PHOTOGEOLOGY

Victor C. Miller

PRESIDENT
MILLER & ASSOCIATES, INC.

Assisted by

Calvin F. Miller

McGRAW-HILL BOOK COMPANY, INC.

New York   Toronto   London   1961

Foreword

In only a few short decades aerial photographs have become useful, indeed indispensable, tools to many men. To no one have they become more useful than to the geologists.

The first step in the evolution of photogrammetry as a science was the mapping of inaccessible areas by means of photographs, first from high vantage points on the ground and later from the air. This started about the time of the First World War. From the very beginning, the geologist saw in this new tool not only a means of making more, better, and less expensive maps, but he also saw a device of the utmost value in helping him to resolve his own special problems in the field—problems relating to geological mapping, to geological structures, and to the interpretation of terrain features.

As the student of photogeology learns how to use this new technique, he is at first utterly dumfounded with the many facts that aerial photographs reveal. He learns to identify on aerial photographs the many details of the landscape that are significant to the geologist, and he becomes adept at interpreting them in terms of geological structure. He learns how to discriminate between what is meaningful and what is not.

He learns to draw inferences and thus to solve problems. Whatever his interest, be it the search for oil or minerals or the building of a dam or highway, he turns first to the aerial photograph for his initial answers.

Dr. Victor Miller has been doing this for many years, in both the United States and Canada. His thorough knowledge of geomorphology, his broad training in geology, his wartime work in photogrammetry, coupled with his wide practical experience in the field, all render him uniquely fitted to contribute to geological science a book of this kind. And more than all of this is his personal integrity, which is an assurance that the principles here presented are sound and dependable.

Associated with Dr. Miller in the preparation of this book is his brother, Calvin F. Miller, a man with several years experience with the U.S. Geological Survey, as well as in photogeological work throughout North America. These two men, each complementing the other, have produced a remarkably well-rounded and comprehensive book.

It is a pleasure indeed for me to commend this work to the whole geological profession.

A. K. Lobeck

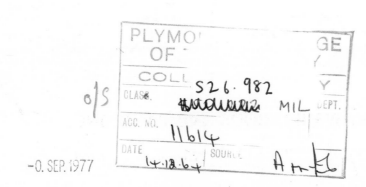

PHOTOGEOLOGY

Preface

Geology is a relatively young science. Photogeology, which is the use of aerial photographs in geology, is one of its youngest and most rapidly growing offspring. Geologists use aerial photographs in many ways in research and exploration. Through a stereoscopic study of aerial photographs they obtain geologic information. In the field they use aerial photographs as base maps. In the laboratory they use precision instruments to make exact measurements on photographs; these data are used in the construction of accurate planimetric, topographic, and photogeologic maps.

Many kinds of data may be obtained from aerial photographs. The science of making precise measurements on aerial photographs is called *photogrammetry*. In many detailed photogeologic mapping projects, photogrammetric instruments are used to calculate stratigraphic thickness, crystalline body dimensions, fault displacement, strike direction, dip magnitude, and fold closure. Some instruments permit the precise plotting of photogeologic data to base maps, and others are used to make detailed structure contour and isopachous maps in areas of well-exposed strata. Controlled mosaics are constructed with the aid of photogrammetric principles and equipment. That part of photogeology which includes advanced photogrammetric techniques may be called *quantitative photogeology*. That part of photogeology dealing with the study, recognition, and *interpretation* of geologic features may be termed *qualitative photogeology*.

Quantitative photogeology is extremely important, and each professional photogeologist must know the basic photogrammetric procedures and principles, whether he has occasion to use them or not. In recent years an increasing number of photogeologists have incorporated the use of photogrammetric instruments into their work. This has resulted in higher standards of planimetric accuracy in the solution of many problems.

There are several reasons why the present book is devoted almost exclusively to *qualitative photogeology*. (1) Though the author appreciates the major role played by photogrammetry, he feels that an incomplete treatment of the subject here would accomplish little. There are numerous excellent comprehensive source books on photogrammetry from which the serious student of the photogeological sciences can obtain a wealth of information. Reference to these will be found in the bibliography at the end of this book. (2) The majority of students who use this book in their university or college courses will be more interested in the understanding of geology than in the more advanced phases of photogrammetry and precise photogeologic mapping. Therefore, it is thought that little would be gained by the inclusion of several chapters involving complex solid geometry and higher mathematics. (3) Regardless of how accurately plotted and constructed a photogeologic map may be, it is essentially *only as valuable as its interpretation is geologically sound*. It is hoped, therefore, that this book will assist the photogeologist to increase the quality, scope, and reliability of his interpretation. If this can be accomplished, then further study in the allied fields of photogrammetry and quantitative photogeology, under the direction of specialists in those fields, should prove most worthwhile and productive.

In governmental survey and commercial exploration, aerial photographs are a tried and proven tool. It is believed that all students of geology, whether they are learning the first principles of the subject or are candidates for graduate degrees, can gain much from the study of selected aerial photographs. Also, there are many practicing geologists who as yet do not employ aerial photographs to their fullest advantage.

The present book is divided into three parts. Part I, entitled "Mechanics," includes the basic principles of aerial photography and stereoscopy, an extremely brief introduction to viewing, plotting, and measuring instruments and to mosaics, and a résumé of preparatory procedures standard to most photogeologic projects.

Part II, which discusses the principles of interpretation, treats such subjects as the various types of photogeologic studies and the criteria used in photogeologic identification. It also lists the many dependent and independent factors which affect the quality and completeness of a given study and interpretation.

Part III consists of a selection of stereoscopic illustrations, most of which are accompanied by an explanatory text or interpretation, and selected questions or exercises. When available and required, corresponding topographic and geologic maps are also included. It should be noted that each illustration-text unit is limited to a single page or a pair of opposite pages. This arrangement permits the convenient examination of the photographs and simultaneous study of the text.

By its very nature, this book need not and should not be used in the same way by all readers. Before proceeding, the reader should determine his position in one or more of the following categories, and in general be guided by the suggestions appropriate to such group or groups.

Beginning Student

The student of elementary geology frequently derives his understanding of the science from two principal sources: the lecture and the standard textbook. It is my hope to supplement these with a three-dimensional pictorial representation of many of the basic landforms and structures studied.

It may well be that no form of illustration other than the aerial photograph can so understandably present topography per se and at the same time impress upon the student the absolute and universal interrelations among landforms, erosion processes, rock types, and geologic structures.

It would be virtually impossible to arrange the illustrations in Part III to follow the order of treatment of any particular textbook in general geology or physical geography. Therefore, the instructor is asked to select those which are most appropriate to the subject or subjects being studied.

Student of Photogeology

The advanced student in photogeology will find this entire volume designed to meet his needs. It is hoped that by it he may be guided to the study of those courses which will give him the best background for a career in photogeology.

Above all, the attempt is made to indoctrinate the serious student in the *philosophy of photogeologic interpretation*. He must learn to think in terms of explaining geologic features as well as identifying and mapping them.

Other Advanced Students

Topography and geologic structure are intimately associated. In most advanced curricula, there are courses in geomorphology, structural geology, topographic and geologic map reading and interpretation, and field geology.

Part III is intended to be used as supplemental material in all these courses. That this is possible attests to the fact that though each course is designed along different lines, involves different teaching techniques, and is conducted under different branches of a geology department, they are all parts of a single major element of geology. In academic and applied geology, the aerial photograph integrates these units into that single element.

The Field Geologist

Whereas few geologists become photogeologists, many thousands devote at least part of their time to field reconnaissance or detailed mapping surveys. Therefore, the collective value to be derived from the proper use of aerial photographs by the field geologists may well exceed that attainable by photogeologists.

For this reason I have tried, in Part II, to instruct the field geologist in the correct field and office uses of photographs, and urge him to a better understanding of their contribution to his operations.

Parts II and III should be thoroughly studied by all geologists whose work takes them into the field.

Senior Personnel

Since photogeology is a new branch of geology, many of the men in the more responsible positions in industry and governmental surveys have not had an opportunity to acquaint themselves with its many applications. Therefore, I feel that if the reader is in charge of large-scale exploration or mapping programs, he will be helped by Part II.

In addition to instructing the student and field geologist, I have included much material in Part II which is designed to explain what photogeology can and cannot do, how personnel can learn to do it properly and effectively, and what types of approach are best suited to different problems.

It should be stressed that mining and economic geologists, as well as those in the petroleum industry, may receive considerable benefit from photogeologic studies.

It is hoped that the following pages will prove ultimately to be a contribution, however small, to the advancement of what to me is the most fascinating and challenging of the sciences.

A long list could be made of the many individuals, companies, professional societies, and governmental agencies who, directly or indirectly, knowingly or unknowingly, have played a part in making this book a reality.

To them all, whether they offered advice or constructive criticism, provided maps or photos, or kindly granted publication releases, my sincere thanks.

I wish to mention a few people individually, however.

To the late A. K. Lobeck, who introduced me to geology and who, during the remaining years of his life, stood as a constant friend, advisor, and towering inspiration, I owe an undying gratitude.

Henry Buthman, Philip Martin, and Howard Thune, professional photogeologists, critically read parts of the manuscript and made many invaluable suggestions for improvement. Stanley Schumm, a geomorphologist, made worthwhile criticisms from the standpoint of the nonphotogeologist.

To Calvin F. Miller, my brother, business partner, and severest critic, I owe much. A word of thanks is inadequate, to say the least.

Victor C. Miller

Contents

Introduction

In recent years such terms as *photogeology, photogeologic mapping,* and *photogeologic interpretation* have been used rather indiscriminately. As a result, they have somewhat lost their meaning. It is therefore felt that these words and terms should be redefined.

Photogeology

Photogeology may be thought of as the use of aerial photographs in the geological sciences. It is a general rather than a specific term. Classroom, field, and office uses of photographs by cartographers, geographers, engineers, photogrammetrists, and geologists alike, may all be parts of photogeology. A *photogeologist* may be defined as a geologist who is trained and experienced in the uses of aerial photographs, especially in their stereoscopic study.

Photogeologic Mapping

Photogeologic mapping is essentially the making of a geologic map with data compiled from photographs. This procedure is frequently referred to as *photogeologic interpretation.* The author has serious objections to this interchange of terms.

Smith (1953) has defined the recognition of specific features on photographs as *photograph reading,* and the understanding of their individual or collective significance as *interpretation.* This is sensible. A geologist who can recognize dips, faults, stratigraphic breaks, and fold axes may assemble his observed data in the form of a photogeologic map. But he may also have enough training and experience to be able to interpret the geology mapped, and to appreciate the significance of structural, stratigraphic, and geomorphic relations which cannot be indicated by standard symbols on a geologic map.

Photogeologic Interpretation

Photogeologic interpretation, then, is the advanced and thorough analysis and understanding of the geology of an area, based primarily on information derived from a study of aerial photographs.

The ranks of professional photogeologists include many persons who have learned to read and map geology. These individuals fulfill a definite need, especially in commercial reconnaissance of little-known areas. Regardless of academic or professional background, the reader should be able to learn the fundamentals of photogeologic mapping with the aid of this book.

However, neither this nor any other volume could conceivably transform any geologist into a competent photogeologic interpreter. A sound university background, followed by long practical experience in certain specialized lines of investigation, is absolutely essential. The academic curriculum must concentrate on those aspects of geology with which the photogeologic interpreter works. Few colleges and universities give all the courses suggested below. However, those that are available should be taken, supplemented with closely associated course work not specifically mentioned and by outside reading and research. The counsel of faculty advisors should be sought at all academic stages.

Suggested Curriculum

All geologists, whatever their training or experience, can use aerial photographs to facilitate their field or mapping programs.

Experience has taught, however, that specialization in photogeology requires a sound background in the following subjects. A geology student who contemplates a career in photogeology is strongly advised to include as many as possible in his curriculum.

Geomorphology. The advanced principles of geomorphology are absolutely essential to the specialist in photogeologic mapping and interpretation. Regardless of the area to be studied, the nature of the geology to be investigated, or the purpose of the study, the stereoscopic examination of aerial photographs entails the viewing and understanding of topography. Topography is the product of the interaction between what are known as the constructive and destructive geologic forces; orogenic and epeirogenic uplift, deformation, weathering, erosion, transportation, and deposition. Geomorphology is the science of investigating, describing, and *understanding* landforms, their development and their evolution.

Frequently it is possible to trace beds and faults, map strikes and dips, and outline intrusive bodies and stratigraphic breaks without paying too much attention to geomorphic criteria. But forest-covered hills can provide stratigraphic and structural information if their geomorphic form is studied. Epeirogenic movements can be detected through drainage and dissection characteristics. In plains areas an understanding of glacial deposition, wind action, and stream erosion may bring to light critical structural information, or reveal leads which can be further investigated by other methods.

Advanced and, if possible, graduate courses, seminars, and

research in geomorphology are strongly recommended. A detailed discussion of the role of geomorphology in photogeology is included in Part II.

Structural Geology. Structural geology is also essential. Since most advanced training in geomorphology entails the investigation of structure, the interrelation of the two is apparent.

Factual and theoretical concepts of tectonics, folding, faulting, jointing, and the like should be thoroughly studied, understood, and appreciated. Whereas geomorphology may occasionally be the more important factor in the recognition of certain features, the thorough knowledge of structural principles permits the evaluation and ultimate interpretation of the geology studied.

Map Interpretation. The student should learn to read and interpret topographic and geologic maps. The geologist who can read both types of map can readily learn to read photographs. One who is experienced in the interpretation of both types of map, especially in visualizing the subsurface relations they represent, is well on his way to qualifying as a potential photogeologic interpreter. Such map-interpretation ability is primarily the product of thorough training in geomorphology and structural geology.

Descriptive Geometry. Perhaps more than any other subject, descriptive geometry can teach the ever-important principles of three-dimensional thinking. While necessary to all geologists, the ability to think and visualize the solid geometry of structural, stratigraphic, and topographic relations is of even greater importance to the photo interpreter. Descriptive geometry should be studied as early as possible, preferably prior to enrollment in one's first course in structural geology.

Field Study. Field trips and field courses are fundamental parts of both graduate and undergraduate training in geology. While the photogeologist may, in later years, spend much of his time at a desk, he must endeavor to become thoroughly acquainted with mapping and the recognition and interpretation of geology in the field. Many field geologists accomplish much without the aid of aerial photographs. Similarly, it is possible to do photogeologic mapping and even some types of photogeologic interpretation without benefit of extensive field training or experience. However, both field and photograph studies can be improved considerably by a thorough knowledge of both techniques and of their interdependence.

Subsurface Geologic Methods. The correlation of data derived from well logs, test holes for coal, and other types of subsurface investigations, may provide the photogeologist with invaluable information. For example, a project area may be extensively blanketed by Tertiary strata, with only a few scattered outcrops of pre-Tertiary rocks. A subsurface "hint" of subcrop structures—facies trends or old tectonic belts—would enhance the final photogeologic interpretation immeasurably.

Photogrammetry. Photogrammetry is the science of the measurement of ground distances and elevations on aerial photographs. By photogrammetric methods, planimetric, topographic, and structure-contour maps may be made, stratigraphic sections measured, and slopes and gradients calculated. These are frequently important parts of photogeology, and should constitute part of one's background instruction. Trips to governmental or commercial photogrammetric plants should prove worthwhile to the student.

Cartography. Since there is so frequently a close coordination of photogeologic interpretation, photogrammetry, drafting, and reproduction of maps, a basic knowledge of cartography is desired. The student should acquaint himself with map-construction methods, reproduction media, drafting, map coloring, scale change, symbolism, and other elements of cartography.

Physical Geography. The science of geology cannot be divorced completely from such related fields as pedology, botany, climatology, and meteorology. In arid climates, carbonate rock resistance to erosion accounts for limestone escarpments and ridges. Under humid conditions limestone solubility is evidenced by sink holes and associated landforms. Bauxite is produced by a certain combination of time, bedrock, climate, and geographical location. Some plants grow more rapidly and abundantly in sandy soil, some in shaly belts, and others grow indiscriminately. Increased moisture along a fault zone may localize darker soil and different plant concentrations. Former prevailing winds may have caused oriented lineations recognizable as dunes. These are but a few of a great number of possible examples of how factors not purely geologic may be important when one studies aerial photographs.

The above, coupled with the fact that a photogeologist may be asked to examine photographs of such diverse areas as Central America, Arabia, Alaska, or Labrador, demonstrates the need for a thorough background in all aspects of physical geography.

Scientific Writing. In rapid regional reconnaissance, the importance of the photogeologic map is unchallenged. In the more advanced field of complete photogeologic interpretation, the thoughts, impressions, hypotheses, and conclusions of the photogeologist must be recorded and presented in clear and understandable terms.

A final report must tell the reader: (1) what was done, (2) how it was done, (3) what criteria were used, (4) how the conclusions were reached, (5) what the results were, (6) what they might signify, and (7) how dependable they are considered.

Most geologists can usually recount verbally and informally what they have done and what they have discovered. Surprisingly few can present, in a logical, clear, and readable way, a discussion of the several elements so necessary in a scientific report.

There are times when that which can be shown on a map is of less importance than that which remains in the mind of the interpreter. Unless he can convey his thoughts through the written word this valuable information may be lost.

Serious students of photogeology, especially those who may later turn to advanced analysis and interpretation, must consider composition, grammar, logic, and clear thinking to be absolutely essential parts of their training.

The Government or Commercial Geologist

The undergraduate who has before him several years of academic study may yet have time to adjust his curriculum along the lines suggested above. This is not true in the case of the trainee of a major oil company, the district geologist of a mining company, or the established member of a state or federal geological survey. Can any of these become competent photogeologists or photogeologic interpreters?

Probably some can and some cannot. Fortunately, most of those who cannot would hardly choose to. Just as it requires a certain interest, aptitude, and temperament to become a professional micropaleontologist, stratigrapher, seismologist, or petrologist, so does it require certain qualities to practice photogeologic mapping or interpretation.

This refutes the relatively common belief that any geologist, through choice or assignment, can almost automatically become a photogeologist after a week or two of orientation. Since all geologists learn how to recognize strikes, dips, contacts, faults, and similar features on the ground, they may all conceivably learn to map obvious features from their appearance on aerial photographs. They would then become *photogeologic mappers*. If that is what is required in their particular assignment or research project, they should succeed.

But should one ask "What does this mean?" or "Why is this anticline faulted and that syncline not faulted?", the importance of specialized academic training in geologic interpretation becomes apparent. By the very nature of his interest and selected schooling, the micropaleontologist or petrologist is frequently less able to answer such questions than is the structural geologist, field geologist, or geomorphologist. The latter individuals are usually more interested in such things as folds and faults, as evidenced by their selection of these specialized subjects.

As a general rule of thumb, a geologist contemplating a change to photogeologic interpretation, or the administrator who wishes to assign one of his staff to such work, should consider the two critical subjects, structural geology and geomorphology. Inadequate training in one or both of these may be overlooked if general geologic mapping alone is required. Both should be strong elements in the background of anyone asked to undertake comprehensive interpretation or evaluation.

Personal Attributes

The life of a photogeologist is rarely one of routine or monotony. One day he may study in minute detail the structural complexities of a few square miles. Another day may be devoted to a regional study of tens of thousands of square miles on small-scale mosaics assembled on a map wall. At some other time he may be involved in attempting to integrate published geologic data, well logs, and his own observed photogeologic information.

He must be able to concentrate on details while thinking in terms of regional relations and history. He must be patient, observant, and adaptable. He must overcome any existing tendencies toward "jumping to conclusions," while developing the ability to grasp and investigate concepts suggested by a minimum of evidence.

Women in Photogeology

There are many women who are extremely interested in the geological sciences. But the opportunities have been restricted. Few women are permitted to "sit on" a well, or to carry out difficult field assignments. Few, in fact, wish to.

Photogeology can open a new and inviting door to the young woman who wishes a career in geology. She should, of course, attempt to follow the curriculum outlined above. Since patience and attention to detail are frequently considered to be feminine attributes, it should follow that her ability in photogeologic investigations would be considerable.

PART | Mechanics

INTRODUCTION

A complete photogeologic analysis may involve (1) a study of aerial photographs, (2) the construction of a map, and (3) the preparation of a report or publication. Prior to such work, the area to be studied must be photographed, and the photographs indexed and otherwise prepared. Frequently, mosaics must be constructed and reproduced. Concurrent with the photogeologic study, information obtained must be transferred either to mosaics or base maps. This may or may not require the use of photogrammetric instruments. In addition, the photogeologist must know and appreciate the fact that aerial photographs are not true maps, and that a stereoscopic model is usually not a true representation of the terrain photographed.

This part of the book will serve to acquaint the student with aerial photography, stereoscopy, and some of the basic procedures necessary to organize and undertake a photogeologic study.

Aerial Photography

TYPES OF AERIAL PHOTOGRAPHS

Aerial photographs are generally classified according to the orientation of the optical axis of the camera. Optical axis may be understood to be the line along which the camera points. It connects the center of the film with the center

of the lens and extends straight out from the front of the camera.

A *vertical aerial photograph* is one taken by a camera which is pointing vertically downward. Some latitude in definition is permitted, since photographs taken when the optical axis is inclined a few degrees from vertical are also classified

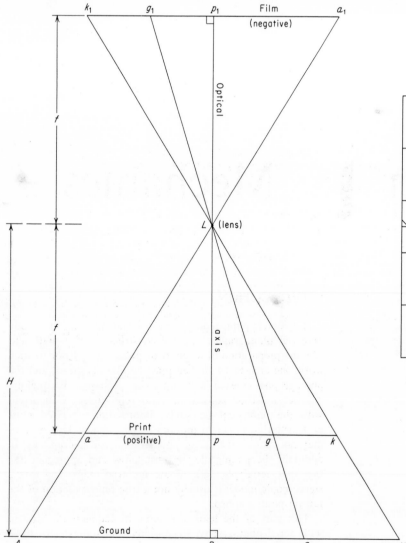

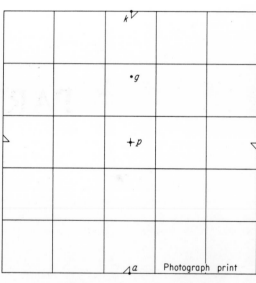

(*B*)

Figure 1-1. (*A*) The geometry of a *vertical aerial photograph,* and the basic relations of film negative, lens, positive print, and the ground. Photograph scale is equal to the ratio of camera focal length to camera height (*f/H*). Ground point *P* lies directly beneath the camera. It is called the *nadir point.* Point *p* is the principal point (center) of the photograph. In vertical photographs, the principal point and image of the nadir point coincide; on tilted or oblique photographs they are separated. (*B*) A vertical "photograph" of a square ground grid. The marks in the centers of the edges of this figure are called *fiducial marks;* lines connecting opposite fiducial marks intersect precisely at the principal point. The principal point is also marked on some photographs.

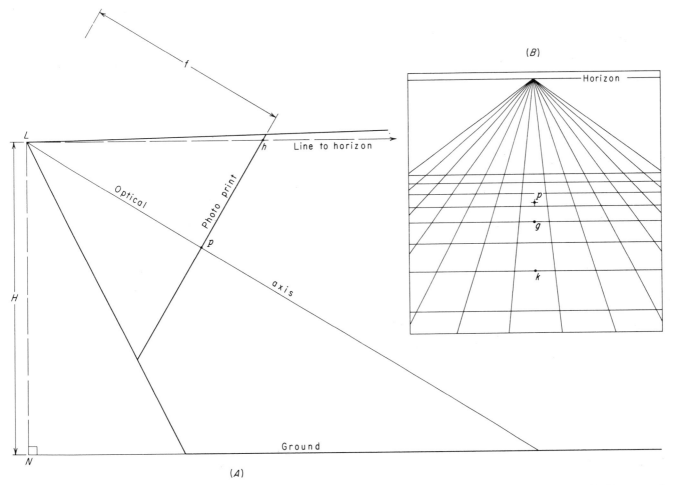

(B)

Horizon

Line to horizon

f

L

Optical

Photo print

p

axis

H

Ground

N

(A)

Figure 1-2. (*A*) The geometry of a *high oblique photograph*. The optical axis is sufficiently inclined to permit the photography of the horizon. The nadir point *N* is not photographed. (*B*) A high oblique "photograph" of a square ground grid. The ground squares are equal to those shown in Figure 1-1*B*.

as vertical photographs. A method of ensuring absolute verticality has not yet been perfected, though with proper control, variation rarely exceeds a few degrees. There are, however, some occasions when excessive variation from the vertical (known as *tilt*) occurs. The resulting photographs are annoying and may be misleading. Tilt may cause erroneous interpretations if not recognized and understood. This subject will be discussed in detail below.

Figure 1-1 diagrammatically illustrates the simple geometric relations involved in vertical aerial photography. Figure 1-1*A* also depicts the negative-positive (film-print) principle. A contact print is dimensionally identical to the negative; its orientation is reversed. Proportional relations between ground and film are the same as between ground and print. For purposes of simplification, subsequent diagrams illustrating aerial photography will include only the contact-print–ground relation. Figure 1-1*B* shows that a square ground grid in a horizontal area maintains its correct shape on a vertical photograph.

Oblique aerial photographs are those taken when the optical axis is considerably inclined from the vertical. When the inclination is sufficiently great to permit the photography of the horizon, they are called *high oblique photographs;* those with less inclination are called *low oblique photographs.* Figures 1-2 and 1-3 diagrammatically depict the geometric conditions existing when high and low oblique pictures are made. Figure 8-6 is a low oblique photograph.

Many parts of the world have been photographed one or more times by governmental agencies or commercial companies. There are many types of aerial photographs available. Some aerial cameras are simple, consisting of a single lens and film magazine. Others are more complex, involving several lenses and film magazines. Some have short and others have long focal lengths; some have more than one.

A relatively common multilens camera is one consisting of four obliquely oriented optical axes arranged to permit the photography of a single large area at one time. The individual pictures are rectified, by projection, to produce prints possessing many of the qualities of vertical photographs. These are then arranged as a composite photograph (see Figures 13-2 and 14-18). Note the stereoscopic effect produced by imperfect matching of the four segments. Four-lens photography is now considered obsolete.

A camera unit formerly used in the reconnaissance photography of large unmapped areas is the *trimetrogon* unit. It consists of three cameras held in a single mount. One camera is held vertically and photographs the area immediately beneath the plane; the others are held obliquely at an angle of 60° to each side. The areas covered by the oblique photos extend from the lateral edges of the vertical coverage to the horizon.

Most oblique photography is difficult to view stereoscopically. It is extremely hard to compile geological data from oblique photographs to base maps. Therefore, when available, vertical photographs are usually used in photogeologic studies.

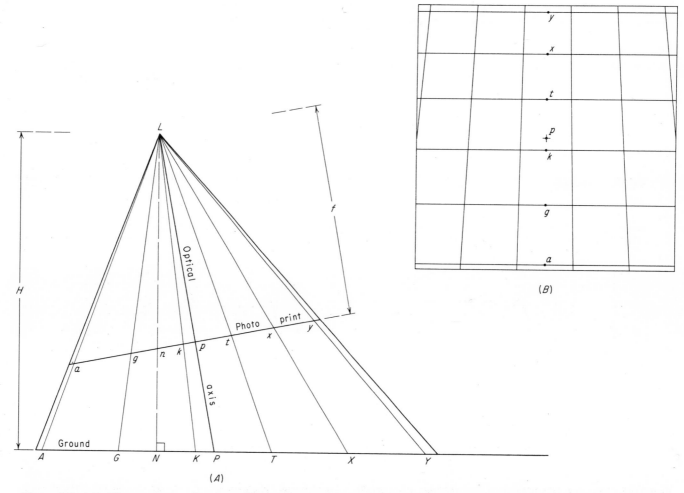

Figure 1-3. (*A*) The geometry of a *low oblique photograph.* Compare with Figures 1-1*A* and 1-2*A*. Camera height *H* and focal length *f* are the same in all three illustrations. Equal ground distances *AG*, *GK*, etc., appear as unequal image dis-

tances *ag*, *gk*, etc., on the low oblique photograph. The nadir point *n* is shown on the photograph. (*B*) A low oblique "photograph" of a square ground grid. The ground squares are equal to those shown in Figures 1-1*B* and 1-2*B*.

GEOMETRY OF AERIAL PHOTOGRAPHS

Scale

Map scale is defined as the ratio of map distance to ground distance. If a ground distance of 1 mile is shown by a map distance of 1 inch, the scale of the map is said to be 1 inch to 1 mile, or, in fraction form, 1/63,360 (there are 63,360 inches in 1 mile). An aerial photograph, for reasons discussed below, has neither a uniform scale nor a regularly changing scale. Therefore, only approximate photograph scale can be determined.

Figure 1-1*A* shows the following geometric relations: ground distance *AP* is photographed by a camera *H* feet above the ground. Camera focal length is *f* feet. The photographic film image of ground distance *AP* is a_1p_1.

(1) $\triangle APL \sim \triangle a_1p_1L$ (parallel sides)

Therefore,

(2) $\dfrac{a_1p_1}{AP} = \dfrac{p_1L}{PL}$ (corresponding sides)

Focal length *f* is defined by the distance p_1L; camera height *H* is defined by the distance *PL*. Therefore, substituting *f* for p_1L and *H* for *PL* in Eq. (2) above, we have the following:

(3) Photo scale $= \dfrac{\text{image distance}}{\text{ground distance}} = \dfrac{a_1p_1}{AP} = \dfrac{p_1L}{PL} = \dfrac{f}{H}$

$\qquad\qquad\qquad = \dfrac{\text{focal length}}{\text{camera height}}$

Lenses used in aerial photography are specially designed and precisely ground. They may nevertheless possess slight imperfections which produce minor image distortions. For the sake of the present discussion, it will be assumed that such distortions or aberrations are either negligible or absent.

Variations in Scale

There are two major factors which cause variations in photograph scale: these are the topographic relief of the terrain photographed and the inclination of the optical axis of the camera. Because of these two factors, ground objects do not photograph in their correct relative horizontal positions, as they would appear on a map.

Scale Variations Caused by Relief. Consider Figure 1-4. Photograph scale, as defined above, is the ratio of photograph image distance to ground distance; this ratio is the same as that of camera focal length to camera height (*f/H*). Since camera focal length is constant in any one camera, changes in the height of the camera above the ground will produce scale changes. In Figure 1-4 horizontal ground dis-

8

tances *AG*, *KP*, and *XY* are of equal length but at different elevations. The height of the camera above ground distance *AG* is greater than it is above *XY*, and less than it is above *KP*. Considering *XY*, *AG*, and *KP* as reference or datum planes, we may say that the camera heights are H_1, H_2, and H_3, respectively.

From the above definition of scale it should then follow that the photographic images of the several lines of equal length should not be equal; that the image of line *XY* should be the longest and that of line *KP* the shortest. As seen on Figure 1-4, the image distances (*ag*, *kp*, and *xy*) are obviously not the same.

There is another relationship illustrated in Figure 1-4. Ground point *G* lies vertically above point *K*, and point *X* lies vertically above point *T*. A map of this area would show points *G* and *K* as one; similarly points *X* and *T* would have a single map position. Note that the photographic images of *G* and *K* are separated (*g* and *k*), with *g* lying farther from the center or principal point of the photograph, point *p*. Photographic images *x* and *t* are also separated, with *x* lying at the greater distance from point *p*. It is therefore apparent that the images of ground points with greater elevations will be displaced outward from the center of a photograph. Conversely, ground points lying below a selected datum plane are displaced radially inward. This is one of the fundamentals of aerial photographs which the photogeologist must constantly bear in mind. Its application in photogeology, and especially in the estimation and measurement of slopes and dips, will be discussed in detail in a later chapter.

Figure 1-5 illustrates the scale variations produced by the photography of the area shown in Figure 1-4. The square grids in the three parts of the *photograph* represent equal ground dimensions.

A significant advance has been made in removing topography-caused image displacements on aerial photographs. The instrument, developed and being improved by the U.S. Geological Survey, is called the *Orthophotoscope*.

A vertical aerial photograph, taken by a camera mounted in an aircraft, is a recorded perspective view of a ground area. A map is an orthographic projection of a portion of the earth's surface. By means of the Orthophotoscope, vertical perspective aerial photographs (Figure 1-6*A*) are converted to the equivalent of orthographic photographs (Figure 1-6*B*).

The principle is relatively simple; the process is necessarily complex, and the instrument is heavy and expensive. Its value to photogrammetry and photo interpretation can only be anticipated at this time. It will eventually put an end to the constant irritation of planimetric error universally present in aerial photographs and mosaics made therefrom.

Since orthographic photographs do not possess image displacements and distortions, they are in effect combined

Figure 1-4. The effect of topographic relief on photograph scale and image position.

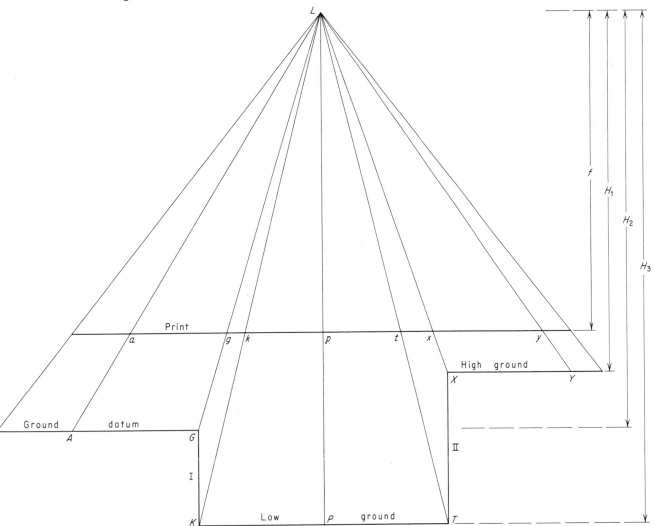

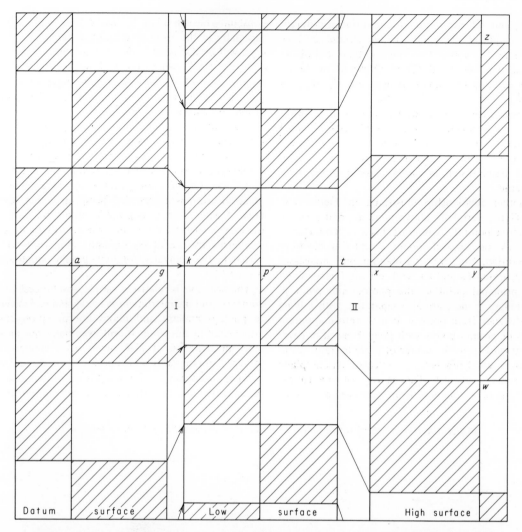

Figure 1-5. The "photograph" shown being taken in Figure 1-4. The squares represent equal ground areas. Ground points *A* and *G* lie on the datum or reference surface. Point *k*, which is the image of ground point *K*, is displaced inward toward the principal point *p*. Arrows, in vertical wall I, show the directions and magnitudes of the image displacements of several other points. The datum plane intersects vertical wall II. Show this intersection on Figure 1-4, and by construction find its photograph position. It can then be indicated on Figure 1-5. The directions and magnitudes of image displacements of points *t*, *x*, and other points at the base and top of wall II can then be determined. The displacements of such points as *w*, *y*, and *z* can also be established by construction.

photographs and planimetric maps. A number of such photographs, reproduced at the same scale, may be assembled as a virtually error-free mosaic. The transfer of annotated data to base maps from such mosaics (or from individual prints) will be rapid and easy. The photographs cannot, of course, be viewed stereoscopically, since the process of stereo vision is based on image displacements on overlapping pictures.

Scale Variations Caused by Tilt. The second factor which introduces variations in photograph scale is that of the inclination of the optical axis. Such inclination is referred to as *tip* and *tilt*. Tilt is defined as the inclination from the vertical such as would be caused by the rotation of the camera about an axis running through the length of the airplane; in other words, the camera is rotated to one side or the other, normal to the direction of flight. Tip, on the other hand, would be produced were the camera rotated about an axis which runs horizontally through it, parallel to the wings of the craft. On a single print the effect would be the same; on a stereo pair the difference would be largely directional.

Since the principles of displacement are the same in both oblique and tilted vertical photographs, the former, with greater displacements, will be used for illustrative purposes.

In Figures 1-2*B* and 1-3*B*, square ground grids are shown to converge toward the upper part of the *photographs*. Such convergence indicates progressive decrease in scale. Figure 1-3*A* shows the geometry of scale change resulting from tilt. Equal ground distances *AG, GK, KT, TX*, and *XY* appear as unequal photograph image distances *ag, gk*, etc.

An important principle of photogrammetry is illustrated in Figure 1-7. A vertical and a low oblique photograph are shown being taken from the same air station *L* (position of the camera in space). The ground surface is horizontal and flat. The vertical photograph retains the shape of the ground area it covers; the oblique photograph distorts the area it depicts. The scale of the vertical photograph is uniform; that of the oblique photograph is greatest along the left (lower) edge and smallest along the right (upper) edge.

Line *ag* is the intersection of the vertical and oblique

Figure 1-6. (*A*) *A contact print* of a vertical photograph negative. (*B*) An *orthophotoscope print* of the same negative. The radial image displacements, caused by topographic relief, have been removed. This print is a true photo map. (*Courtesy of U.S. Geological Survey.*)

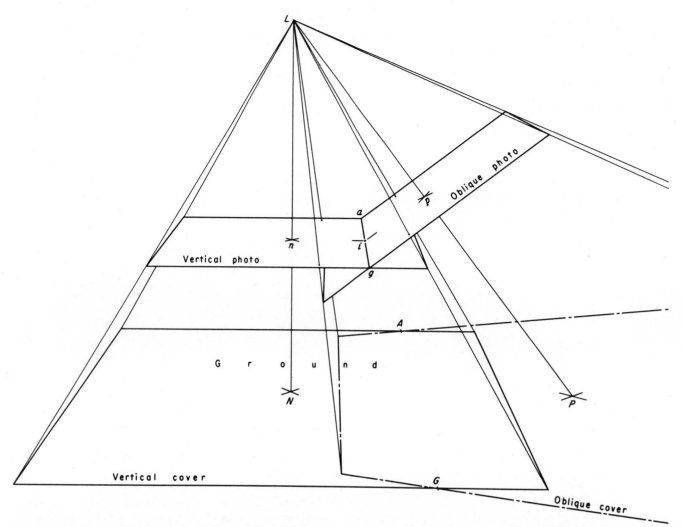

Figure 1-7. The relation between oblique (tilted) and vertical photographs. Line *ag*, which is the intersection of the two photographs, is called the *axis of tilt*. Only along this line is the scale of the oblique photograph equal to that of the vertical photo-graph. The isocenter *i* lies on line *ag* midway between points *n* and *p* (principal points). Image displacements caused by tilt are radial from the isocenter and *not* from the principal point of the tilted photograph.

photographs. It is a horizontal line referred to as the *axis of tilt*. To the right of the axis of tilt the scale of the oblique photograph is less than that of the vertical photograph; left of this line it is greater.

Points *n* and *p* are the principal points of the two photographs. Midway between them, on line *ag*, is a point called the *isocenter*, symbolized *i*. Photographic image displacements due to tilt are radial outward from or inward toward the isocenter. On vertical photographs, displacements due to topographic relief are radial from the principal point *n*. It is extremely important, therefore, to ascertain the presence of tip or tilt in vertical photographs if radial control of any kind is to be used. In the case of minor tilt, the assumption that all displacements are radial with respect to the principal point is permitted, since resulting errors will be negligible. When tilt is severe, the isocenter must be located, or the photographs must be rectified.

1. It is suggested that the student show on Figures 1-2*A* and 1-3*A* the positions of vertical photographs taken from the same air stations as the oblique photographs shown. Focal length should be the same.

2. The isocenters should then be located on these figures and transferred to Figures 1-2*B* and 1-3*B*.

3. Transfer points *g* and *k* from Figure 1-2*B* to the oblique *photo* depicted in Figure 1-2*A*, and determine the ground positions of these points.

4. Transfer the image of the nadir point *n* from Figure 1-3*A* to Figure 1-3*B*.

5. Mark the centers of ground distances *AG*, *GK*, etc., on Figure 1-3*A*, show the photographic images of these new points, and transfer them to Figure 1-3*B*.

6. Assuming that the ground squares depicted on Figure 1-5 are 1 mile square (sections of land), compute the *photograph* scale in the three parts of the figure.

FLIGHT PROCEDURES

Aerial photography is an exacting and delicate operation. It demands painstaking preparation and professional execution. Many factors must be considered and many problems must be solved before the photographic plane leaves the ground.

EXERCISES

The principles presented in Figure 1-7 were employed in the construction of Figures 1-2*B* and 1-3*B*.

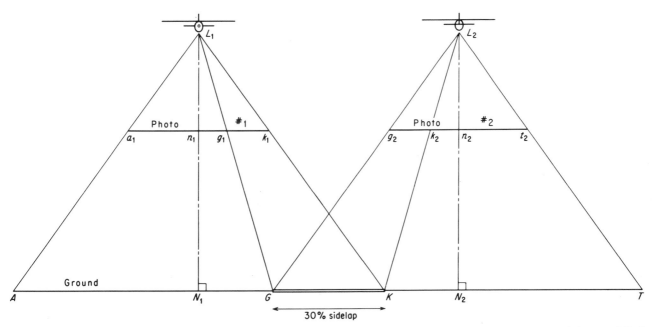

Figure 1-8. The obtaining of *sidelap* photographic coverage. The plane at station L_1, flying toward the reader, photographs ground area AK. At air station L_2, while flying away from the reader, it photographs area GT. The area common to both is area GK, the sidelap area.

The purpose of the project will determine the scale and other characteristics of the photography to be obtained. The proper camera will be selected, as will necessary filters, suitable film, and other special equipment. A well-trained photographic crew will be assigned.

In photographing an area, the plane flies back and forth across it, following predetermined parallel flight lines. These lines are equally spaced. The photographs of one flight line cover a long band or belt of ground. Those of the second line should include a narrow marginal strip of ground originally photographed by the first flight line. The common marginal strip is called *sidelap,* and is usually about 30 per cent (Figure 1-8). Since scale is known, the width of ground covered by a single photograph or flight strip is readily calculated. To permit 30 per cent sidelap, adjacent flight lines are planned at a separation equal to 70 per cent of this width.

Within a single flight line, photographs must be taken frequently enough to permit all ground objects to appear on at least two consecutive photographs. The area of common coverage is called *overlap,* or *forward lap* (Figure 1-9). In practice, overlap of 60 per cent is prescribed to ensure com-

Figure 1-9. The obtaining of *overlap* photographic coverage. From station L_1, area AK is photographed; from Station L_2, area GT is photographed. The overlap shown (GK) is 60 per cent. The nadir points N_1 and N_2 are included in the overlap area and appear on both photographs. Locate camera station L_3. By construction, show that part of overlap area GK is included in the coverage of the third photograph.

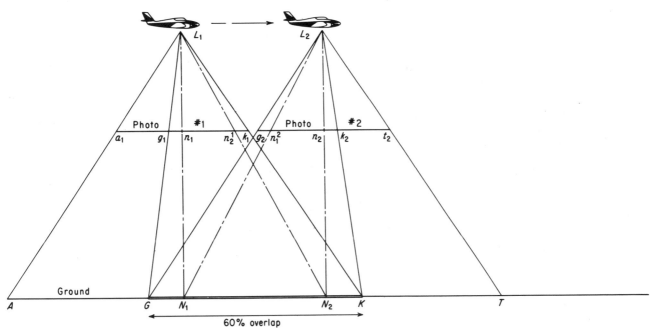

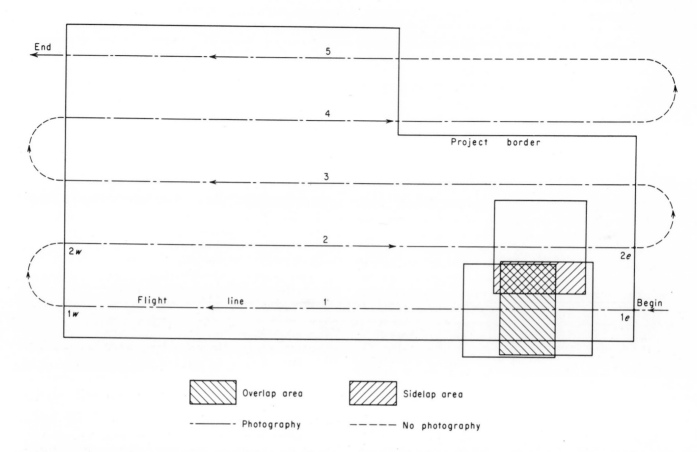

End 5

4

Project border

3

2

2w

Flight line 1

1w

2e

Begin

1e

▨ Overlap area ▨ Sidelap area

------ Photography ----- No photography

Figure 1-10. Flight lines planned to photograph a project area. The lines are parallel, and spaced to afford 30 per cent sidelap. Note that photography is obtained along the entire length of line 4, to ensure coverage along the northeastern border of the project area. Two photographs from flight line 1 are shown to illustrate 60 per cent overlap, and one from flight line 2 is added to illustrate sidelap with flight line 1. Assuming that the photographs are 9 by 9 inches, that camera focal length is 6 inches, and that photograph scale is 1:63,360, calculate: (1) camera height, (2) the ground area covered by a single photograph, (3) the overlap area covered by two successive photographs, (4) the ground width of sidelap between adjacent flight lines, (5) the dimensions of the project area, and (6) the minimum number of photographs required to afford stereoscopic coverage of the project area. Points 1e, 1w, 2e, and 2w indicate the ends of the first two flight lines. Reference to the photographs of these points will be made in a later chapter.

plete stereoscopic coverage, despite slight overlap variations caused by changing ground speed or exposure interval, or by topographic irregularities. Figure 1-10 shows the principle of flight lines, overlap, and sidelap in the photography of a small project area.

Most aerial cameras are held in rather intricate mounts which permit their rotation about three mutually perpendicular axes. Exposure time, aperture opening, and similar adjustments are controlled by the photographer. A level bubble attached to the camera unit allows him to maintain relatively correct camera orientation. If topographic relief is moderate to low, and ground speed relatively constant, the timing of successive exposures is predetermined, and a regulator called an *intervalometer* is set to trigger the camera at the proper time interval. A ground glass permits the observation of ground passage; intervalometer settings may be readjusted when necessary, or the exposure interval may be varied or maintained manually.

Cross or oblique winds may force the pilot to head the plane diagonally into the wind; the plane will point in one direction but will move along a different line. This is referred to as "crabbing." When this occurs, it is necessary to turn the camera till its sides are parallel to actual flight direction. The relations of wind and flight directions as well as plane and camera orientations are shown in Figure 1-11.

Figure 1-11*A* shows the photographic overlap produced when camera and plane orientations are parallel; Figure 1-11*B* illustrates overlap produced by proper compensation for crab.

THE SIGNIFICANCE OF SCALE

Photograph scale is important for several reasons. On small-scale photographs, many ground features are too small to be recognized and identified. On large-scale photographs it may be possible to see more detail, but some subtle regional relations may be missed because the stereoscopic field is too restricted. Camera focal length and camera height influence the stereoscopic impression of depth or relief; changes in either or both factors produce noticeable changes in the three-dimensional appearance of ground features.

One of the more important considerations is that of the cost of purchasing photography of different scales. Individual photographs may range in price from 50 cents to several dollars. Suppose that a single contact print costs one dollar and that one wishes to obtain stereoscopic coverage of the area shown in Figure 1-10. Investigation shows that the area has been photographed twice in recent years. The photographs depicted in Figure 1-10 are from one set of photography; its scale is 1 mile to the inch. The scale of the other set is 1 mile to two inches. Both sets have the usually prescribed 60 per cent overlap and 30 per cent sidelap, and both were obtained under favorable conditions. The choice must then be between greater or less detail on the one hand, and relatively high or low cost on the other.

The unit overlap of the smaller-scale photographs covers an area measuring 5.4 by 9 miles. That of the larger-scale photographs is 2.7 by 4.5 miles. While the dimensions vary at a ratio of 2:1, the areas vary at a ratio of 4:1 (48.6:12.15 square miles). The general rule of thumb is that photographic costs vary directly with the square of the change in scale. Coverage of the area, at a scale of 1:15,840 (4 inches equal one mile), would therefore be estimated to cost about 16 times as much as the 1:63,360-scale photography.

Another point to consider is the possibility of mosaic construction. Using 1:63,360-scale photographs, one can assemble a mosaic of the project area in a lay-down measuring about 30 by 57 inches. A lay-down of the same area, made with 1:31,680-scale photographs, would cover an area 60 by 114 inches. Many photogeologists do not have proper mosaicing facilities. However, one could easily assemble the small-scale photographs on a 4 by 8 foot composition board or Beaverboard. The larger scale would introduce a problem. It would be necessary to divide the area and to assemble each part separately. The factor of photograph scale in mosaic construction must therefore be taken into account when time schedules or personnel costs are calculated.

Many photogeologists who use the simpler viewing stereoscopes prefer a photograph scale of 1:20,000. This scale is relatively large, permitting the recognition, mapping, and interpretation of many details of structure, lithology, and terrain. The cost of such photography is usually within the limits of most individuals and companies.

In many areas the available coverage is of much smaller scale. For example, throughout much of western Canada, where the interest in petroleum has recently stimulated extensive photogeologic exploration, 1:40,000-scale photographs are common. In other Canadian areas the only coverage available is at a scale of about 1 mile to the inch.

The trend toward the increased use of precision measuring and plotting instruments, such as the Kelsh Plotter, has created a greater demand in the United States for smaller-scale photography. It is believed that in such work a scale of about 1 mile to the inch is optimum. The Kelsh Plotter enlarges positive transparencies five times. A pair of photographs having a scale of 1 mile to the inch will be projected to form a stereoscopic model having a scale of about 1:12,700.

MOSAICS

"The Manual of Photogrammetry" (1952) defines a mosaic as ". . . an assembly of individual aerial photographs fitted together systematically to form a composite view of an entire area covered by the photographs."

There are numerous techniques applied in mosaic construction and reproduction. The basic problem is to fit the photographs together in such a way that there is minimum image offset, duplication, or omission, and at the same time to maintain over-all shape and proportion.

An *uncontrolled* mosaic (Figure 1-12) consists of an assembly of photographs, with the greatest possible degree of image tie or match, but with little or no adjustment to planimetric control. Since primary attention is generally directed toward image continuity, uncontrolled mosaics usually possess noticeable planimetric errors. Both directions and distances may be incorrect. In addition, photographs of various scales, and those possessing excessive tilt, may be used in the construction of uncontrolled mosaics. In mountainous or dissected plateau areas scale variations on individual photographs may be great enough to prevent acceptable match within a flight or between adjacent flights.

A similar uncontrolled assembly, with the individual photograph reference or index numbers exposed, is called a *photo index*. Photo indexes permit the location of photographs on hand and also provide reference numbers for ordering new photographic coverage.

When facilities and equipment are available, and time permits, an experienced photogrammetrist can make an extremely accurate *controlled mosaic* (Figure 1-13). This requires that the individual photographs be of uniform scale and that they do not possess tip or tilt. Usually the photographs must be corrected by precise projection printing, which is an expensive process. The photographs used in controlled mosaic construction should have a uniform tone. When fitted together, adjacent photographs will thus afford the impression of being a single over-all picture. The importance of uniformity of photographic tone may be appreciated by comparing Figures 1-14 and 1-15. The photographs used in Figure 1-14 were printed in the conventional manner. Those shown in Figure 1-15 were automatically "dodged" by an electronic printer. Almost absolute tonal uniformity is produced in this way.

It is well to caution the student not to attempt to interpret mosaics made with electronically dodged prints. Frequently, especially in low-dip basin, plains, and coastal areas, slight natural tonal anomalies are the only clues to underlying structural anomalies. Electronic dodging would, of course, destroy such important tonal variations.

Prior to the assembly of a controlled mosaic, a complete system of ground-control points must be established and

Figure 1-11. (*A*) Overlap photography obtained when camera is oriented parallel to airplane during *crab*. (*B*) Overlap photography obtained when camera orientation is adjusted to compensate for crab.

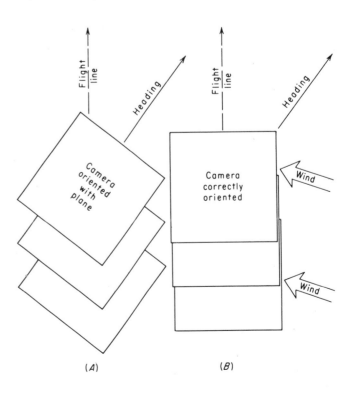

(A)   (B)

39N-99E

Figure 1-12. A stapled *uncontrolled mosaic*. Entire photographs were used in its construction. Note the several instances of tonal contrasts between adjacent photographs. In many places cultural and natural features are offset where the photographs are joined. The numbers which appear in the northwest corner of each photograph indicate the date of photography. This is not a *photo index*. The code or index numbers, which are probably in the northeast corners, are hidden. Compare this mosaic with Figure 1-13, a controlled mosaic of the same area. (*By permission from Edgar Tobin Aerial Surveys.*)

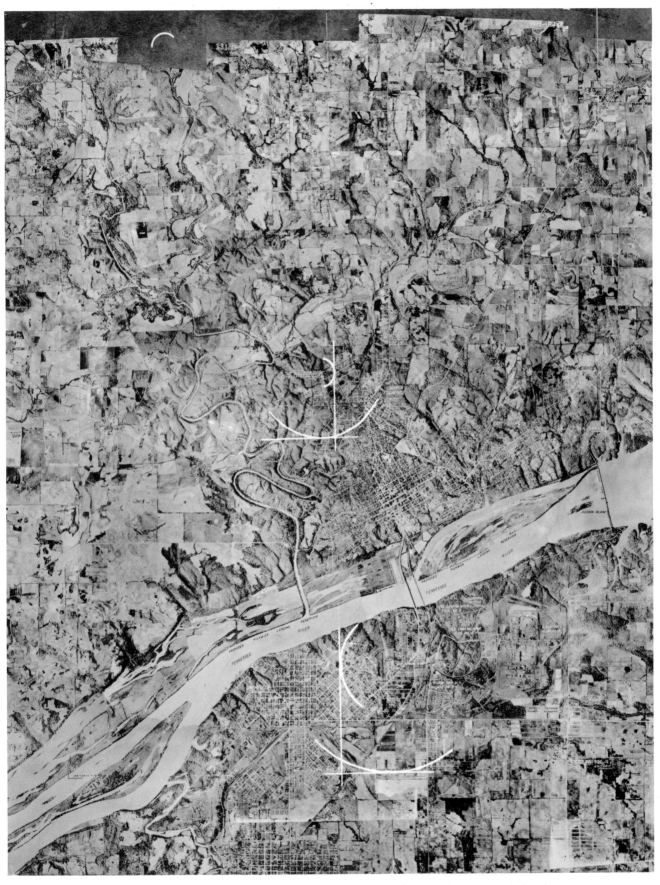

Figure 1-13. A *controlled mosaic* of the area shown in Figure 1-12. (*By permission from Edgar Tobin Aerial Surveys.*)

Figure 1-14. An uncontrolled mosaic made with conventional undodged photographs. (*Photographs courtesy of Mark Hurd Aerial Surveys, Inc.; mosaic reproduction by Hotchkiss Mapping Company.*)

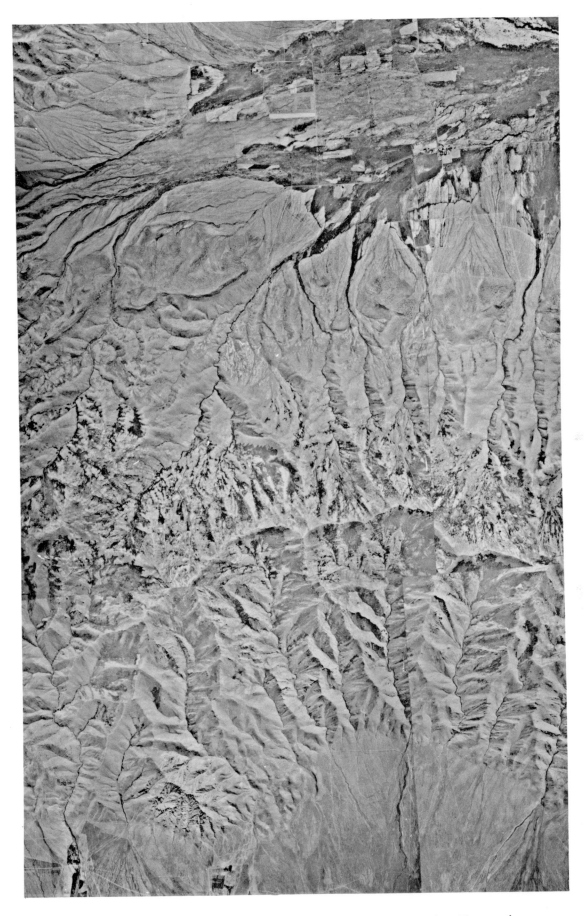

Figure 1-15. An uncontrolled mosaic made with electronically dodged prints. The negatives used were the same as those from which the undodged prints of Figure 1-14 were made. (*Photographs courtesy of Mark Hurd Aerial Surveys, Inc.; dodging device manufactured by LogEtronics, Inc.; mosaic reproduction by Hotchkiss Mapping Company.*)

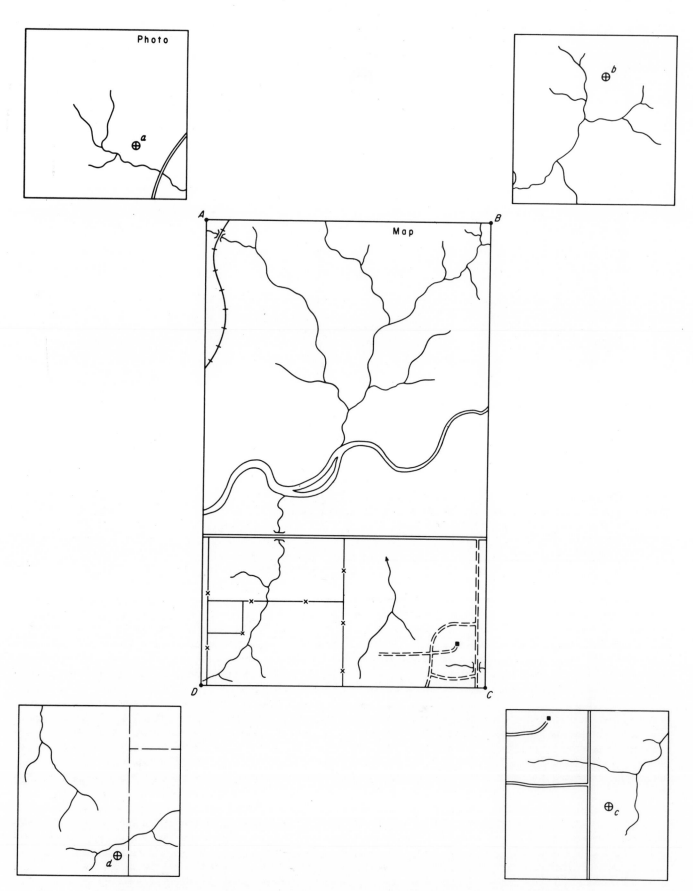

Figure 1-16. Mosaic corner points located on map and identified on photographs. Capital letters are map corners; lower-case letters are corresponding photographic points.

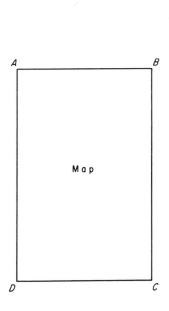

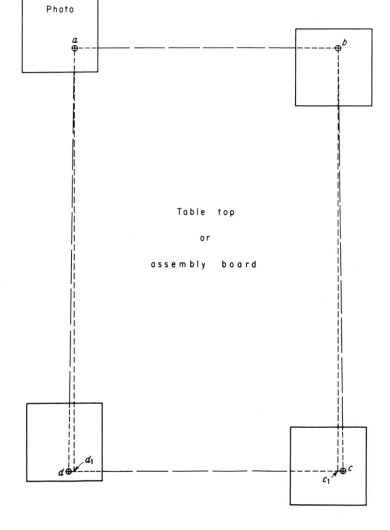

Figure 1-17. Mosaic corners *a, b, c,* and *d* positioned to provide correct dimensional proportions. Flight line from point *b* to point *c* may be laid out first; then distances *ab* and *cd* may be computed to correspond with map distances *AB* and *CD.*

plotted on the layout table or board surface. Through a complex procedure the assembled aerial photographs are oriented and located with reference to the control and to each other. Only the central portion of each photograph is used; minimum image displacements due to topographic relief occur in this part of a photograph.

Photogeologists use, but rarely have the opportunity or the need to construct, controlled mosaics. It is important, however, that the principles and methods of mosaic construction and reproduction be learned. Several excellent references are available, including the "Manual of Photogrammetry" (1952). In addition, an increasing number of courses in applied and theoretical photogrammetry are being conducted in colleges and universities throughout North America.

Uncontrolled mosaics may be made by all persons reasonably well acquainted with the geometric qualities of aerial photographs and with maps in general. There are several approaches to the construction of uncontrolled mosaics. One frequently used consists of the placing of each photograph against or over the next, in such a way that the corresponding images match or fit together with least offset, overlap, or duplication. In areas of uniformly low or moderate topography, this method may be acceptable, since photograph scale is relatively constant. In areas of severe topographic relief, or of variable topography, this method may produce serious differences in mosaic scale from one part to the next. A large square ground area, for example, may appear as a quadrangle having four sides of different lengths and three or four nonrectangular corners. This is especially disadvantageous if several mosaics, which are later to be fitted together, are to be made. Of course, if there is no planimetric control available, there is no alternative.

If the area to be mosaiced is covered by a reasonably accurate topographic or planimetric map, a dimensionally proportional mosaic can be constructed. For example, Figure 1-16 depicts a 15-minute quadrangle map of ground area *ABCD,* for which a mosaic is required.

The first step consists of locating on the photographs the images of the four corner points, *a, b, c,* and *d.*

Sides *AD* and *BC* are of equal length. If the area is in the northern hemisphere, side *AB* is shorter than side *DC,* and both are shorter than side *BC.* The proportional lengths of sides *AB* and *DC* to side *BC* can be obtained by measuring these sides on the map. More precise proportions can be obtained from standard tables which list the exact lengths of 15 minutes of longitude and latitude in the area.

In the area shown, assume that $AB:BC = 63:100$, and that $DC:BC = 64:100$.

On the assembly board or table, lay out the photographs that cover side *BC,* maintaining the closest possible image match (Figure 1-17). Measure the distance *bc.* The lengths of sides *ab* and *dc* can be calculated, using the above proportions.

Area *abcd* will not be a rectangle. It will be a quadrangle, as is the map. Lines *ab* and *dc* must not be laid off perpendicular to side *bc*. Their direction can be determined by construction.

A quadrangle may be thought of as consisting of a rectangle (abc_1d_1) plus two marginal wedges (d_1ad and c_1bc). If, in the present case, side *dc* is 0.2 inch longer than side *ab*, the south end of each wedge will be 0.1 inch wide.

Measure 0.1 inch in from point *c* to point c_1. Lay a straightedge along line bc_1. Erect perpendiculars to ends *b* and c_1, and measure off distance *ab* on the north line and *ab* +0.1 inch on the south line. Mark points *a* and *d* at the ends of these lines.

The photographic images of these two points, previously identified on the photographs, are then placed in their proper tentative positions and secured by sharp pins inserted through the corner image points *only*. The photographs are thus free to rotate as required.

The fill-in photographs along the three remaining sides are then arranged, held in place by paperweights or map weights, and the "fit" is examined. If, as a result of scale changes, it is found that along two sides there are image omissions, and along the other two an equal amount of duplication, this is usually accepted as the solution with minimum necessary error. If the total duplication exceeds the total omission, the original flight line is relaid with small repeated omissions, in the attempt to approach a more acceptable average scale. The converse procedure is followed if there is more over-all omission and less duplication. When the four sides have been assembled and stapled down, the interior portion of the mosaic is then filled in with the remaining photographs.

This method is purely a matter of trial and error, but it is usually adequate when time is important and detailed accuracy impossible. It is the type of procedure which students and commercial geologists alike, especially those who have little or no background in photogrammetry, should find quite easy to understand and adopt.

Following mosaic construction, the usual practice is to identify and delineate in ink such features as rivers, lakes, towns, railroads, and highways. A white border is stapled to the mosaic board. A bar scale and the name or numerical designation of the mosaic area are drafted on the border. Finally, the geographical or survey coordinates are indicated. The mosaic is then photographed and reproduced.

If facilities are available, the mosaic negative may be made at final print scale, and a contact print obtained. If not, the mosaic may be photographed on a 7- by 9- or an 8- by 10-inch negative and enlarged by projection. Small negatives are less expensive, and their use permits projection printing to any larger or smaller scale or scales. Also, small mosaic negatives can be filed in manila envelopes in a standard filing cabinet. One of the disadvantages of small negatives is that when appreciable enlargements are made, some image detail is invariably lost. This may occur, for example, when a 7- by 9-inch negative is enlarged to 28 by 36 inches or larger.

If finances permit, the ideal practice is to obtain both a large negative for contact printing at final map scale and a smaller negative for possible future projection printing at different scales. Once committed to a contact-size negative, it is impossible to change scale through projection.

SOURCES OF PHOTOGRAPHS AND MOSAICS

Many governmental agencies and private aerial photograph companies sell mosaics, as well as individual aerial photographs of many areas.

An extremely valuable general index to aerial photograph coverage in the United States and its possessions is the "Status of Aerial Photography" map, compiled by the U.S. Map Information Office. It may be obtained free from the Map Information Office, U.S. Geological Survey, U.S. Department of the Interior, Washington, D.C. It shows that, with few exceptions, the entire country has been photographed at least once. Numerous areas have been photographed two or more times.

A second reference map, compiled and distributed by the Map Information Office, is "Status of Aerial Mosaics." It should be cautioned that though this map is published annually, mosaic construction is proceeding at such a rapid rate that it may be out of date in some areas by the time of publication. Therefore, in the case of areas shown as not covered by available mosaics, further inquiries should be directed to both governmental and commercial agencies before one undertakes a mosaic-construction program.

In Canada, the "Air Photographic Coverage" map may be obtained from The Map Distribution Office, Department of Mines and Technical Surveys, Ottawa, Ontario. There is no comparable index showing available mosaic coverage in Canada. For detailed information on particular areas, the National Air Photographic Library, Department of Mines and Technical Surveys, Ottawa, Ontario, should be consulted.

In general, published controlled mosaics are of excellent quality. It is virtually impossible for the average photogeologist to construct mosaics of equal control and accuracy. Therefore, it is usually advisable to purchase rather than to construct mosaics. It is important to learn the date of the photography from which such mosaics were made, however. Occasionally, available mosaics were constructed from old photographs, while stereoscopic coverage obtained may be of a more recent date. In such cases, new roads and other cultural or agricultural changes, included on the newer contact prints, will not appear on the mosaics. It is most convenient to use mosaics made from the contact prints which are to be studied.

When only particularly poor uncontrolled mosaics or photo indexes are obtainable, better results may be had by constructing one's own mosaics. Since the quality of available mosaics cannot always be anticipated, it is advisable to purchase a sample for study and comparison. If many mosaics are involved, such a precaution may effect a considerable saving of time and funds.

In some instances, only mosaics of certain scales are available. In others, the agency or company may be able to reduce or enlarge their mosaics to any scale desired. If a photogeologic map is to be made at a given scale, mosaics of the same scale should be obtained, if possible. Therefore, a preferred scale should be designated when ordering or requesting information about mosaics. The transfer of data from a mosaic to a map of the same scale is not usually difficult. Different scales may require the use of plotting instruments, or may even render such a transfer impossible in some cases.

When the photogeologist constructs his own mosaics, or orders them made, he can, of course, have them reproduced at the desired scale. Upon receipt, purchased mosaics of different scales may be enlarged or reduced photographically to facilitate the transfer of data to the base map.

For most photogeologic studies, contact prints of aerial photographs are used. In special cases, it may be necessary to obtain the photographic coverage in other forms. The various other types of prints available may include (1) enlargements, (2) film positives, (3) copy negatives, (4) multiplex diapositives, (5) Kelsh plates, and (6) transformed prints, made from either convergent or transverse low oblique photography. An order for photographic coverage should specify the type desired, and should also indicate the following: (1) agency, (2) roll numbers, and (3) photo numbers, if indexes can be consulted prior to ordering. If this information is not available, identify the area for which coverage is desired by state, province, county, and geographical or survey coordinates. The type of paper and finish should also be indicated (i.e., double- or single-weight, glossy or semimatte, etc.). For stereoscopic study, complete stereoscopic coverage is needed and consecutive prints must be requested. If the topographic relief of the area is moderate to low, and the photographs are needed solely for mosaic construction, considerable savings can be made by ordering alternate prints only.

U.S. Governmental Agencies

The following U.S. Governmental Agencies hold available photographs and mosaics:

U.S. Geological Survey

Rocky Mountain Region
Covers: Texas, New Mexico, Colorado, Wyoming, Montana, parts of southeast Utah and northeast Arizona, and Alaska east of longitude 160° W.
Address: Rocky Mountain Regional Engineer
U.S. Geological Survey
Denver, Colo.

Pacific Region
Covers: Washington, Idaho, Oregon, California, Nevada, Utah, and Arizona.
Address: Pacific Regional Engineer
U.S. Geological Survey
Sacramento, Calif.

Central Region
Covers: North Dakota, South Dakota, Nebraska, Kansas, Oklahoma, Minnesota, Wisconsin, Iowa, Illinois, Missouri, Arkansas, Louisiana, and Mississippi.
Address: Central Regional Engineer
U.S. Geological Survey
Rolla, Mo.

Atlantic Region
Covers: All eastern states.
Address: Map Information Office
U.S. Geological Survey
U.S. Department of the Interior
Washington, D.C.

Soil Conservation Service
Covers: All states from one central office.
Address: Director, Cartographic Division
Soil Conservation Service
U.S. Department of Agriculture
Washington, D.C.

Commodity Stabilization Service (formerly Production and Marketing Administration)
Western Laboratory
Covers: Washington, Oregon, California, Idaho, Nevada, Arizona, Utah, Montana, Wyoming, Colorado, New Mexico, North Dakota, and Kansas.
Address: Western Laboratory, Performance Division
Commodity Stabilization Service
U.S. Department of Agriculture
Salt Lake City, Utah

Eastern Laboratory
Covers: All eastern and central states not listed under the Western Laboratory.
Address: Eastern Laboratory, Performance Division
Commodity Stabilization Service
U.S. Department of Agriculture
Washington, D.C.

U.S. Forest Service
Western Division (divided into six regions)
Region Number 1
Covers: Montana, northwest South Dakota, northern Idaho, eastern Washington, and northwest portion of Wyoming.
Address: Regional Forester
U.S. Forest Service
Missoula, Mont.

Region Number 2
Covers: All South Dakota except northwest corner, Nebraska, Kansas, Colorado, and the eastern two-thirds of Wyoming.
Address: Regional Forester
U.S. Forest Service
Denver, Colo.

Region Number 3
Covers: New Mexico and Arizona.
Address: Regional Foester
U.S. Forest Service
Albuquerque, N.Mex.

Region Number 4
Covers: Utah, Nevada, western third of Wyoming, and southern half of Idaho.
Address: Regional Forester
U.S. Forest Service
Ogden, Utah

Region Number 5
Covers: California.
Address: Regional Forester
U.S. Forest Service
San Francisco, Calif.

Region Number 6
Covers: Oregon and western two-thirds of Washington.
Address: Regional Forester
U.S. Forest Service
Portland, Ore.

Eastern Division
Covers: All states not listed in the Western Division.
Address: Chief, Forest Service
U.S. Department of Agriculture
Washington, D.C.

U.S. Air Force
   Photographic Records and Services Division
   Washington, D.C.
Corps of Engineers
   Office, Chief of Engineers
   Department of the Army
   Washington, D.C.
Bureau of Reclamation
   U.S. Department of the Interior
   Washington, D.C.
Tennessee Valley Authority
   Maps and Surveys Division
   Chattanooga, Tenn.
Coast and Geodetic Survey
   U.S. Department of Commerce
   Washington, D.C.
Special Photography
   High-altitude Aerial Photography (1:60,000)
      Flown for the Army Map Service. Most of the United
      States, with the exception of parts of the coast, is cov-
      ered by this photography. For information, contact:
      Map Information Office
      U.S. Geological Survey
      U.S. Department of the Interior
      Washington, D.C.
   Orthophotographs (not yet available to the public)
      Inquiries concerning the progress of this program and
      the future availability of prints should be directed to:
      Map Information Office
      U.S. Geological Survey
      U.S. Department of the Interior
      Washington, D.C.

Commercial Agencies Holding Photos and Mosaics

The following list includes the names of most of the companies which undertake aerial photography projects in the
United States. Aerial photograph and mosaic coverage of
parts of the United States can be obtained from many of
these companies. Those interested in using aerial photographs in future studies are advised to request photo and
mosaic coverage indexes from these commercial companies.
Such indexes are usually procured free of charge upon
request.

Abrams Aerial Survey Corporation
Lansing, Mich.

Aero Service Corporation
Philadelphia, Pa.

Jack M. Ahearn
Salt Lake City, Utah

Air Survey Corporation
Arlington, Va.

Jack Ammann Photogrammetric Engineers, Inc.
San Antonio, Tex.

Michael Baker, Jr.
Air Maps, Inc.
Rochester, Pa.

Chicago Aerial Industries, Inc.
Melrose Park, Ill.

Fairchild Aerial Surveys, Inc.
Los Angeles, Calif.

Mark Hurd Aerial Surveys, Inc.
Minneapolis, Minn.

Lockwood, Kessler & Bartlett, Inc.
Syosset, N.Y.

Muldrow Aerial Surveys Corporation
Midland, Tex.

Pacific Air Industries
Long Beach, Calif.

Park Aerial Surveys, Inc.
Louisville, Ky.

Raynor Aerial Surveys
Georgetown, Conn.

Robinson Aeroflex, Inc.
Aerial Surveys Division
Newark, N.J.

Ryall Engineering Co.
Denver, Colo.

James W. Sewall Company
Old Town, Maine

Edgar Tobin Aerial Surveys
San Antonio, Tex.

Aerial Photograph and Mosaic Coverage by Special Contract

If available governmental or commercial photo or mosaic
coverage of a specific area is not of the required scale, type,
or date, it is possible to procure coverage by special contract.
Bids and consultation regarding the best methods of obtaining the desired photography can usually be arranged by
submitting a request to such companies as those listed above.

Foreign Aerial Photography

Most federal governments have map-information offices to
which inquiries may be directed relative to the availability of
aerial photograph coverage. Usually there are certain politi-
cal and military restrictions which must be satisfied before
such coverage can be obtained. Therefore, though coverage
is known to exist, a foreign project should not be con-
templated until all requirements have been met. Persons in
the United States wishing information concerning foreign
coverage may contact:
   Map Information Office
   U.S. Geological Survey
   U.S. Department of the Interior
   Washington, D.C.
Several commercial photograph companies have considerable coverage of foreign areas. These companies may also
contract to photograph other areas in which coverage is not
yet available. The consent of the government concerned is
usually required prior to the initiation of such a contract.
The major companies offering such coverage and services
include:

Aero Service Corporation
Philadelphia, Pa.

The Aircraft Operating Company of Africa, Ltd.
Selby, Johannesburg, South Africa

Jack Ammann Photogrammetric Engineers, Inc.
San Antonio, Tex.

Compania Mexicana Aerofoto, S.A.
Mexico, D. F., Mex.

Fairchild Aerial Surveys, Inc.
Los Angeles, Calif.

Hunting Aerosurveys, Ltd.
London, England

King Associates
Van Nuys, Calif.

Hunting Survey Corp., Ltd.
Toronto, Canada

2

Stereoscopy

VIEWING INSTRUMENTS

With training and practice, one may become proficient in the stereoscopic examination of aerial photographs without the aid of a stereoscope. Hewever, all beginners must first learn to use a stereoscope. In addition, most practicing photogeologists find that their work is greatly facilitated when a viewing device is used.

The main function of the stereoscope is to assist the viewer to focus his eyes on the photographs. It also assures the maintenance of a constant viewing distance. The two principal types of stereoscope are the *lens* and the *mirror* stereoscopes.

The *lens* stereoscope (Figure 2-1) consists of two lenses mounted in a simple frame supported by short legs. The more useful models, such as the one shown, are adjustable; lens separation can be changed to correspond with the eye base of the individual viewer. Since the lenses are fixed focus, spectacles may be worn when using this type of stereoscope. A major oil company is reported to have installed prescription lenses in the personal stereoscope of each of its photogeologists. This is an excellent idea, since it prevents possible scratches to one's glasses. However, the cost is considerable, and the more casual use of such an instrument would probably not warrant such an expenditure. Also, if more than one geologist were to use a single instrument, prescribed lenses would be precluded.

When many photographs are to be studied, and time does not permit careful positioning of the individual stereo pairs, it is common practice to place two overlapping photographs on the desk or table and move them around beneath the stereoscope until a clear three-dimensional image is obtained. In precision photogrammetric work, and when a single stereo pair is to be studied for a considerable time, greater care must be exercised to prevent errors, eyestrain, and fatigue. With individual modifications, the following procedure is suggested. The two photographs, the stereoscope lenses, and the eye base of the viewer must be parallel. The eyes of the viewer, then, will occupy a line parallel to the direction of flight.

1. Select two overlapping vertical aerial photographs.

2. Locate and mark the principal point (center) of each (points x_1 and y_2, Figure 2-2A).

3. Locate and mark on each the photo image correspond-

Figure 2-1. A lens or pocket stereoscope. This model has adjustment for lens (eye) separation. (*Courtesy of Abrams Instrument Corp.*)

ing to the principal point of the other (points y_1 and x_2, Figure 2-2B).

4. Draw a straight line across each photo, passing through the principal point and "transferred" principal point (Figure 2-2C).

5. Place the photographs on the desk, one overlapping the other, with about 2 inches between corresponding images. Using a straightedge or scale, adjust the center lines to a common control line (line VW, Figure 2-2D).

6. Place the stereoscope over the photographs. Look at the photos, and if necessary rotate the stereoscope until a single line is seen (in a twisted position, the single line appears as two).

7. If stereoscopic vision is not obtained, slowly slide one of the photographs in or out along the established line. An adjustment of less than ½ inch is usually sufficient if the viewer is accustomed to three-dimensional viewing. The beginner may find that a photographic image separation of about 1 inch is optimum. With practice, he will find an increased separation more convenient.

8. When good stereoscopy is obtained, the photographs may be secured in position with drafting or masking tape. Scotch tape is not advised, since it tends to tear the emulsion when removed. Small pieces of tape at the outer two corners of each photo are usually sufficient. The pictures can be held flat with the hands. Some photogeologists prefer to work on a flat metal plate and hold the photos in place by small but strong magnets.

It is, of course, not possible to view the entire overlap area at one time when using the lens stereoscope. Two 9- by 9-inch photographs, with 60 per cent overlap, include a common area of about 5½ by 9 inches. Average eye base is approximately 2½ inches. When the photographs are correctly positioned for stereoscopic examination, less than one-half of the overlap area can be viewed. The overlap area must, therefore, be studied in several steps. The following is suggested (a left-handed person would reverse the procedure). Assume a photograph separation of 2¼ inches.

1. Arrange the photographs for stereoscopic study (as described above) with the right photograph lying partly over the left photograph (Figure 2-3A). With the photographs in this position, study the available 2¼-inch wide left-hand strip of the overlap area. Make necessary annotations on the right photograph, in area L_2.

2. Place the left photograph partially over the right photograph (Figure 2-3B). If the photos are secured only along their outside edges or corners, this will not necessitate removing either from the desk. With the photographs thus arranged, the 2¼-inch wide right-hand strip of stereoscopic coverage may be examined, and annotation made on the right photograph, in area R_2 (Figure 2-3B).

3. There remains a 1-inch-wide central strip (M) of the area of stereoscopic coverage which has not yet been viewed. The only convenient way to uncover this area on the lower (right) photograph is to bend up the right edge of the left photograph (Figure 2-3C). While the thumb and forefinger of the left hand are used to curl up the edge of the left photograph, the remainder of the hand holds it flat on the desk. The right hand is thus free to annotate on the right photograph in area M_2.

The *mirror* stereoscope (Figure 2-4) consists of two mirrors at positions A, supported at an angle of 45° to the horizontal, and either two 45° prisms or two small mirrors at positions B. The chief advantage of the mirror stereoscope

is that it permits the simultaneous examination of all or most of the overlap area, since the photographs are separated and do not obscure one another. Its disadvantage is that the photographs appear to be at about arm's length; hence, the scale of the image is quite small. Several mirror instruments have binocular attachments (such as shown in Figure 2-4), which permit the viewing of part of the overlap area at an enlarged scale. Thus, in the study of a stereo pair, one may obtain a small-scale regional impression first, and then introduce the binoculars to study selected critical features in more detail. This combines the better features of the mirror and lens stereoscopes.

The correct procedure for positioning photographs for viewing with the mirror stereoscope is essentially the same

Figure 2-2. Arranging photographs for viewing with lens stereoscope. (A) Mark principal point of each photograph. (B) "Transfer" principal points y_1 and x_2. (C) Establish line through principal point and "transferred" (conjugate) principal point of each photograph. (D) Adjust lines to single control line (VW), separation to be determined by eye base and instrument used.

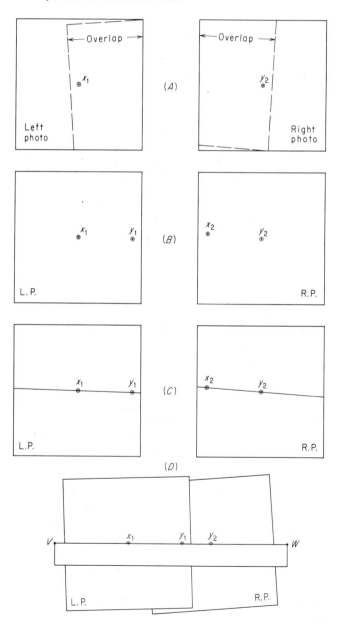

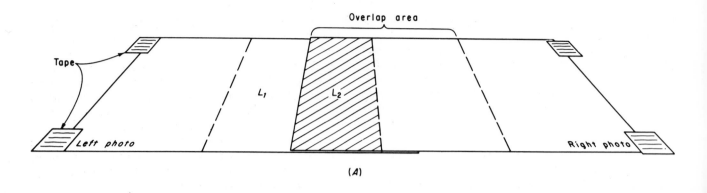

(A)

(B)

(C)

Figure 2-3. Method of studying entire overlap area when using lens stereoscope. (*A*) With right photograph overlapping, examine left part of overlap area (*L₁* and *L₂*). (*B*) With left photograph overlapping, examine right part of overlap area (*R₁* and *R₂*). (*C*) Curl up right edge of left photograph and examine middle part of overlap area (*M₁* and *M₂*).

as for the lens stereoscope. The principal points are marked and "transferred," and the extended center lines are drawn. The parallel arrangement of center lines and stereoscope is required. Only the separation of the photographs is different. The photographs should be securely fixed to assure their lying as flat as possible during study and annotation.

A special type of reflection stereoscope is the Old Delft Scanning Stereoscope (Figure 2-5). It is mounted with the oculars inclined at an angle of 45°. This affords a more comfortable viewing position and, as shown, has the particular advantage of permitting the simultaneous study of a single stereo pair by two persons. In school laboratories and in commercial training programs this is especially useful, since both student and instructor can view the same features at the same time.

NORMAL VISION AND DEPTH PERCEPTION

The process of three-dimensional vision is extremely complex. Since a detailed analysis of this subject cannot be given here, the following discussion will be limited to the two most important and most easily understood factors in normal seeing: focus and eye convergence.

In Figure 2-6*A*, the left eye l is directed along line lA toward object A. Its lens accommodates to focus at distance lA, which may be represented by the approximate viewing distance d_a. The right eye r is directed along line rA; it also focuses at distance d_a. The lines of sight converge at point A to form angle α. Focus and convergence are intimately coordinated; a convergence of α is automatically accompanied by focus adjustment to viewing distance d_a.

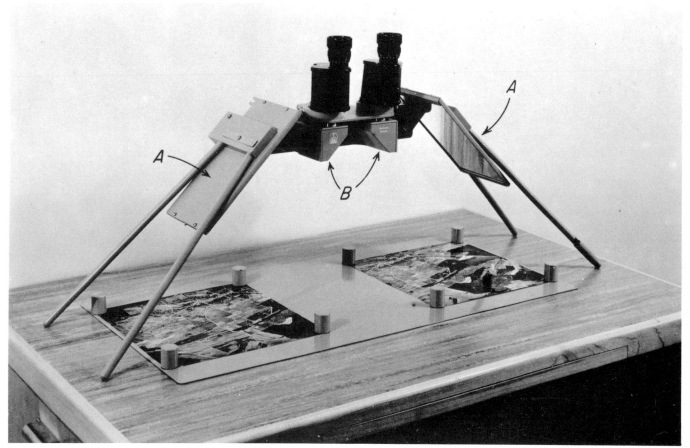

Figure 2-4. A mirror stereoscope, with binocular attachment. Mirrors at 45° to the horizontal are at *A;* mirrors or prisms, also at 45°, at *B*. Photos are held flat on metal plate by small magnets. (*Courtesy of Transmares Corporation, sole agents for Zeiss Aerotopograph.*)

Figure 2-5. Two Old Delft Scanning Stereoscopes positioned for simultaneous examination of a single stereo pair by two persons. (*Courtesy of N.Y. Optische Industrie "De Oude Delft."*)

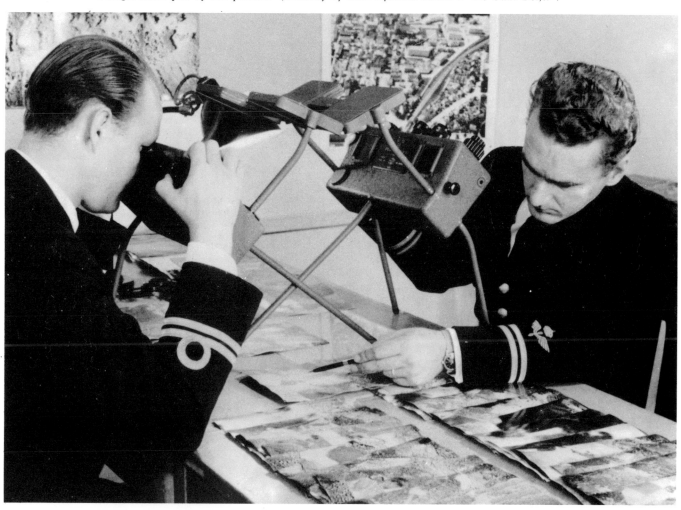

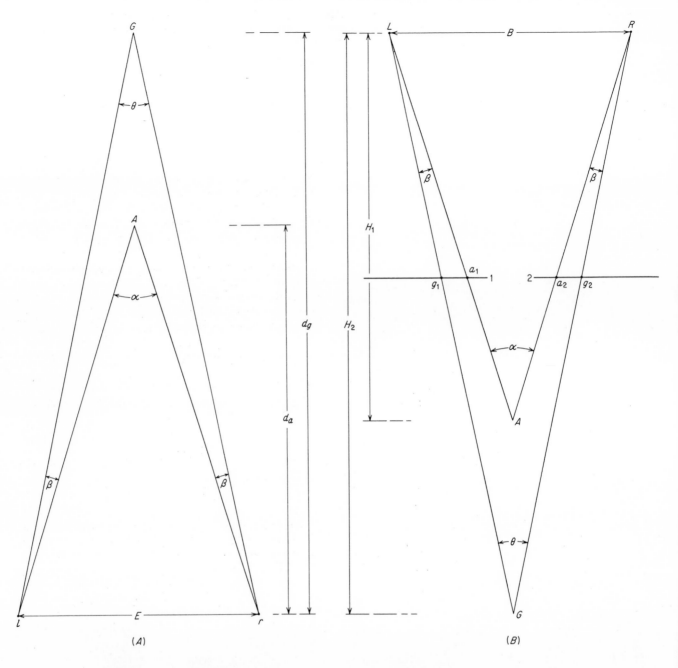

Figure 2-6. (*A*) Eye-object relation in normal three-dimensional viewing. (*B*) Camera-object relation in stereoscopic aerial photography.

When point *A* is viewed, the convergence and focus do not permit the simultaneous coordinated viewing of point *G*. To *look at* point *G* clearly, the eyes must be rotated through the angles β, to converge at this point. The new, smaller angle of convergence is angle θ. The viewing distance (focus) is increased from d_a to d_g.

The geometry of the eye-object relation is duplicated in the camera-ground relation in aerial photography (see Figure 2-6*B*). Low ground point *G* and high ground point *A* are photographed from camera positions *L* and *R*, which are separated by distance *B* (air base). Camera height above *A* is H_1, and above *G* is H_2. Rays of light from point *G* pass along lines *GL* and *GR*; those from point *A* pass along lines *AL* and *AR*. These rays form angles θ and α. The angles between the incoming rays, at the camera stations, are small angles β.

Lines 1 and 2 in Figure 2-6*B* represent prints of the photographs obtained from camera stations *L* and *R*. The light rays from the two ground points intercept the prints at image points g_1, a_1, a_2, and g_2. There is a direct relation between angles β and image distances g_1a_1 and a_2g_2. Since angles β are determined by the vertical ground distance *GA*, it follows that image distances g_1a_1 and a_2g_2 *represent* vertical ground distance *GA*. Image distances of this type are called *parallax* differentials produced by relief. Instruments have been devised to measure parallax differences on aerial photographs. Such data can be used to obtain accurate ground heights, slope gradients, and the like. Several photogrammetric instruments are described briefly in a later chapter.

Next, consider the process of *mentally* viewing an object. In Figure 2-7, the left eye *l* views side *AG* of the triangle more squarely than it does side *GK*. Conversely, the right *pean eye* (*c*). The combined focus-convergence device may be said to instruct the cyclopean eye as to the correct distance that the model should be projected. We may refer to this type of projection as *cyclopean projection,* as distinguished from the concept of *convergence projection.*

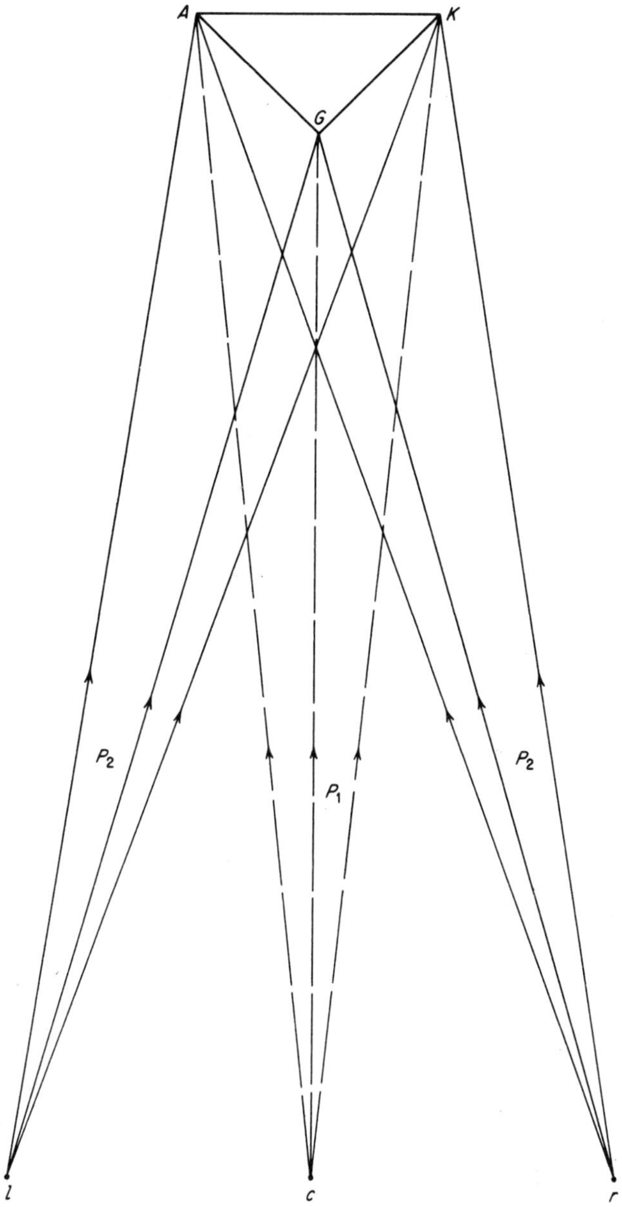

According to the convergence theory, the brain, after receiving the retinal images, composes them into a solid model and projects them back outward, through the eyes, along the lines followed inward by the light rays from the object viewed. This projection would follow lines P_2 in Figure 2-7.

For considerable time the principles of stereoscopy have been illustrated by geometric constructions designed to fit the convergence theory. Such figures are easy to construct, but they do not appear to adhere to reality, since experience and experimentation indicate that something very similar to cyclopean projection actually takes place. However, the latter phenomenon cannot be depicted by simple understandable geometric figures. Therefore, in order to show the effects of the several photographic and stereoscopic variables on the stereoscopic model, convergence-type drawings will be used in the following discussion.

STEREOSCOPIC VISION

The geometry of stereoscopic vision, as explained by the convergence theory, is illustrated in Figure 2-8. Object A is viewed from eye positions l and r. Viewing distance may be said to be d. Eye convergence is angle α. Were two glass plates (1 and 2) placed at distance d_1 from the eyes, light rays from object A to eyes l and r would pass through the plates at points a_1 and a_2.

Figure 2-8. Geometry of stereoscopic vision and the establishment of the *virtual fixation point* A_2 and the *virtual fixation distance* d_2. (*Adapted from Raasveldt, 1956, Fig. 5.*)

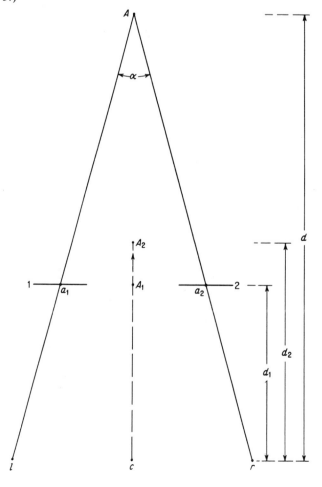

Figure 2-7. Comparison between *convergence* and *cyclopean* projection theories, in normal vision. (*Adapted from Raasveldt, 1956, Fig. 1.*)

eye r receives a fuller impression of side GK than of side AG. The two unlike retinal images are transmitted to the brain, where they are combined into a solid mental impression or model of the original figure. But we do not *see* or *experience seeing* objects inside our brains; we see them in what is usually their correct positions in space before and around us. This can only be true if the brain can somehow *project* the model outward. Such a process can only be imagined. The remarkable thing is that two flat optical images are received and one solid mental model must be projected!

Raasveldt (1956) proposes that while the optic nerves deliver the two unlike images to the brain, an imaginary third eye, located in the middle of the forehead, accomplishes the external projection of the solid model (along lines P_1 in Figure 2-7). He calls this third eye the *mental* or *cyclo-*

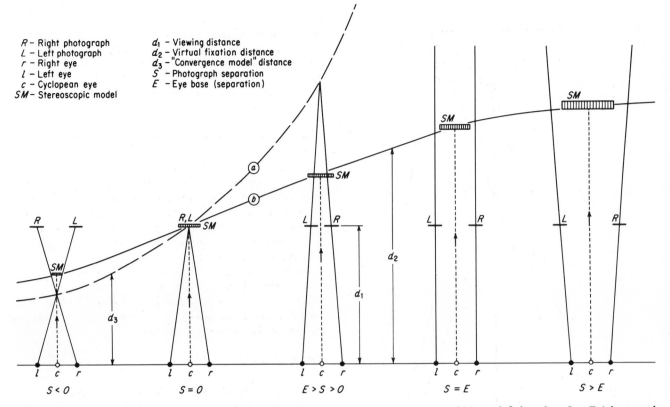

R – Right photograph
L – Left photograph
r – Right eye
l – Left eye
c – Cyclopean eye
SM – Stereoscopic model

d_1 – Viewing distance
d_2 – Virtual fixation distance
d_3 – "Convergence model" distance
S – Photograph separation
E – Eye base (separation)

Figure 2-9. Changes in *virtual fixation distance* (along line *b*) with changes in photograph separation. Dashed line *a* would be the positions of the stereoscopic model, according to the convergence theory; it would be at infinity when $S = E$ (photograph separation equals eye separation). (*After Raasveldt, 1956, Fig. 5.*)

Let us suppose that plates 1 and 2 were instantly transformed into photographic prints and held in their present positions, with photograph *images* a_1 and a_2 located where shown. Thinking in terms of light rays, projection, and convergence only, it would be reasonable to assume that the eyes would receive the impressions of points a_1 and a_2, transfer them to the brain, and that the brain would then mentally project the model outward, back to its correct position in space (point A).

But this is not what happens! *Both* viewing distance (focus) *and* convergence must be considered. The convergence apparatus would say that the model should be at point A. But the eyes are focused at distance d_1. Therefore, the focus apparatus would insist that the model not be beyond point A_1. A compromise must be and is reached. The model is *seen* to lie at point A_2, between the two extremes but closer to point A_1.

Point A_2 cannot be located by direct geometric construction, since its distance from the eyes is determined by a complex mental process involving several factors. It can best be visualized as being projected outward from the cyclopean eye c a distance d_2 mutually agreeable to the convergence and focus mechanisms. Point A_2 is termed the *virtual fixation point* by Raasveldt (1956). Its distance (d_2) from the eye base may be referred to as the *virtual fixation distance*.

The location of the virtual fixation point will vary with different viewing conditions. Figure 2-9 qualitatively shows the positions of this critical point for various photograph separations.

VERTICAL EXAGGERATION—INTRODUCTION

The three-dimensional mental model obtained by the stereoscopic study of two aerial photographs is seldom an accurate replica of the terrain depicted. In most cases, the relief appears more severe than it actually is in nature. This is produced when the vertical scale of the model exceeds the horizontal scale (positive exaggeration). When the vertical scale is the smaller, the model is said to have *negative exaggeration*.

Vertical exaggeration is extremely important when one must estimate slopes, dips, strata thicknesses, and fault displacements. During the past few years several technical papers have been written presenting qualitative and quantitative analyses of exaggeration and other model distortions. Since the general subject is still being investigated by various authorities, and since there remains some disagreement as to methods of calculating the exaggeration factor, the following material is presented in a descriptive and generalized form. The advanced student of photogeology should study the several papers dealing with this subject.

The relation of vertical exaggeration to slope or dip exaggeration is diagrammatically illustrated in Figure 2-10. Point J represents the peak, and line AG the base of a hill which has been photographed. Suppose that when the photographs of this hill are observed stereoscopically, the peak appears to be at point K. Point K is twice as high, relative to base AG, as the original peak J. The hill appears vertically exaggerated; the exaggeration factor is 2.00.

The angle JAG (α) is equal to the true slope of side AJ. This true slope will appear on the exaggerated terrain model as apparent slope KAG (β). Whereas the hill appears twice as high as it really is, the apparent slope β is not twice that of the true slope α.

$$\text{Tangent of angle } \alpha = \frac{JG}{AG}$$

$$\text{Tangent of angle } \beta = \frac{KG}{AG}$$

Since the base of the hill (AG) may be considered as unity, the *tangents* of the angles (α and β) are seen to vary with vertical exaggeration. When reducing apparent model dip and slope estimations to their true values, one must use their tangent relation.

Vertical exaggerations frequently range from 2 to 5 or more. Those of 2.5 to 4 are the more common. Figure 2-11 is a graph showing the relation of true and apparent dip (slope) and vertical exaggeration. An estimated apparent dip or slope value, when checked against the exaggeration factor, can be converted to a true value.

Before some of the methods of determining the amount of vertical exaggeration are considered, the various reasons for its presence will be examined.

If possible, concepts should be presented graphically. Figure 2-7 illustrates the basic relation between the convergence and cyclopean projection theories in normal vision. Experience and experiment combine to support the cyclopean theory in normal vision and as a way of understanding stereo vision. The comparison is expanded, in Figure 2-12, to include the basic geometric principles involved in the stereoscopic viewing of a solid form.

Figure 2-12A depicts the viewing of photographs 1 and 2 from eye positions l and r. The photographs contain images of a pyramid.

When these photographs are viewed stereoscopically, the convergence theory would assume that the solid mental model created would be pyramid G, a distance D_1 from the eyes. Model G is obtained geometrically by extending the lines of sight from the eyes to the photographs (i.e., from l and r to images a_1 and a_2).

The cyclopean theory suggests that rather than appearing as model G, the pyramid will appear as model K, at a distance d_1 from the eyes (virtual fixation distance).

Note that model K appears less elongate vertically than model G.

Should one or more factors (to be discussed below) cause the convergence model G_1 (in Figure 2-12B) to fall farther away from the eyes (distance D_2) and appear even more extended (exaggerated), the corresponding cyclopean model K_1 would similarly retreat (to virtual fixation distance d_2) and become more exaggerated. This is an illustration of an observed phenomenon. It is not a geometric proof. The importance of these figures is that they demonstrate that it is possible to show, by using such models as G and G_1, the manner in which the corresponding cyclopean models K and K_1 are affected by what may be termed the *exaggeration variables*.

FACTORS AFFECTING VERTICAL EXAGGERATION

What causes vertical exaggeration? Why is it not the same for all aerial photographs? When two individuals look through a stereoscope at a given pair of photographs, do they actually *see* the same terrain? If not, why not? These are some of the questions which must be considered and for which answers must be sought.

When a ground feature is photographed from two air stations, as in Figure 2-13A, there is established a fixed ratio between camera height H and air base B. Were it possible to view the two photographs in such a way that the same ratio could be achieved, as in Figure 2-13B, between virtual fixation distance d_1 and eye base E, a true three-dimensional

scale model of the terrain would be seen. This would require that the eyes be positioned above the respective photograph principal points p_1 and p_2. Mirror stereoscopes may permit the eyes to be, in effect, above the principal points, but distance d_1 would, in most cases, be much too long. Lens stereoscopes preclude the possibility of such an eye-photograph relation. Since stereoscopic conditions cannot simulate the geometry of overlap photography, an unreal, exaggerated stereoscopic model is to be expected.

What factors of photography and stereoscopy may vary and thus cause or change vertical exaggeration? Variable photographic factors are air base B, focal length f, and camera height H. Variable stereoscopic factors are viewing distance d, photograph separation s, and eye base E. A change in any one of these variables will produce a change in the amount of vertical exaggeration, as geometrically illustrated below. Again note that the diagrams used here are drawn according to the convergence theory. They are intended to illustrate, in principle, the corresponding variations brought about in the cyclopean model.

Photographic Variables

When aerial photography is planned, camera focal length f, approximate or average camera height H, and approximate air base B are predetermined. Thus, before the plane leaves the ground, several of the factors which affect vertical exaggeration are relatively fixed. In any two missions, one or more of the factors may be changed. Therefore, different photography should be assumed to possess different amounts of vertical exaggeration until proven otherwise. Also, it should be remembered that air base frequently varies within a single flight, or between adjacent flights, though usually this variation is relatively small. Occasionally, variation in air base is sufficiently great to cause a noticeable variation in exaggeration.

Air Base. Desired overlap is determined prior to photography. Usually 60 per cent overlap is prescribed. Greater or less overlap may result from changes in ground speed, significant topographic relief differences, or other factors for which the photographer is not able to compensate. There are other occasions when greater or less overlap is desired. Hence, the photogeologist should realize that though there is a standard desired overlap, the photographs with which he is working may have a different overlap, or even a

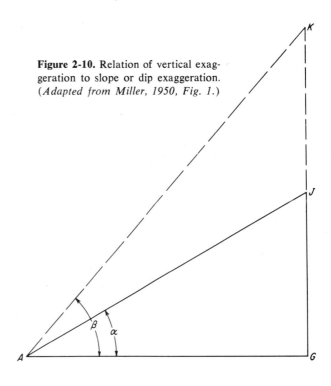

Figure 2-10. Relation of vertical exaggeration to slope or dip exaggeration. (*Adapted from Miller, 1950, Fig. 1.*)

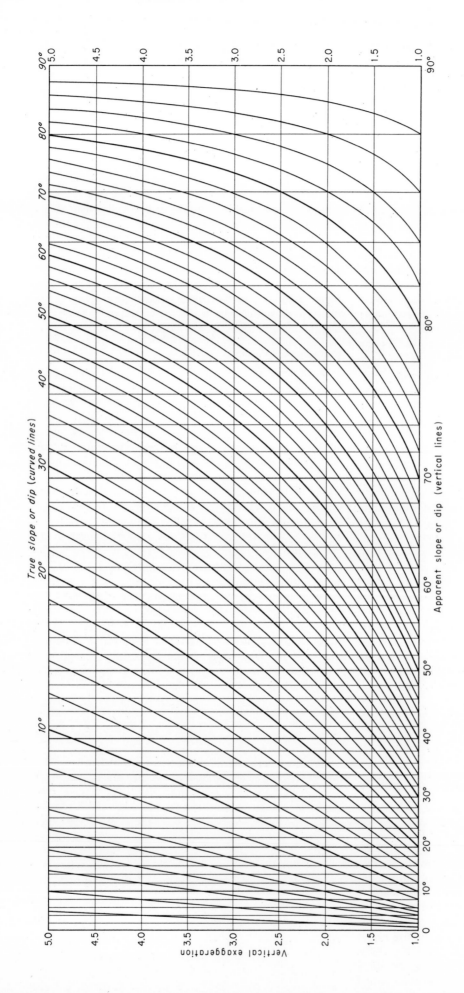

Figure 2-11. Graph showing relation of true and apparent dip and slope and vertical exaggeration. Graph is plotted on log paper for greater clarity in higher dip range.

varying overlap. In areas of low to medium relief, where overlap is primarily determined by air base, changes in overlap indicate changes in air base; the greater the overlap, the shorter the air base.

Figure 2-14A illustrates the relations existing when short-air-base B_1 and long-air-base B_2 photography are used to obtain overlapping coverage of a pole (AG) and given ground distance (JK). Pole height is half the ground distance. For the sake of simplicity, only those portions of the photographs which intercept the light rays from ground to lenses are shown.

Figure 2-14B shows the viewing of photographs 1 and 2, which were obtained from air base B_1. Figure 2-14C shows the viewing of photographs 3 and 4, taken from air base B_2. In both instances, photograph separation s, eye base E, and viewing distance d are the same.

The vertical exaggeration of the model shown in Figure 2-14C is considerably greater than that of Figure 2-14B, where the photographs used were taken with the smaller air base. This indicates a *direct relation between air base and vertical exaggeration.* Since air-base variation produces in-

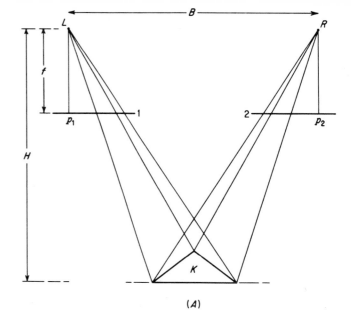

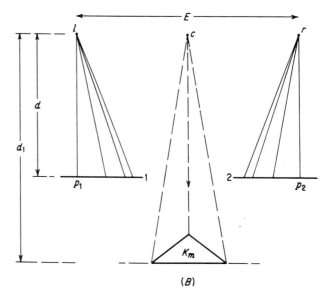

Figure 2-13. (A) Overlapping aerial photography taken from camera height H and air base B. (B) Hypothetical stereoscopic viewing of the overlap photography obtained in part (A), with ratio of eye base to virtual fixation distance (E/d_1) equal to photographic base-height ratio (B/H). Stereoscopic model (K_m) is *not* exaggerated vertically.

verse overlap change, vertical exaggeration may also be said to vary *inversely with overlap.*

Figure 2-15A is a constructed stereogram of a pyramid. The overlap represented is 30 per cent. Figure 2-15B is a constructed stereogram of the same pyramid; overlap is 60 per cent. A study of these figures streoscopically will demonstrate the change in vertical exaggeration caused by overlap (air-base) change. For practice, the student may wish to estimate the apparent slopes in each pyramid model. Since true slope is 45°, the vertical exaggeration for each model can be determined by referring to Figure 2-11.

Focal Length. Focal length is one of the two factors which determine photograph scale. Photographs 1 and 2 in Figure 2-16A have a smaller scale than photographs 3 and 4 in the same figure, since a change in focal length produces a corresponding change in scale, when camera height H remains constant. Air base B is also shown as constant.

Figure 2-16B depicts the viewing of photographs 1 and 2. Figure 2-16C shows the viewing of photographs 3 and 4.

Figure 2-12. Change in stereoscopic model (G to G_1), shown by construction following the convergence theory, and comparable change in cyclopean theory model (K to K_1), which cannot be shown by construction.

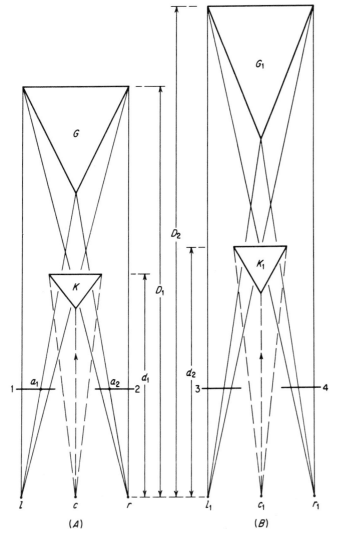

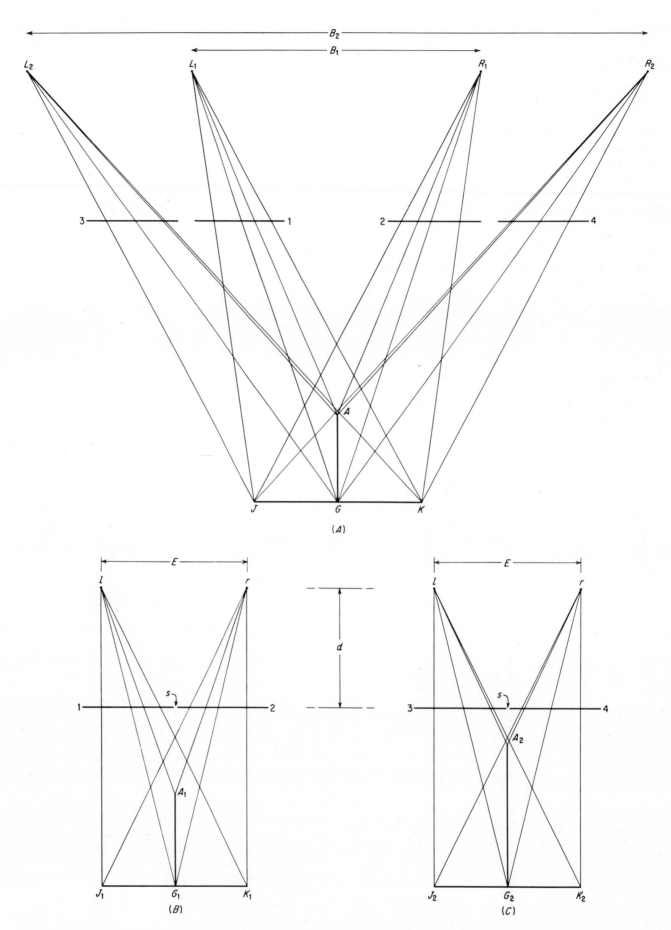

Figure 2-14. Effect of air base (overlap) on vertical exaggeration. (*A*) Overlap photography from camera stations L_1 and R_1 (short-air-base B_1) and from L_2 and R_2 (long-air-base B_2). (*B*) Viewing photographs 1 and 2 (short-air-base photography). (*C*) Viewing photographs 3 and 4 (long-air-base photography). (*Adapted from Miller, 1953.*)

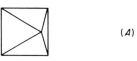

Figure 2-15. Illustration of effect of overlap on vertical exaggeration. (*A*) Stereogram representing 30 per cent overlap. (*B*) Stereogram (of same pyramid) representing 60 per cent overlap.

Figure 2-16. Effect of focal length on vertical exaggeration. (*A*) Short-focal-length (f_1) photography, pictures 1 and 2; and long-focal-length (f_2) photography, pictures 3 and 4. (*B*) Viewing photographs 1 and 2 (short-focal-length photography). (*C*) Viewing photographs 3 and 4 (long-focal-length photography). (*Adapted from Miller, 1953.*)

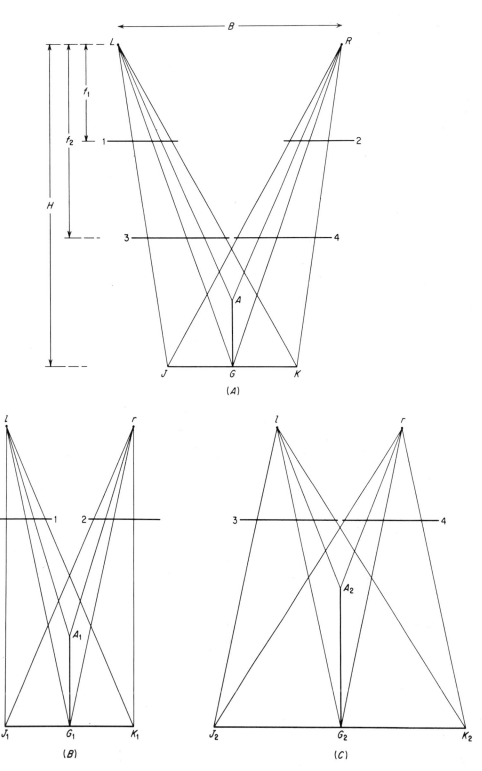

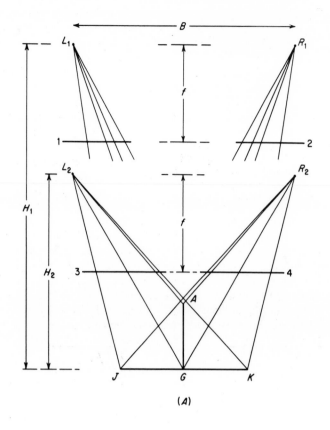

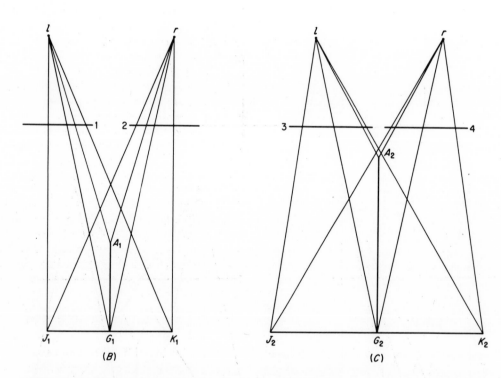

Figure 2-17. Effect of camera height on vertical exaggeration. (*A*) Photographs 1 and 2 are taken from greater camera height (H_1) than are photographs 3 and 4 (H_2). (*B*) Viewing greater-camera-height photographs 1 and 2. (*C*) Viewing lesser-camera-height photographs 3 and 4. (*Adapted from Miller, 1953.*)

The vertical exaggeration resulting from viewing photographs 1 and 2 is greater than that produced by viewing photographs 3 and 4 under the same conditions. This illustrates that there is an *inverse relation between vertical exaggeration and focal length.*

Note that both sets of photographs were taken from the same air stations (L and R). In general, a change in focal length (with height constant) is accompanied by a change in air base, to maintain adequate overlap. Therefore, it must be cautioned that though Figure 2-16 demonstrates the principle of the effect of focal-length change, it does not show a representative situation. When photo dimensions (i.e., 9 by 9 inches) are the same, an increase in focal length must be accompanied by a decrease in air base. These would reinforce each other, since each change would cause a decrease in vertical exaggeration.

Camera Height. Variations in camera height produce inverse variations in scale; an increase in height, for example, produces a decrease in photograph scale. Photographs 1 and 2 in Figure 2-17A have a smaller scale than photographs 3 and 4; focal length f is the same in both instances. Air base B is also shown as constant.

Figure 2-17B diagrammatically depicts the stereoscopic examination of photographs 1 and 2. Figure 2-17C shows the examination of photographs 3 and 4 under the same viewing conditions. The vertical exaggeration shown in Figure 2-17B is substantially less than that in Figure 2-17C. Vertical exaggeration varies *inversely with camera height.*

Each of the three illustrations discussed above demonstrates the effect produced by variations of *one* of the photographic variables; air base, focal length, or camera height. Usually, contrasts between different photography result from changes in more than one of the variables. These changes may either reinforce or cancel each other in their cumulative effect on vertical exaggeration.

Stereoscopic Variables

The several variable factors described above involve aerial photography; their effects on vertical exaggeration are impressed at the time the photographs are made. The variable factors described in the following paragraphs involve stereoscopy. They may be changed, with or without the photogeologist's knowledge, at the time the photographs are being viewed. For one individual, of course, eye base is constant. If several persons study the same photographs, eye base is usually a variable.

Figure 2-18 illustrates the effects of the stereoscopic variables on vertical exaggeration. When referring to this figure, the student is again cautioned to remember that whereas the figures illustrate the principles involved, the diagrams themselves are not intended to be true dimensional representations of the geometry of stereoscopy. While the variable effects shown in Figure 2-18 are pronounced, some of the actual corresponding variations in vertical exaggeration experienced during stereoscopy may be extremely small.

Viewing Distance. Figure 2-18A shows the viewing of photographs 1 and 2 from eye positions l_1 and r_1, a distance d_1 from the photographs. The hypothetical mentally projected stereoscopic model seen by the viewer is shown as pole image A_1G_1 and ground distance image J_1K_1. In Figure 2-18B, the same photographs, with the same photograph separation s_1, are seen from eye positions l_2 and r_2. Eye separation E_1 is the same as in Figure 2-18A, but the viewing distance d_2 is greater. Note the effect of increased

viewing distance on the stereoscopic model. Pole image height A_2G_2 is much greater compared to ground image distance J_2K_2. Vertical exaggeration is thus greater when viewing distance is increased. *Vertical exaggeration varies directly with viewing distance.*

If the student can view photographs stereoscopically without the aid of a stereoscope, he may demonstrate the effect of changing viewing distance. It is usually easiest to obtain unassisted stereoscopic vision by holding the photographs a distance of about eighteen inches from the eyes. Common images on the two photographs should be separated approximately two inches—slightly less if the viewer is inexperienced. One of the stereograms in this book may be selected for this purpose. After stereoscopic vision is obtained, the student should study the terrain carefully, noting the relative relief, slope grades, and object heights. Then, slowly but steadily the photographs should be moved closer to the eyes, until a strain is felt in the eye muscles or stereoscopic vision is lost. Repeated, back and forth, the movement of the photographs will cause slight variations in apparent topographic relief and slopes. As viewing distance is decreased, hills and ridges will become more subdued, slopes will become more gentle, and valleys less deeply incised. Conversely, with increased viewing distance, these features will become more bold and severe. Note the mentally located (projected) position of the stereo model as this experiment is carried out. When the photos are near, the model should appear to lie immediately behind them; when they are held more distant, the model should retreat to greater distances behind the page.

Photograph Separation. When two photographs are placed beneath the stereoscope, their separation is determined by the viewer. If he wishes, he may vary the separation while maintaining stereoscopic fusion. When one studies aerial photographs repeatedly, he will develop the habit of maintaining a relatively constant separation. The main reason for this is that for each person there is a separation at which eye strain is minimum or zero. However, the element of fatigue may influence one's selection of photo separation. Albrecht [1] has pointed out that he has observed a tendency to decrease separation toward the latter part of the afternoon, following several hours of intensive photo study.

If photograph separation is not kept constant, the viewer should realize that its variation introduces a similar (though usually slight) variation in vertical exaggeration. Parts (A) and (C) of Figure 2-18 show the relative change in vertical exaggeration produced by a change in photograph separation. In Figure 2-18A the separation s_1 is less, as is the vertical exaggeration. When the photographs are moved apart, the stereoscopic model appears to retreat from the eyes, but the lower topographic points (J_1, G_1, K_1) retreat more (to points J_3, G_3, K_3) than do the topographic highs (point A_1 to point A_3). The result is an increase in the apparent relief seen, hence an increase in vertical exaggeration. *Vertical exaggeration is a direct function of photograph separation.*

Using any two overlapping photographs, the student may test this relationship. He will note that unless his eyes are capable of considerable accommodation, his impressions of changing relief will not be great, since the amount of separation change is limited. It is believed that normal variations in photograph separation introduce minor changes in exaggeration. If photograph separation be maintained relatively

[1] Dr. J. C. H. Albrecht, personal communication.

39

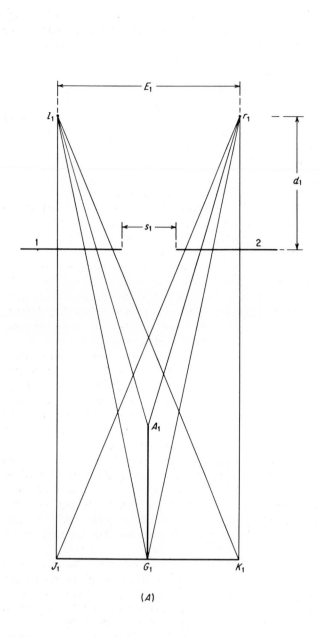

(A)

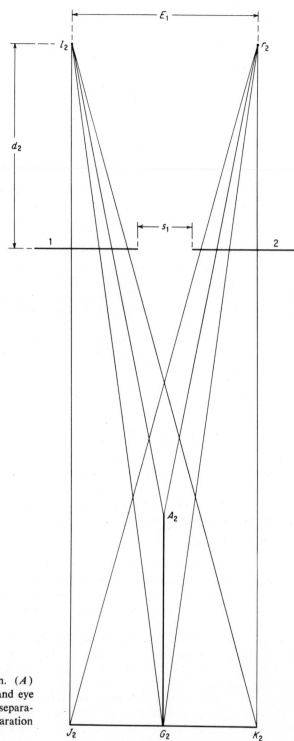

(B)

Figure 2-18. Effect of stereoscopic variables on vertical exaggeration. (*A*) Viewing a stereo pair from distance d_1, with photograph separation s_1 and eye base E_1. (*B*) Increase viewing distance to d_2. (*C*) Increase photograph separation to s_2. (*D*) Increase eye base to E_2, with increased photograph separation s_2. (*Adapted from Miller, 1953.*)

constant in practice, this factor need not be given undue attention.

Eye Base. Any one individual's eye base is, of course, fixed; hence variation in eye base must only involve the eye bases of two or more persons. If one person is conducting a photogeologic study he is not concerned with eye base as a variable. However, when two or more persons have occasion to study the same photographs, the question must be asked, "Do they *see* the same apparent stereoscopic topography, or does one see a more or less severe topography than the other?"

Compare parts (*C*) and (*D*) of Figure 2-18. In each case, viewing distance d_1 and photograph separation s_2 are the same, but eye bases E_1 and E_2 are different. When the person whose eye base is E_2 views the photographs, his impression is that he *sees* pole A_4G_4 and ground distance J_4K_4. Relative to the ground distance, the height of the pole appears more moderate to him than it does to the viewer whose eye base is E_1. *Vertical exaggeration varies inversely with eye base,* when photograph separation and viewing distance are the same.

In practice, two persons with different eye-base dimensions

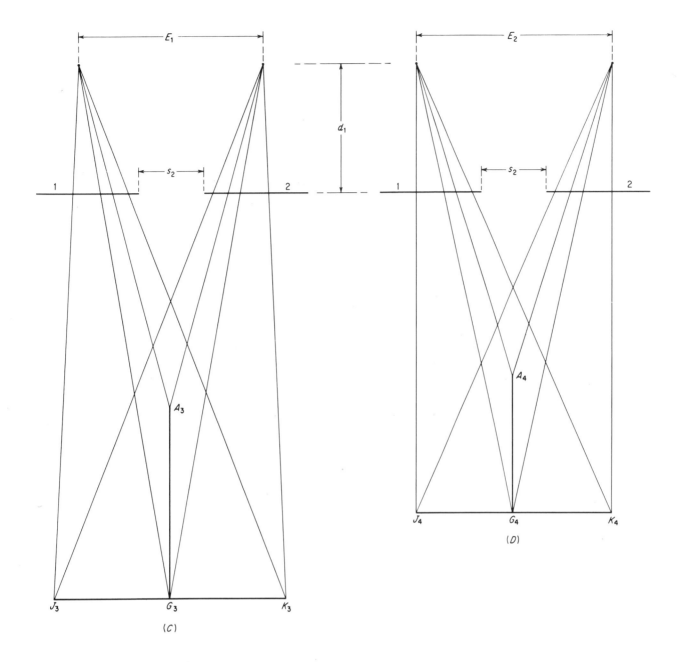

(C)

(D)

will usually select different photograph separations when each arranges his photographs for stereoscopic examination. If photo separation varies commensurately with eye base, differences in vertical exaggeration will tend to be minimized, if not entirely removed. The person with more widely spaced eyes would be expected to employ a larger photo separation. A comparison between parts (A) and (D) of Figure 2-18 illustrates this principle; in Figure 2-18A both eye base and photo separation are less than in Figure 2-18D. The two stereoscopic images are of different drawn sizes, but their proportions are approximately the same.

If, however, a person with narrowly spaced eyes habitually holds his photographs far apart, and his companion, with larger eye base, holds his photographs quite close together, they will not see the same model. Also, if one adjusts his stereoscope and photographs, and requests that another "take a look" and estimate dip, it should not be assumed that each sees the same apparent dip. Differences in dip estimation may frequently be explained on the basis of this fundamental relation.

Summary

The following facts regarding vertical exaggeration should be stressed:

1. In any one set of photographs, focal length is, of course, not a variable and need not be considered as a factor in vertical-exaggeration variation.

2. In any one set of photographs, camera height is usually relatively constant. Variation will depend on the topography photographed. In most cases, the differential relief will not be great as compared with average camera height, but in mountainous areas photographed by short-focal-length cameras the height variable may introduce noticeable exaggeration changes.

3. In any one set of photographs, constant or changing overlap may indicate constant or inversely changing air base. Variations in overlap may exist, and the photogeologist should check this factor from time to time as he studies each flight strip.

4. When different sets of photographs are used in a photogeologic study, they may possess different vertical-exaggera-

41

tion factors. If a given area is only partially covered by one set of photographs, and the remaining coverage involves another set, it is customary to obtain some duplicate photography, to facilitate ties and to ensure complete photo coverage. When such common coverage exists, the apparent topography seen in each may be compared directly, to determine the presence and effect of possible differences in vertical exaggeration. When no such common photographic coverage is present, the vertical exaggeration of each set of photographs should be obtained or estimated.

5. Generally, when stereoscopic practice is established and is more or less routine, stereoscopic variables may be considered inconsequential in comparison with photographic factors. Photograph separation is usually relatively constant, and if a single stereoscope is used, viewing distance and eye base must of necessity be constant for any one person.

In brief, vertical exaggeration varies:
1. Directly with air base B (inversely with overlap)
2. Inversely with camera focal length f
3. Inversely with camera height H
4. Directly with viewing distance d
5. Directly with photograph separation s
6. Inversely with eye base E

These variable influences may be summarized in the following qualitative expression. This is *not* a formula or equation!

$$X \alpha \frac{Bds}{fHE}$$

where X is the vertical-exaggeration factor.

DETERMINATION OF VERTICAL EXAGGERATION

At the present time, numerous individuals, companies, and governmental agencies are conducting exhaustive tests and experiments in the study of vertical exaggeration. Unfortunately, many valuable findings are still confidential and, therefore, not available. Some may never be released.

Meanwhile, there have appeared several technical papers dealing with the subject. There is a general agreement as to what factors influence exaggeration. There is none with respect to its determination.

Qualitatively speaking, the consensus appears to be that as variables, air base B, camera height H, and viewing distance d are more important than focal length f, eye base E, and photo separation s.

Some of the earlier tests to be published were those carried out by R. F. Thurrell, Jr. and V. C. Miller, and reported by the former. In his paper, Thurrell (1953) stresses the significance of air base and camera height. He states that, for any one stereoscopic viewing arrangement, exaggeration is essentially determined by the base-height ratio (B/H). By establishing the base-height ratio, one is able to obtain the corresponding approximate exaggeration.

Data were obtained through controlled experimentation. Using stereo pairs mounted at a fixed separation and a pocket lens stereoscope (fixed viewing distance), a number of photogeologists and nontechnical persons were asked to estimate the observed or apparent slopes of photographed prisms. The relations of apparent to true slope values were then used to construct exaggeration curves. That this was possible indicates the relatively small influence of eye base as a variable.

The data are assembled in Figure 2-19, which shows the relation between base-height ratio and exaggeration. Note that the dots (representing selected individual results) average out to give a straight line. The spread among the dots is interpreted to result from a general inability to estimate apparent slope precisely.

Figure 2-20 shows the calculated relations between base-height ratio and per cent overlap for photography of various focal lengths and dimensions. Figure 2-21 combines the two sets of data (from Figures 2-19 and 2-20) and permits the reading of the *average* exaggeration factor when photograph specifications (dimensions and focal length) and per cent overlap are known. It should be stressed that these charts apply only when a two-power 4½-inch focal-length lens stereoscope is used.

Several individuals and companies report that Thurrell's graphs have proven extremely helpful in dip-estimation problems. A modification or correction is usually necessary, however, because of image distortion, which is considered below.

Thurrell's work suggests that similar graphs can be constructed by further experimentation with (1) different stereoscopes and (2) different viewing conditions. It is understood that the U.S. Geological Survey is currently making a series of tests involving mirror stereoscopes.

Two papers to which attention is directed are those of Goodale (1953) and Raasveldt (1956). These authors attempt to determine mathematically accurate equations for obtaining vertical exaggeration. Goodale states, regarding his equation:

For use of the equation, the only information needed is the focal length of the air-camera lens. All other terms can be measured on a stereo pair of contact prints. The eye base and viewing distance will correspond to the individual observer and the stereoscope used, and can easily be measured.

His several illustrations and detailed analysis will not be presented here. His equation is as follows:

$$E_v = \frac{f_s (b_e + s)(b + d)}{f_a (b_e)(b_e + md)}$$

when E_v = approximate vertical-exaggeration ratio
f_s = viewing distance, or stereoscope focal distance (our d)
f_a = focal length of air-camera lens (our f)
b_e = eye base (our E)
s = print separation (our s)
b = photo base (photo image of ground distance traveled between exposures)
d = image displacement (parallax differential)
md = image displacement multiplied by the magnifying power of the stereoscope

When print separation is equal to eye base ($s = b_e$), his formula is simplified to

$$E_v = \frac{2f_s(b + d)}{f_a(b_e + md)}$$

Note that the equation does not include camera height H and air base B. However, the value d (image displacement) is determined by camera height, air base, and the differential relief of the ground object photographed (see Figure 2-6B).

Raasveldt's equation appears to be simpler than Goodale's, though one of his factors is the intangible virtual fixation

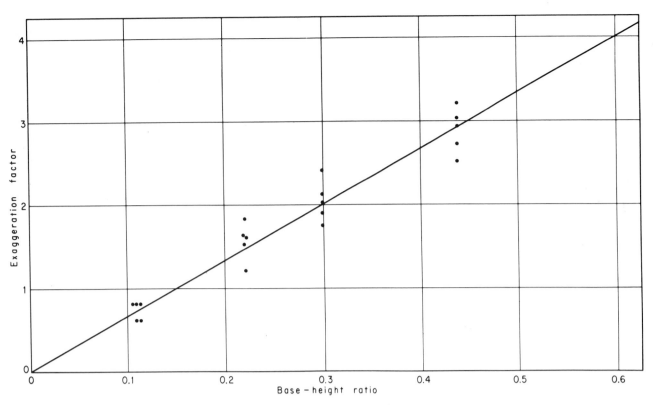

Figure 2-19. Straight-line relation between average vertical-exaggeration factor and base-height ratio. (*After Thurrell, 1953, Fig. 5.*)

Figure 2-20. Relation of film size, overlap, and focal length to base-height ratio. (*After Thurrell, 1953, Fig. 6.*)

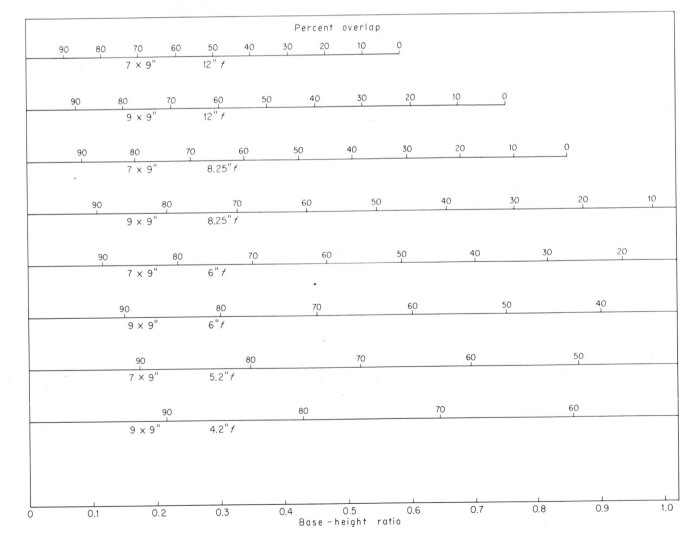

distance (F_v) determined by several variables. The equation is

$$E_v = \frac{F_v b}{Ef}.$$

when E_v = vertical exaggeration
$\quad F_v$ = estimated distance of virtual fixation point
$\quad b$ = photo base
$\quad E$ = eye base
$\quad f$ = focal length of photography

This equation does not contain viewing distance d, photo separation s, camera height H, or air base B. However, photo base is a function of H, B, and f, and F_v is established by d, s, and E.

In different forms, then, Goodale and Raasveldt directly or indirectly include factors for camera height and focal length, air base, eye base, viewing distance, and photo separation. Goodale also incorporates topographic relief, parallax, and stereoscope lens magnification into his equation.

When the photogeologist does not know the camera focal length or other information required to calculate vertical exaggeration, he may approach the problem in several other ways. These may be called the *map, field,* and *temporary-approximation* methods. In discussing each of these methods, Figure 2-11 is used as reference.

Map Method

Reliable topographic maps of the photographed area are required. Map scale should be large and contour interval small. Select about ten uniform slopes in the central parts of one or more stereo pairs. Locate them on the maps. Estimate the apparent slopes seen on the stereo model. Using contours and map scale, compute their true inclinations. By comparing the true and apparent readings, an exaggeration factor for each slope can be obtained. For example, if the apparent slope is 30°, and the true slope is 13°, the exaggeration will be read as 2.5.

Very few photogeologists attain the ability to estimate apparent slopes and dips to within a few degrees. Therefore, the individual exaggerations will not be the same for all ten slopes. If care is taken, and estimates are consistent and reasonably accurate, the range in exaggerations should not be great and an average approximate exaggeration can be calculated by arithmetic.

Once the average factor is obtained, all subsequent estimates of apparent slope *and dip* can be reduced to their true values by the use of Figure 2-11.

Field Method

In principle, the field method is the same as the map method. Prior to going into the field, select and estimate

Figure 2-21. Relation of per cent overlap to average vertical-exaggeration factor, for eight common combinations of focal length and film size. (*After Thurrell, 1953, Fig. 7.*)

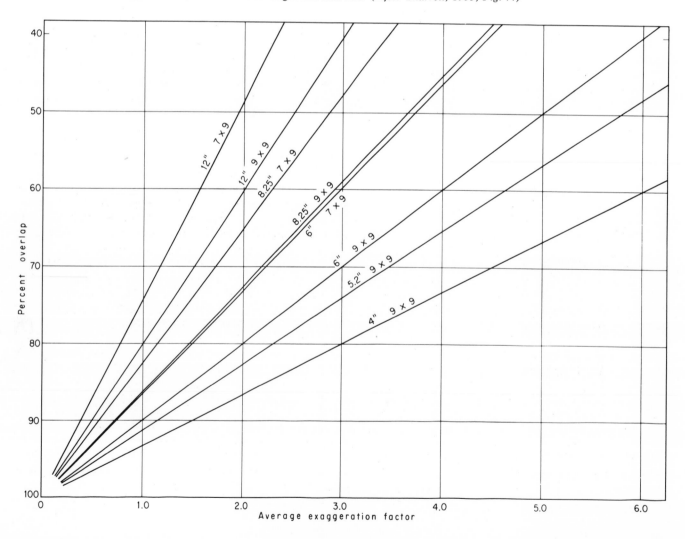

the apparent inclinations of at least ten uniform slopes or dips. To avoid difficulty, choose only slopes which are relatively accessible and which you think can be measured easily in the field. In the field the true slopes or dips are measured and recorded. The two sets of data are then referred to Figure 2-11, and the average exaggeration determined.

If a dependable geologic map, showing field-measured dips, is available, it can be used in place of or in support of one's own field data.

Temporary-approximation Method

This method should only be used if no others are possible or practicable. It consists merely of studying the terrain on the photographs and deciding that a certain exaggeration *appears* to exist. Each area will have to provide its own clues or hints. Training, experience, and a highly developed sense of observation and understanding on the part of the photogeologist determine his choice of evidence.

Such a feature as a talus slope may be important. Suppose that a coalescing talus apron lies at the base of a major escarpment. The average talus slope appears to be about 55°. The average angle of repose of most talus material is about 30°. Older accumulations may be more gentle; fresh slopes may attain 35°. An apparent slope of 55° and a true slope of 30° indicate an exaggeration of 2.5. A true slope of 35° would mean an exaggeration of 2.0. A choice of either factor, as an estimated "working" value, would place subsequent reduced or converted slope and dip readings reasonably close to their actual values.

The use of an assumed, if possibly inaccurate, vertical-exaggeration factor has several distinct advantages. First, an experienced photogeologist should be able to estimate its approximate order of magnitude. His reduced dip or slope estimations will, therefore, be much more nearly correct than were he to use apparent readings only. Second, in areas of moderate to low relief, the reduced values will be mutually proportional. The relative asymmetry of folds, for example, will be logically recorded when an assumed exaggeration factor is used. A subsequent field check, or the obtaining of other reliable control data, will permit the revision of all dips to their true values in a uniform and efficient way.

When using an assumed or computed exaggeration factor, one variable element should be kept in mind; the topographic relief of the area. Since camera height influences vertical exaggeration, appreciable topographic relief can produce variations in exaggeration within a given stereo model. Reductions to "true" dip and slope values should be somewhat greater when the original estimates or measurements are made of high mountain features, and somewhat less in the case of valley or lowland features.

MODEL DISTORTION

The term *distortion* is generally used to designate an unnatural apparent or actual change of shape. As understood by most photogeologists, distortion is restricted to mean all changes in the form of a stereoscopic model *except* in the vertical direction. The position of the eyes or stereoscope determines the apparent shape of a feature viewed. Changes in viewing position, in a plane parallel to the photograph surfaces, produce changes in the form of hills, valleys, slopes, and the like. Such changes *do not* affect the magnitude of vertical exaggeration.

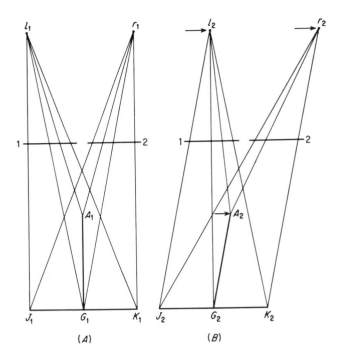

Figure 2-22. Distortion of stereoscopic model caused by horizontal movement of the eyes to one side. (*Adapted from Miller, 1953.*)

Studying Figure 2-22, we see overlapping photographs being viewed from two positions. In Figure 2-22A, when the eyes are at l_1 and r_1, the pole image A_1G_1 appears to stand vertically. In Figure 2-22B, the eyes have been moved to the right, to positions l_2 and r_2. This is accompanied by a pronounced leaning of the model of the pole (A_2G_2). Note that in both instances ground distance JK appears horizontal, and that the height of the pole is unchanged.

It is common practice to view photographs from directly above. That is to say, as a stereo pair is studied, the stereoscope is moved about so that each small area can be viewed from above. There is only one point on a stereo pair where viewing from directly above produces a distortion-free, vertically exaggerated stereo model. This point, which Raasveldt (1956) calls the *perspective center for stereoscopic vision*, lies midway between the two nadir points or photo centers. Ground points near the perspective center are slightly distorted when viewed from directly above; more distant points are severely distorted (see Figure 2-23).

Figure 2-23A shows the overlap photography, by a plane moving normal to the page, of pole AG and ground distance JK. The nadir points are at N; the photo centers at p. The features photographed lie in a marginal position. Note that photographic images a and g are considerably separated, though they would appear as a single point on an orthographic map projection.

Parts (B) and (C) of Figure 2-23 show the viewing of the photographs from two positions. In the first, the eyes are directly over the photographic images; in the second, the head is moved "back" toward the photo centers p, and the eyes are looking out slightly, somewhat similar to the way in which the camera originally "viewed" the ground and pole. Viewing from directly above creates a leaning pole model (A_1G_1). Viewing from a more central position *pulls A_2 back* till the pole appears vertical. It removes the pronounced distortion, though the vertical exaggeration remains the same.

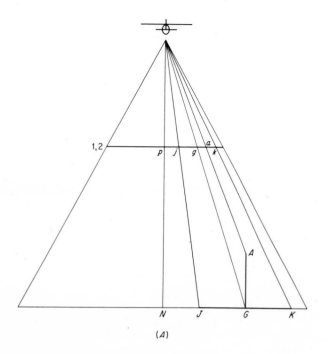

(A)

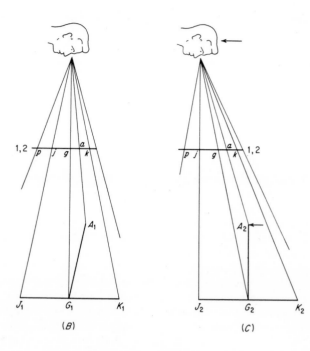

(B)   (C)

Figure 2-23. Importance of photographic image position and viewing position. (*A*) Overlap photography of object in marginal position. (*B*) Viewing marginal images from directly above. (*C*) Viewing marginal images from position inward toward centers of the photographs. (*Adapted from Miller, 1953.*)

These figures illustrate the importance of viewing position in the mapping of steeply dipping strata. A vertical bed at point G (Figure 2-23A), the strike of which is parallel to the flight line, would appear to dip toward the left (as pole A_1G_1 in Figure 2-23B) when viewed from directly above. Beds dipping steeply away from the photograph centers may even appear to dip toward the centers when viewed in this manner.

A lens stereoscope stands about four inches above the photographs. It is not possible to place it over the photo base and examine the entire area of overlap. At the same time, it is not absolutely necessary to view all points from directly above, though most photogeologists agree that nearly vertical viewing is essential to avoid lens-caused distortions and eyestrain. It is suggested that at least *some* of the model distortion can be removed by positioning the stereoscope between the marginal images and the photo base.

Consider Figure 2-24, a sketch showing the overlap photography of ground area $VWYZ$ from air stations L and R. Ground points N_1 and N_2 are the nadir points of the two vertical photographs. Stream junction P lies midway between points N_1 and N_2; it represents the perspective center of the stereo pair. If we may imagine the cameras as photographic "eyes," we may say that, in viewing point P, camera eye L looks down and inward toward the right. Similarly, camera eye R looks down and inward toward the left.

Hill Q lies beyond the photo base, but closer to point N_1 than to point N_2. Camera eye L looks down and outward, in a plane almost at right angles to the photo base. Camera eye R looks down, obliquely outward and to the left. Correspondingly, butte T is seen in different ways from the two camera stations. In fact, it lies to the right of camera eye R.

In viewing each feature stereoscopically from directly above, only stream junction P can be seen free of distortion. The crest of hill Q will appear to lie outward and to the left, along a projection of line PQ. The top of butte T will

appear to lie outward (toward the reader) and toward the right, along a projection of line PT. Raasveldt (1956) refers to lines such as PQ and PT as *radial vectors*.

When the photographs of ground area $VWYZ$ are positioned for viewing with a lens stereoscope (Figure 2-25), all corresponding images, including those of the radial vectors, have a separation equal to or slightly less than eye base. Some, if not all, model distortions can be removed if the stereoscope lenses are held above the radial vector of each object being viewed. For example, when hill Q is studied, the stereoscope lenses should be placed above lines p_1q_1 and p_2q_2, at some points such as g_1 and g_2. Positions too close to points q will permit too much distortion of this marginal feature. Positions too close to points p will result in eyestrain and lens-caused distortions. Optimum stereoscope positions can be determined only through practice and long experience.

Figure 2-26 is a constructed stereogram of identical pyramids. It should be used as an exercise in viewing features in different orientations, and at different distances from the perspective center. The perspective center is at points P in the center of pyramid VII. Points p_1 and p_2 are the principal points of the two "photographs."

First, study each pyramid from directly above. Estimate the apparent slopes of the twenty-eight sides. Assume a vertical exaggeration of 3.00, and reduce the estimated values to true values.

Then study each pyramid from a stereoscope position along its radial vector. For example, when viewing pyramid IV, place the left lens (or the left eye) above point k. From this and comparable radial vector viewing positions, again estimate the twenty-eight apparent slopes, and reduce the estimated values to true values. Compare the two sets of reduced slope values. Pyramid VII, lying on the perspective center, should be viewed vertically in both instances.

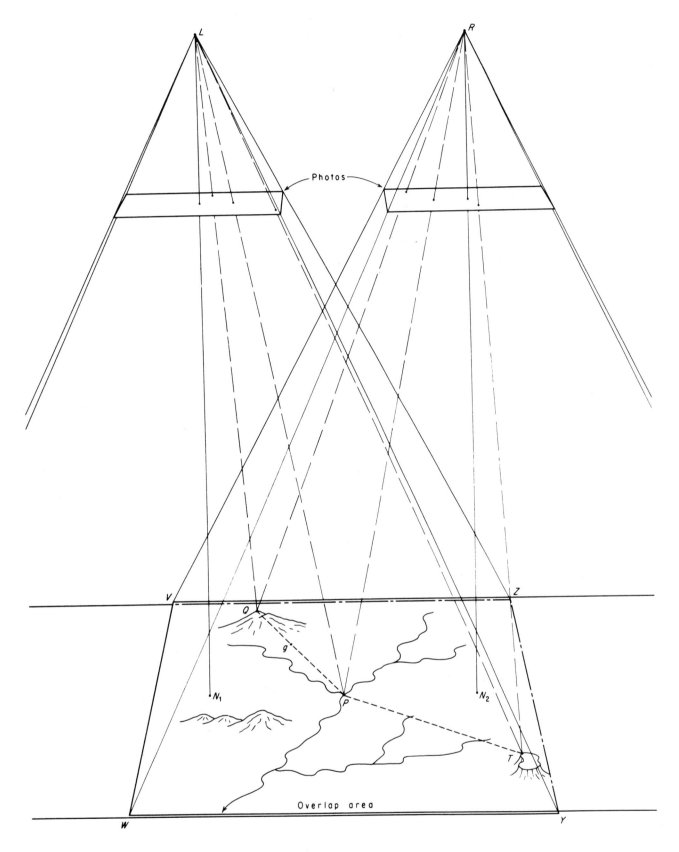

Figure 2-24. The overlap photography of area *VWYZ*. Ground points N_1 and N_2 are the *nadir points* of the two photographs. Ground point *P*, midway between points N_1 and N_2, is the *stereoscopic perspective center*. Stereoscopic model distortions are radial from this point (i.e., along lines *PQ* and *PT*).

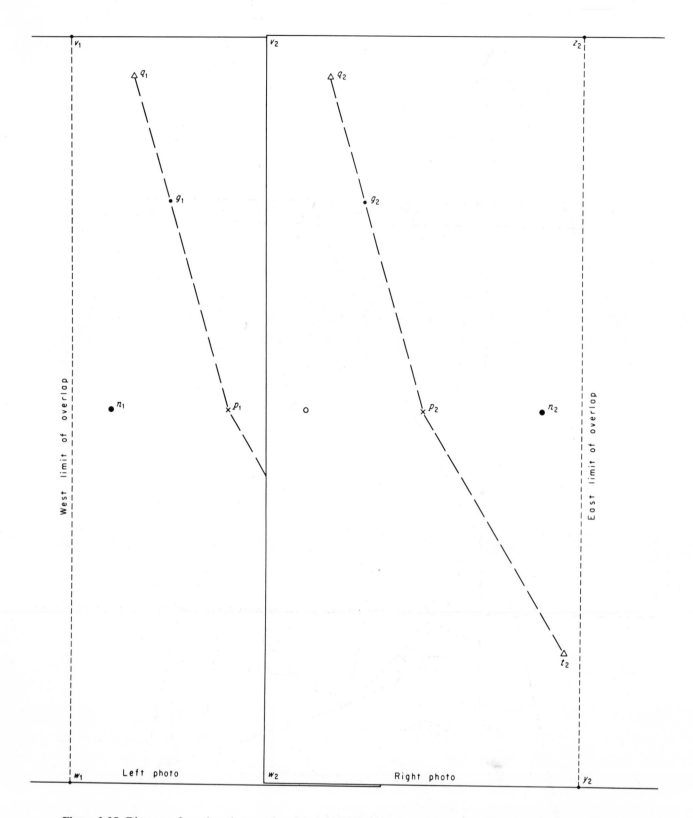

Figure 2-25. Diagram of overlap photographs of area $VWYZ$ (see Figure 2-24), arranged for stereoscopic study.

Two factors determine the amount of distortion of a given slope or dip. These are (1) its image distance from the photographic perspective center, and (2) its orientation with respect to its radial vector. Compare pyramids I and VII (Figure 2-26) when each is viewed from directly above. Pyramid I is considerably distorted; pyramid VII is not. Side 1 is oversteepened; side 4 is elongate and gentle. The other six sides appear to be equal. Side 2, for example,

may be considered as an extension of side 26. Its strike coincides with its radial vector. The strike of sides 1 and 4 is normal to their radial vector. Sides 2 and 3 are *skewed*, but their apparent inclinations are not affected by distance from the perspective center.

It is possible to construct tables to correct for distortion. The only factor which must be known is the focal length of the aerial camera. The photogeologist should decide whether

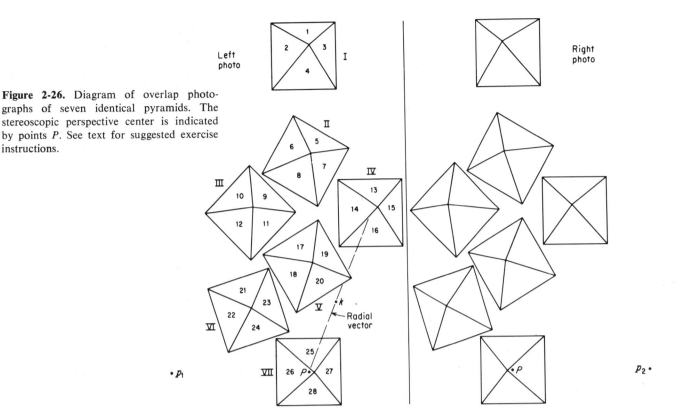

Figure 2-26. Diagram of overlap photographs of seven identical pyramids. The stereoscopic perspective center is indicated by points *P*. See text for suggested exercise instructions.

he wishes to try to remove distortion by oblique viewing from a radial vector position, or to view all features vertically and use a correction table. In some instances a combination of the two may be advisable.

One method of obtaining data for table construction is illustrated in Figure 2-27. This represents the geometric condition prevailing when pyramids are photographed with a camera having a 6-inch focal length. Point *P* represents the perspective center. The model pyramids lie 1, 2, 3, and 4 inches from the perspective center. The true slope of the pyramid sides is 45°. The pyramid sides are oriented parallel to and normal to the radial vector *PQ*. When the pyramids are viewed individually from directly above, and the vertical exaggeration is 3.00, they will appear as indicated by the dotted outlines. Reduction of the exaggerated values will give values as indicated by the dashed outlines (nonexaggerated distorted models). The correction table should provide data to permit the correction of these values to true values.

Consider the pyramid 4 inches from *P*. Its peak *A* appears at point *a* on the photographs. When viewed stereoscopically, it is vertically exaggerated *and* distorted and appears to be at point A_{ed}. The reduced slope values would lower the peak to point A_d. The correction would restore it to the original point *A*. The significant relation, then, is between points A_d and *A*. Point A_d lies above point *a* and at a height equal to that of *A*. Construction is simple: draw the pyramid outline, extend line *BA* to point *a*, erect a vertical to A_d, and add the dashed sides of the pyramid.

A series of sketches similar to Figure 2-27, using different original slopes (i.e., 10, 20, 30°, etc.), will provide the required data for the correction table. In each, the angles of the dashed pyramid sides are measured and recorded. For example, in Figure 2-27, the slopes inclined toward *P* decrease to 41, 36½, 33, and 30½°. The slopes inclined away from *P* increase to 50, 56½, 64½, and 73½°. The

Figure 2-27. Relation of true (solid), distorted (dashed), and exaggerated-distorted (dotted) stereoscopic models, when focal length is 6 inches and vertical exaggeration is 3.00. (*Adapted from Thurrell, 1953, Fig. 9.*)

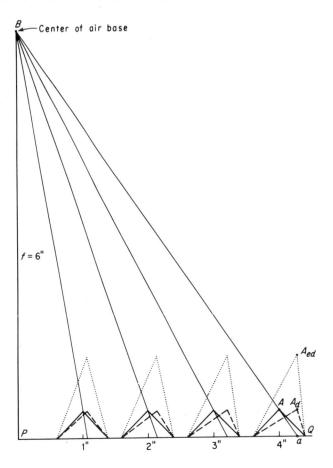

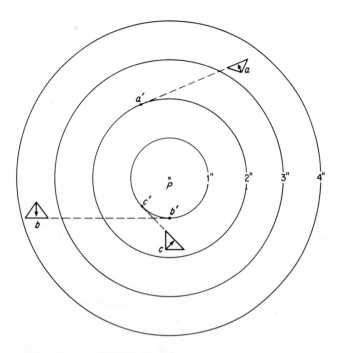

Figure 2-28. Relation of direction of strike and effective image distance from the stereoscopic perspective center *P*. For use in correcting for stereoscopic model distortion.

increase is appreciably greater than the decrease (at 4 inches it is 28½°, compared to a decrease of 14½°).

It should be stressed that the slopes shown in Figure 2-27 are normal to the radial vector. A slope oriented obliquely to its radial vector is less distorted at any given distance. Figure 2-28 shows how such obliquely oriented slopes can be corrected. Slope *a* lies about 3.4 inches from perspective center *P*. Its strike, however, is tangent to a circle 2 inches from point *P*. Its slope distortion is the same as it would be were it at point *a'*. Slope *b* can be corrected by considering it to be at point *b'*, 1 inch from point *P*. Slope *c* may be considered to be at point *c'*, also 1 inch from point *P*. All slopes, whatever their location and orientation, may be converted to equivalent slopes trending at right angles to radial vectors.

When the correction table has been prepared, it is used in the following manner:

1. Determine the vertical-exaggeration factor.

2. Estimate a given apparent slope or dip when viewed vertically.

3. Reduce the exaggerated distorted estimate to a nonexaggerated distorted value.

4. Convert the nonexaggerated distorted value to true value.

Several authorities have proposed a quantitative approach to distortion correction. In most instances their formulas require lengthy calculations for each correction. In areas of complex structure it is frequently necessary to estimate tens and even hundreds of dips on a single stereo model. As a general rule, time and economic considerations do not permit the calculation of each dip correction by such formulas.

The advanced student may wish to consult Raasveldt (1956) to learn of a representative quantitative solution to distortion problems.

3

Measuring and Plotting Instruments

INTRODUCTION

There are two basic principles on which photogrammetric instruments operate. One is that differences in ground elevation can be determined by measurements made on the aerial photographs (parallax); the other is that the true ground or map position of an object can be located by intersection from two known points (centers of radial displacement on two overlapping photographs).

Figure 2-6B shows the relations among relief differential (height GA), combined convergence change (angles β), and parallax differentials (a_1g_1 and a_2g_2). The sum of image distances a_1g_1 and a_2g_2, measured parallel to photo base, provides a quantitative indication of the relief difference between ground points G and A. The most convenient way of obtaining this sum is to measure distances a_1a_2 and g_1g_2, and subtract the smaller from the larger.

Referring to Figure 3-1, we note that it diagrammatically shows two overlapping vertical photographs of ground points A, G, K, M, and T. The elevation of point A is 1,000 feet; that of point M is 1,120 feet. The elevations of points G, K, and T must be determined. The photographs are securely fixed in position in their proper orientation. Their separation is arbitrary, since only the *difference* in image separation is important. If measurements are to be made while the photos are being viewed beneath a stereoscope, separation is dictated by the type of stereoscope used.

Image separations are as follows:

a_1a_2	2.25 inches
g_1g_2	2.18 inches
k_1k_2	2.32 inches
m_1m_2	2.11 inches
t_1t_2	2.145 inches

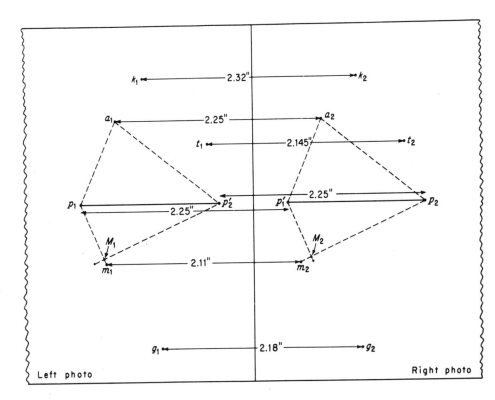

Figure 3-1. Differences in image separation (differential parallax) caused by topographic relief, and the intersection method of obtaining the true map position of a ground point.

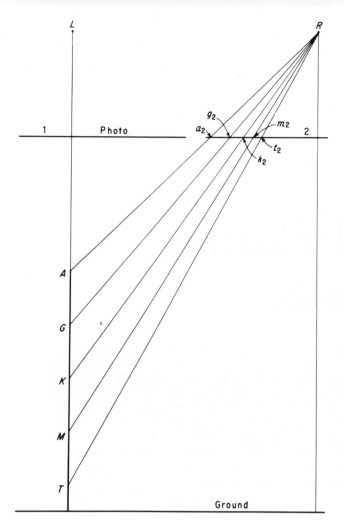

Figure 3-2. Equal vertical intervals and their unequal photographic images. Parallax tables correct for this variation.

Using the ground elevation of point A (1,000 feet) as datum, the parallax differentials of ground points G, K, M, and T are:

G	− 0.07 inch
K	+ 0.07 inch
M	− 0.14 inch
T	− 0.105 inch

Ground point M is 120 feet higher than ground point A. This height differential is represented by a parallax differential of 0.14 inch. The parallax-relief relation may be used to determine the approximate elevations of the other points. A parallax differential of 0.07 inch corresponds to a difference in height of 60 feet, and one of 0.105 inch corresponds to 90 feet. Since an increase of parallax indicates a decrease in elevation, ground point K must lie below 1,000 feet, and points G and T above 1,000 feet. Their computed elevations are, therefore:

G	1,060 feet
K	940 feet
T	1,090 feet

Such direct conversions from parallax differentials to ground heights can be made when the total topographic relief is moderate to low, compared with camera height, and when great accuracy is not required. In areas of extreme relief, or when precision is essential, a further consideration is required (see Figure 3-2). In greatly exaggerated proportions, a series of equal vertical-height intervals is photographed from camera stations L and R. For the sake of simplicity, the ground points are shown to lie directly beneath L. All parallax differentials are thus recorded on photograph 2, made from station R. Note that the higher intervals produce greater parallax differentials (i.e., a_2g_2), while the lower intervals are represented by shorter displacements (i.e., m_2t_2).

The influence of significant height range is compensated for by the use of the standard differential parallax equation:

$$\Delta p = \frac{bh}{H - h}$$

where Δp = differential parallax, hundredths of millimeters
  b = photo base, measured to nearest 0.1 millimeter
  h = relief or height differential, feet
  H = camera height, above a given datum level, feet

Tables have been prepared, based on this equation, which permit the rapid conversion of parallax readings into differential ground-height measurements.

Figure 3-1 may also be used to demonstrate the second principle; that of determining the correct planimetric positions of ground points included in overlap vertical photography. On a tilt-free vertical photograph, all image displacements caused by topographic relief are radial from the principal point. On tilted or oblique photographs, displacements are radial from the isocenter. When tilt is extremely small, it is acceptable to assume that the isocenter and principal point coincide; that is, that angular readings from the principal point are directionally correct.

Points p_1 and p_2 are the principal points of the photographs depicted in Figure 3-1. Points p_1' and p_2' are the transferred or conjugate principal points.

Consider triangles $a_1p_1p_2'$ and $a_2p_1'p_2$ in Figure 3-1. Ground points A, P_1, and P_2 lie at the same elevation, as indicated by their equal parallax measurements. It is assumed that the photographs are tilt-free. The triangles are congruent; they are exact small-scale map replicas of the corresponding ground triangle AP_1P_2.

Ground point M, however, is considerably higher than points P_1 and P_2. The images of M are therefore displaced on both photographs. But lines p_1m_1 and p_2m_2, drawn radially from the principal points, are directionally correct. The correct map position of point M can be obtained by drawing, from point p_2', a line parallel to line p_2m_2, or by drawing from point p_1' a line parallel to line p_1m_1. The intersections of these lines with the corresponding radial lines (points M_1 and M_2) are the desired map positions of point M, as it would appear were its elevation equal to that of points P_1 and P_2.

It follows that any ground point can be mapped correctly, at any desired scale, by the process of intersection familiar to geologists who have undertaken field traverses, Brunton surveys, or alidade mapping.

MEASURING INSTRUMENTS

There are numerous instruments which are used to measure parallax differentials and to ensure correct planimetric plotting. Under favorable conditions parallax measuring devices can obtain data with which to do the following:

1. Determine strike direction and dip magnitude
2. Calculate the thickness of geologic sections
3. Construct geologic and topographic profiles
4. Make isopachous and structure contour maps
5. Plot or compute stream gradients and longitudinal profiles

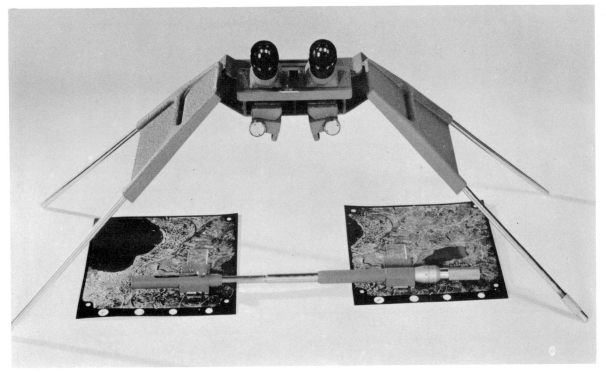

Figure 3-3. Mirror stereoscope and stereometer (parallax bar). (*Courtesy of Wild Heerbrugg Instruments, Inc.*)

6. Compile accurate topographic maps and determine spot heights

Instruments for obtaining such data may be fitted into two general classifications: (1) those used with lens or mirror stereoscopes; and (2) high-order stereo-plotting instruments. Other photogrammetric instruments provide accurate methods of transferring photographic data to base maps. Some of the high-order stereo-plotting instruments can be used to make parallax measurements, plot and construct a base map in a single operation. The limited scope of this book precludes the discussion and illustration of the many varieties of instruments available to the photogeologist. A few representative examples have been selected for inclusion here. It must not be assumed that those omitted are in any way inferior.

The Stereometer

Figure 3-3 shows a stereometer or parallax measuring bar arranged for use beneath a mirror stereoscope. The separa-

tion of two glass plates, which are affixed to a horizontal bar, can be regulated by a delicately tooled knob. Separation can be read on a micrometer drum. A small dot marks the center of each plate. When seen through the stereoscope, the dots are fused stereoscopically and appear as a single dot having a fixed position in space. As the separation is changed, the dot appears to rise or fall. By proper adjustment it can be *placed* on any feature on the stereo-model surface. For each ground position selected, a given separation reading may be obtained. Thus differential parallax, involving control and points of unknown elevation, can be calculated, as in Figure 3-1. Instruments such as these are said to employ the *floating-dot* principle. They are portable, inexpensive, and relatively easy to learn to operate.

The Stereo-slope Comparator

The Stereo-slope Comparator (Figure 3-4) has recently been developed by the U.S. Geological Survey. It was designed specifically to determine dip and strike of planar

Figure 3-4. Stereo-slope Comparator. (*Courtesy of U.S. Geological Survey.*)

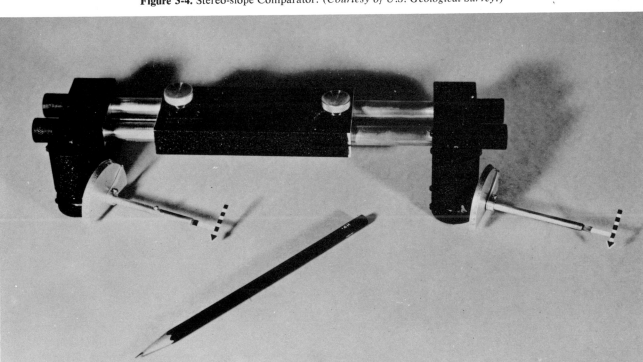

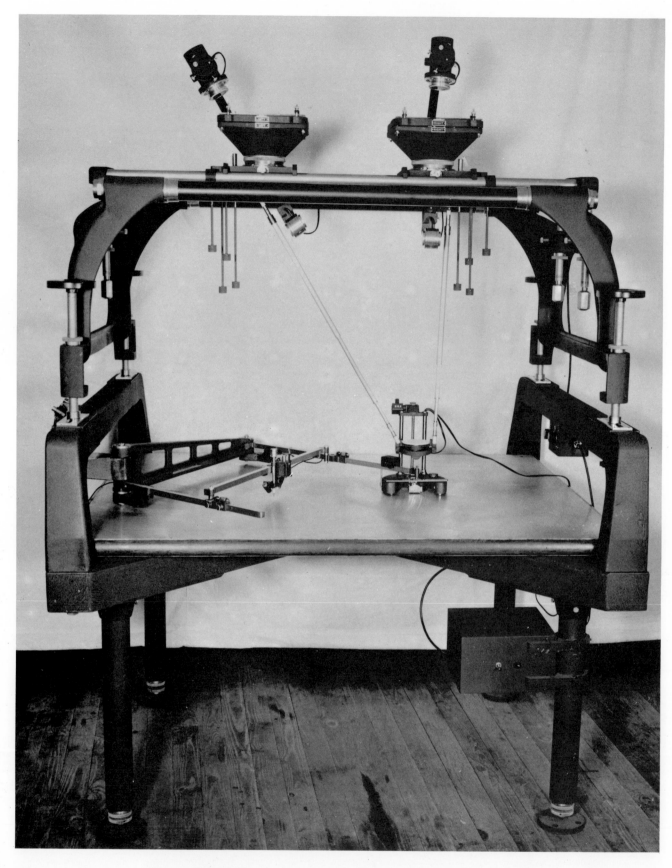

Figure 3-5. Kelsh Plotter. (*Courtesy of the Kelsh Instrument Company, Inc.*)

surfaces. It uses two small targets that may be fused stereo-scopically into a single model. The target model, which can be raised or lowered by changes in separation, can also be tilted to conform with the slope or dip of any selected photographic model plane. Since it measures the exaggerated slope values, its readings must be reduced to their corresponding true values by reference to a graph similar to Figure 2-11.

The Kelsh Plotter

The Kelsh Plotter (Figure 3-5) is one of several excellent precision stereo-plotting instruments available to photogeologists. It is well described in U.S. Geological Survey Bulletin 1043-A, as follows:

KELSH PLOTTER

The Kelsh Plotter projects an image from glass-plate diapositives to a viewing surface below the projectors; measuring and plotting are done with attachments to a small movable carriage mounting a platen on which the stereoscopic model is viewed. The anaglyph principle is used to create the third dimension.

The Kelsh Plotter uses 9- by 9-inch glass-plate diapositives on which the photograph image is the same scale as the original photography. The projected model scale is about $5\times$ that of the original photography. Only that part of the Kelsh model appearing on the platen is illuminated; this results in a greater concentration of light and a more brightly illuminated model. However, this concentration of light prevents viewing of the entire model at any one time.

Because of the $5\times$ enlargement of the original photography scale plus the use of diapositives the same size and scale as the original photographs, thus preserving a high degree of resolution in the projected model, high-altitude photography at scales of 1:60,000 to 1:70,000 can be used in the Kelsh Plotter in routine photogeologic compilation where 1:20,000-scale photographs are normally employed with simpler photogrammetric instruments. This may reduce by as much as 90 percent the number of stereoscopic models that would normally be oriented for interpretation and plotting using 1:20,000-scale photographs. In detailed studies the use of 1:20,000-scale photography, enlarged to 1:4,000 in the Kelsh Plotter, gives the interpreter a great advantage in interpreting geologic data as well as positioning such data on the base map. Interpreting, measuring, and plotting geologic data can be done in one continuous operation with the Kelsh Plotter.

During recent years, the U.S. Geological Survey has utilized high-order stereo-plotting instruments to obtain quantitative geologic and topographic data to supplement several of its large geologic mapping programs. The rapid advances made in techniques and instrumentation are in part explained by the fact that expensive plotting equipment, diapositive plates (transparent prints), and highly trained personnel were availabe for such work without an appreciable increase in budget. In private industry, a trend toward such methods can only be accomplished after a careful analysis of the finances involved. Unfortunately, private research is extremely confidential, and no reliable cost estimates are presently available. However, some general observations and tentative conclusions may be made.

The use of high-order stereo-plotting instruments, combined with the stereoscopic study of contact prints and a thorough field check, can produce excellent geologic maps. These maps are superior in geologic detail and planimetric accuracy to those made by photo study and mosaic annotation alone. In certain areas of very low dip, where adequate surficial expression of mappable units exists, it is felt that photogrammetric methods can compete financially with detailed field mapping. Similarly, many structure contour and isopachous mapping problems can be undertaken more inexpensively by photogrammetry.

However, some reservations and qualifications are in order. Unless the stratigraphic section in sedimentary areas and the crystalline rock units in hard-rock areas are known thoroughly, rock identification demands field examination, sample collection, and similar firsthand investigations. Secondly, precision instruments can contribute only to the mapping of geology, *not* to its understanding. Therefore, regardless of financial or time considerations, one must also ascertain the *primary objective* for a given photogeologic study.

PLOTTING INSTRUMENTS

Tilt and relief displacements render the accurate transfer of photo data to base maps extremely difficult. In the U.S. Geological Survey this problem has been solved by the use of high-order stereo-plotting instruments, such as the Kelsh Plotter. In private industry the cost of transferring data to manuscript sheets by such means has been prohibitive in most cases. In general, in commercial photogeologic studies the emphasis has been placed on the obtaining of maximum geologic data while sacrificing some planimetric accuracy. When this philosophy is followed, the geologic information is usually compiled on semicontrolled mosaics, or on mosaic overlays, and thence transferred to base map linens by tracing. Occasionally anomalous or favorable-appearing areas are selected for controlled plotting by precision instruments.

Plotting instruments range in cost and complexity of construction from those of the camera-lucida type to the previously mentioned variety represented by the Kelsh Plotter. A few of the more commonly used plotting instruments are described briefly below.

The Vertical Sketchmaster

The Vertical Sketchmaster (Figure 3-6) is relatively inexpensive and easy to use. It operates on the camera-lucida principle. It is a monocular instrument, having a semitransparent mirror at the eyepiece. The map is placed beneath the instrument and is viewed directly through this mirror. The photograph is seen by reflection from a first-surface mirror and the semitransparent eyepiece mirror. The insertion of various miniscus lenses beneath the eyepiece mirror permits the use of several map scales. Further scale change is afforded by raising or lowering the instrument by leg adjustments. Minor tip and tilt errors can be removed in this way.

When photo images and base map are properly fused, geologic and additional cultural and hydrologic detail can be transferred to the map or a transparent map overlay.

Most satisfactory results are to be expected in areas of low to moderate relief, since topographic displacements cannot be removed by the use of the Sketchmaster.

The Double Reflecting Projector

The instrument shown in Figure 3-7 was designed to provide a simple means of changing the scale of a drawing, map, or photograph. Its construction provides the user with an unobstructed drafting surface on which to compile his map. If it is used to change or to add to a base map, the map used must be either transparent or extremely translucent.

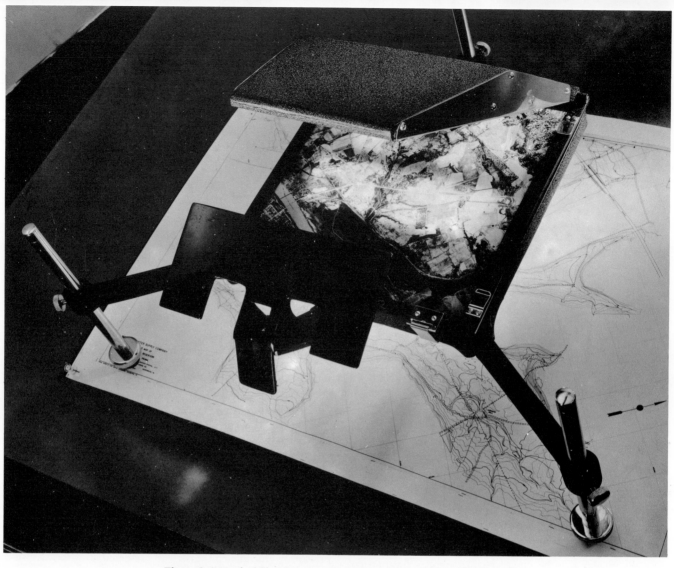

Figure 3-6. Vertical Sketchmaster. (*Courtesy of Aero Service Corporation.*)

Figure 3-7. Double Reflecting Projector. (*Courtesy of Philip B. Kail Associates.*)

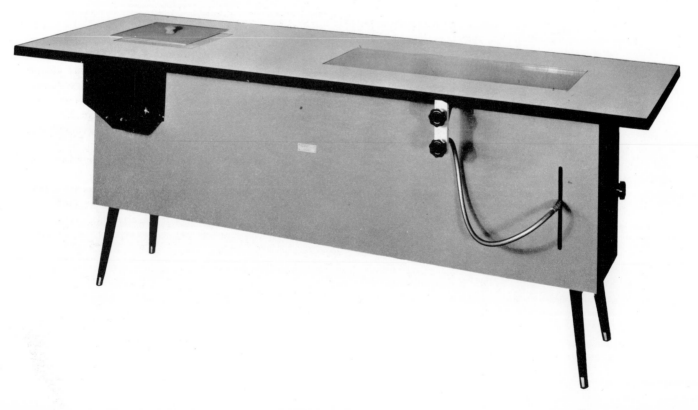

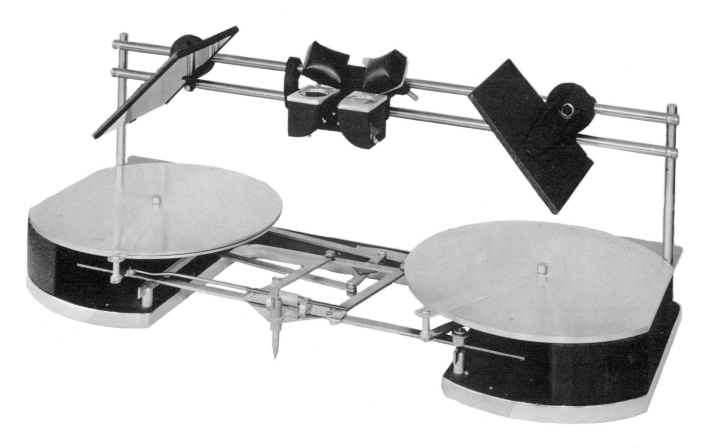

Figure 3-8. Radial Planimetric Plotter. (*Courtesy of Philip B. Kail Associates.*)

Figure 3-9. KEK Stereoscopic Plotter. (*Courtesy of Philip B. Kail Associates.*)

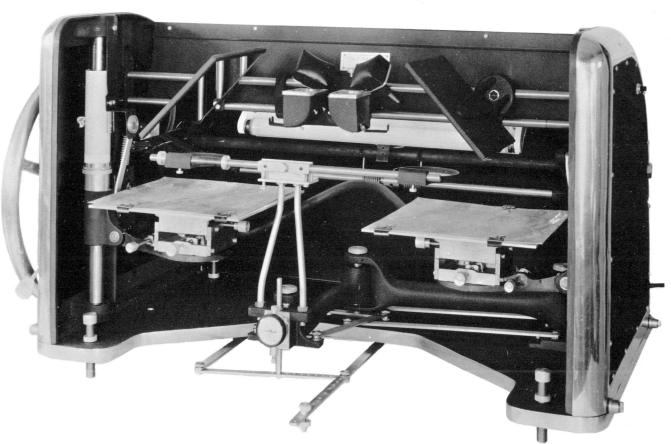

To plot photogeologic data to a base map, the annotated photograph is placed face down on the left-hand glass plate. The photo image is reflected from the left-hand mirror (hidden in Figure 3-7), through a lens to the right-hand mirror, and up to the base map on the right-hand glass plate. Possible scale changes range from a 3:1 reduction to a 1:3 enlargement. Scale change is controlled by a knob which raises or lowers the mirror and lens platform inside the projector.

Since this instrument cannot remove distortion due to tilt or topographic relief, its use is restricted to tilt-free photographs of areas of low to medium-low relief.

The Radial Planimetric Plotter

The Radial Planimetric Plotter (Figure 3-8) consists of a mirror stereoscope mounted above two photograph tables. A transparent plastic arm with a centrally scribed line extends from and pivots around the center of each table. These arms are linked to a pantograph attachment.

This instrument is based on the principle of azimuthal intersection in the location of true map positions of objects delineated on aerial photographs.

Overlapping vertical aerial photographs are placed on the photograph tables and oriented for proper stereoscopic viewing. Control points on the photos are oriented to control points on the base manuscript. As the plastic arms radiate from different centers, they cross to form the so-called *plotting cross*. Movement of the pantograph attachment moves the plotting cross over the stereoscopic model and permits the tracing of photograph detail on the base map. One of the chief advantages of this plotter is that it removes relief-caused photograph displacements. Also, the instrument is easily set up and requires little specialized training and skill to operate.

In private industry the Radial Planimetric Plotter appears to be an economically feasible substitute for mosaic-type compilation when accurate planimetric maps are available.

The KEK Plotter

The KEK Plotter (Figure 3-9) consists of a stereoscope, two photograph tables, a floating-dot assembly, and a drawing attachment. Since it operates on the floating-dot principle, it may be more difficult for some persons to use than the Radial Planimetric Plotter. The plotting cross of the latter instrument is replaced on the KEK Plotter by a fused dot floating in space. By raising or lowering the photograph plates, one may *place* the floating dot on the terrain model surface. The vertical motion of the photograph plates is linked to a drum scale on which relative heights can be read directly, in feet. Movement of the pantograph drawing attachment permits the sketching of geologic detail directly on the map base. During this sketching the fused dot must be *held* on the model surface by the simultaneous movement of the photograph tables.

Because the photograph tables may be tilted to make an approximate correction for tilt, this instrument is more precise than the Radial Planimetric Plotter, which has no such adjustment. Another advantage of the KEK Plotter is that it permits contouring. However, for many geologic map compilation problems, the somewhat less accurate but simpler and less expensive Radial Planimetric Plotter is preferred.

Procedures

PRELIMINARY PROCEDURES

Before aerial photographs are studied, they must be obtained, processed, organized, indexed, and filed. Some of these steps are especially important if a large area is being investigated, and hundreds or thousands of prints are required. Good preliminary organization can save time, work, and expense.

For most purposes, double-weight semimatte photographs are needed. It is difficult to annotate glossy prints, and single-weight paper does not stand up under repeated handling.

"Photographic coverage" may be interpreted to mean sufficient photographs of an area to afford complete ground coverage. Such coverage can usually be obtained by using alternate prints of each flight strip. In most photogeologic projects, stereoscopic study of the photographs is required; therefore, *all* photographs must be obtained. In placing an order for aerial photographs, the term "complete stereoscopic photographic coverage" is strongly recommended to avoid possible misunderstanding and delay.

Photographs may be ordered by area or by reference numbers. In the United States, governmental agencies require that the purchaser first obtain photo indexes, make a list of the photos requested, and submit full payment with his order.

In Canada, the standard procedure is to submit a small sketch map outlining the area for which coverage is desired. Virtually all available photo coverage in Canada is held by federal and provincial governments. The agency then determines the cost of the coverage, bills the purchaser, and on receipt of payment initiates processing of the photos.

When commercial companies hold the desired photo coverage, it is usually advisable to inquire as to correct ordering procedures.

Whether or not photo indexes are needed in ordering photographs, they should be obtained as a matter of routine. If mosaics are available, they should also be ordered at this time.

Usually the first step necessary is the trimming of all pictures, cutting off the black borders, leaving only the aerial photograph images. This is not required if a mirror stereoscope is used and mosaics are purchased. When the lens stereoscope is used, or when the pictures are to be used in mosaic construction, the borders must be removed. Pretrimmed prints may be obtained at a slight additional cost.

The next step is the arrangement of the photos into flight strips. Photo indexes or index maps are required for reference. As each strip is gathered and arranged numerically, its corresponding center line is marked in a prominent color on the map or photo index. When all lines have been so

marked, any remaining gaps will be noted, and the necessary fill-in coverage can be ordered directly.

The photographs may then be filed in manila folders according to flight lines. It is sometimes convenient to use their original numbering system. To simplify flight identification, the photogeologist may assign his own numerical values to the project flight lines, and file the photos accordingly. For example, if the flight lines run east and west, the southernmost may be designated flight 1, the next flight 2, and so on northward across the project area. If more than one project is planned in the region, the first project may be termed "Project A," and its photos indexed as flights A-1, A-2, etc. When using one's own index system, it is suggested that the back of each photo be stamped according to its new flight-line designation. It is rarely necessary to renumber each print within a flight line.

Frequently, colored pencils will not make a clear impression on aerial photographs. Better color markings can be assured by the application of a prepared solution to the photograph surface. There are several mixtures in use. They consist of various combinations of powdered resin, turpentine, and benzine. Small amounts of ether may also be added. The standard solution used by the writer consists of the following:

Six ounces of powdered natural resin are dissolved in 6 ounces of turpentine. This is permitted to stand 24 hours. A gallon of benzine is then added and the mixture stirred rapidly. If ether is used, about 4 ounces may be included at the time the benzine is added.

Very little solution is needed for optimum results. A tissue or wad of cotton may be used to apply it evenly over the photograph. If too much is used, the photograph surface will remain sticky after drying. Work in a well-ventilated room; it is toxic and highly inflammable!

ANNOTATION OF THE PHOTOGRAPHS

All photographic annotation should be done while the pictures are being viewed stereoscopically. On many occasions some features will appear so obvious and well defined on a single print that one might argue that no such need exists. No time is saved by attempting single photograph annotation, since the errors resulting from this practice inevitably require erasures and correction.

There is no unanimity of thought as to what media to use in photograph annotation. Some experienced photogeologists insist on black or colored inks applied with an extremely thin pen point such as a crow-quill. It is their belief that at the usual photograph scale, the width of a pencil line represents too great a ground width. In addition, they feel that pencil is generally less accurate, and that it obscures valuable geologic features.

There are others, equally experienced and trained, who almost invariably use colored pencils for marking photographs. Their reasons are probably more diverse. Time, the purpose of the study, and the nature of their final map may be some of the factors on which they base their practice.

There are many elements to consider with regard to procedure. One that is frequently overlooked is human temperament. Some individuals are by nature extremely thorough and painstaking. Precision and neatness are undoubtedly important to such persons. Others place greater emphasis on the study of details, on trying to see and understand as much as humanly possible in a given amount of time. To them, a wider pencil line, drawn at a certain point or along a certain line, represents the result of their fullest geologic concentration, reasoning, and analysis. The meaning of the line, rather than its characteristics as a line, may to them be the more important.

Numerous practical factors must also be taken into account. For example, compare the atmosphere under which a research or governmental-survey photogeologist works with the atmosphere typically present in a district office of an oil company. In the first instance, where publication is expected, accuracy and precision in plotting details must be maintained. In the second, there may be a rapidly approaching deadline, an acreage block may be coming up for bid, or a limited field season may shortly begin. In consulting photogeology, a client may want a finished interpretation by a certain date. These and many other factors are vitally important, and it is well that the reader, especially if he be a student, know and appreciate them.

In general, one may be guided by the following suggestions. When time is not a factor, when planimetric detail and accuracy are required and will be maintained by the use of photogrammetric instruments, and when funds permit, colored inks should be considered. They are neat in appearance, do not smudge with use, and in most instances are satisfactory. When time or funds are limited, when less accurate plotting and mapping procedures are to be employed, and when the nature of the problem is such that certain areas will have to be restudied, interpretations revised, and erasures made repeatedly, colored pencils are generally the more logical choice.

When using pencils, the highest possible order of accuracy and neatness should nevertheless be maintained. A handy and efficient instrument is the rubber-base, portable, desk pencil sharpener. Such a simple device as this can save countless hours otherwise spent going to and from a sharpener fixed to a wall.

There are several brands of colored pencils used by artists, draftsmen, and geologists. The Eagle Prismacolor pencil is excellent for most photograph annotation. Though the reader may wish to devise his own color system, the following is frequently used:

Blue	Streams, lakes, marshes and muskegs
Brown	Roads and trails
Black	Cultural features, except roads and trails (fences, houses, railroads, dams, tanks, bridges, etc.)
Yellow ochre	Quaternary alluvium (outlined)
Orange	Quaternary general (fans, pediment cappings, slump, landslides, moraines, dunes)
Red	Geologic structures (dips, strikes, faults, fold axes)
Pink	Extremely doubtful interpreted structures (possible faults expressed by linear streams, etc.)
Purple	Stratigraphic contacts and crystalline body boundaries
Green	Stratigraphic breaks (key beds, intraformational divisional breaks, etc.)

In annotating aerial photographs, one must decide what to indicate, and in what detail. In populated or cultivated areas, it is not always necessary to trace all roads, trails, fences, and other cultural features. A photograph study directed to the understanding of the geomorphic history of the area, or attempting to locate an extension of a major tectonic zone or a mineralized body, would probably not require the mapping of all cultural features. Or, in a photogeologic search for sand and gravel deposits, the omission of geologic structure and stratigraphy in nearby mountains would be expected. The purpose of the study, then, dictates the selection of features to be mapped.

The detail of annotation depends largely on the scale at which the data will be assembled in map form. In geologic mapping, the relative structural complexity is also important. For example, on 1:20,000-scale aerial photographs, an inch represents a ground distance of approximately one-third mile. If the final map scale is to be 1 mile to the inch, and the geology of the area is relatively simple, map dip symbols need not be less than 1 inch apart. On the photographs a spacing of dip symbols of about three inches is therefore adequate. Closer spacing would be occasioned by changes in dip magnitude or in strike, and by the presence of numerous small folds. Faults, of course, should be mapped as completely and accurately as possible. Stratigraphic units, intrusive bodies, and crystalline boundaries should be traced and transferred as faithfully as map scale will permit.

FLIGHT-STRIP ANNOTATION

In photograph annotation, each stereo pair must be considered as part of the entire area, and not as an independent unit. All annotated lines which extend from one stereoscopic model to the next must be made to match. In this way, when they are transferred to a mosaic or a base map, they will form continuous and not broken or interrupted lines. All streams, cultural lines, geologic contacts, fold axes, faults, and similar linear features, which are in the marginal zone of one model, must be extended (tied) across to the next. The method of tying a series of photographs appears complicated on the printed page. However, if it is followed one or two times, it will become largely a matter of automatic procedure and can greatly increase the efficiency and reliability of the study.

Figure 4-1 should be used as a reference for the following discussion. On it two viewing positions, L (left) and R (right) are shown, as are four "stack" positions, I, II, III, and IV. The photographs may be placed in one stack position, studied and annotated, and eventually transferred to another stack position.

When a series of photographs is to be annotated, it should be placed in stack position I, if the interpreter is right-handed. The photographs should be arranged numerically face up, in such a way that when the first two are taken from the stack and placed beneath the stereoscope, the top photo-

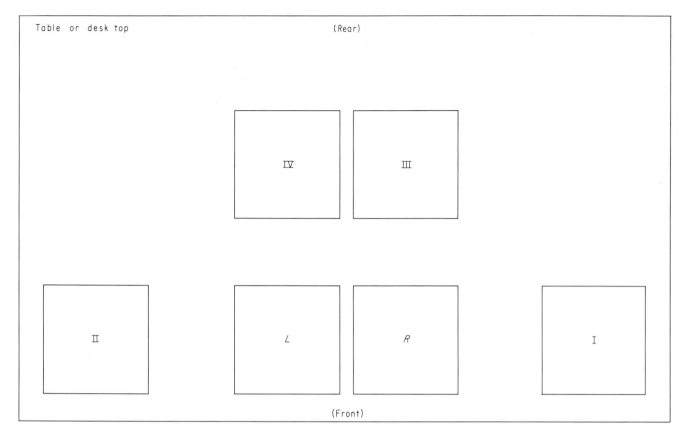

Figure 4-1. Arrangement of photograph viewing (*L* and *R*) and stacking (I to IV) positions on desk or study table.

graph (1) will automatically fall in viewing position *L* and photograph 2 in viewing position *R*. When the overlap area has been studied and necessary annotations made on photograph 2, photograph 1 is discarded to stack position II.

Photograph 2 is then moved to viewing position *L*, and photograph 3 taken from stack I and placed in viewing position *R*. This process should continue throughout the study and annotation of the entire flight.

The overlap area between photographs 2 and 3 includes a narrow strip of the original annotated overlap area between photographs 1 and 2. The annotations, recorded on photograph 2, extend into the stereoscopic field when photographs 2 and 3 are viewed. All such annotations should be continued across the second overlap area. When the data are later transferred to a mosaic or base map, continuity and completeness will thus be assured.

The above method of annotating a strip of photographs may be followed when the annotated photographs are not to be used later in the field, when mosaics have been purchased or previously constructed, or when the data are to be transferred directly to a base map. If, after interpretation, the same photographs are to be used to construct a mosaic, a different procedure is necessary. Mosaics may be made by using alternate prints. If all annotation is carried out on even-numbered photographs, it is possible to use only the unmarked odd-numbered prints in mosiac construction. Also, in the field it is preferable to have as much information as possible on a single photograph. This reduces handling, and affords a more complete representation of the geology on the least number of photos. In addition, field notations can be made on the unmarked prints.

In such cases, it is advisable to annotate alternate prints completely; the other photographs are thus left unmarked. The geologist might set the following rule to follow: an-

notate only even-numbered prints and use only odd-numbered prints in mosaic construction or for other purposes.

When alternate prints are to be annotated, the above procedure of continuous annotation must be revised. If the student will select four or five consecutive prints from a flight strip and very slowly follow the instructions step by step, he will find that the procedure is both logical and surprisingly simple. The procedure described applies to a right-handed person; left-handed individuals should reverse the process.

1. Place the photographs in position I, arranged so that when photograph 1 is removed it will lie in viewing position *L,* and when photograph 2 is removed it will lie in viewing position *R*.

2. Annotate on photograph 2 the entire area of overlap.

3. Discard photograph 1 and place it in stack position II.

4. Rotate photograph 2 180°.

5. Remove photograph 3 from stack I, rotate it 180°, and place it in viewing position *L*. This photograph, with photograph 2, will afford stereoscopic coverage of the remainder of photograph 2. Annotate photograph 2.

6. Rotate photograph 3 180°.

7. Rotate photograph 2 180° and place it on top of photograph 3 in viewing position *L*.

8. Remove photograph 4 from stack I and place it in viewing position *R*.

9. Study photographs 2 and 4 stereoscopically (only a narrow marginal strip will be stereoscopically covered by these two photographs, but there will be enough common area to permit the transfer of marginal annotations from photograph 2 to the edge of photograph 4).

10. Remove photograph 2 and place it on top of photograph 1 in stack II.

11. Stereoscopically examine photographs 3 and 4, and

61

continue on photograph 4 the annotations transferred to it from photograph 2.

12. The above procedure is followed for the entire strip. The cycle begun in step 1 is repeated, starting with photographs 3 and 4.

Figure 1-10 illustrates overlap and sidelap existing on two adjacent flight lines. The above method of maintaining continuity of annotation, when a series of photographs is being studied. applies only when that series is taken from a single flight line; for example, the group of photographs which comprises flight 1. Now consider the problems of annotating flight 2. Not only must continuous annotations be maintained throughout flight 2, but attention must be given to the strip of sidelap between flights 1 and 2. All annotations in this area of sidelap, which were drawn when flight 1 was being studied, must be continued onto the photographs of flight 2. This may be accomplished in many ways, but the following has proved most useful: (Again, the assumption is made that the geologist is right-handed.)

The photographs of flight 1 are placed in stack position II; those of flight 2 are placed in stack position I. Within the stacks the photographs should be numerically arranged so that the top photograph in each stack sidelaps the top photograph of the other. Figure 1-10 shows the relative positions of the photograph numbers of flights 1 and 2. If annotation transfer is to be carried out employing photographs from these two flights, the top pictures of the two stacks should be 1w and 2w or 1e and 2e.

The top photographs from each pile should be placed beneath the stereoscope; that from stack II, for example, should always occupy viewing position L. The area of sidelap is viewed stereoscopically, and all marginal annotations are transferred from the left-hand photograph to the right-hand photograph. Following the transfer of the annotations, the two photographs are discarded to begin two more stacks. The most convenient positions for these discards are in front of the geologist (in stack positions III and IV, Figure 4-1).

By the above method, all of the marginal annotations of the sidelap area are transferred from flight 1 to flight 2. Flight 1 photographs may then be assembled and returned to the files. Flight 2 photographs are then ready to be fully annotated, care being taken to continue all annotations transferred over from flight 1. Frequently, when a photogeologist is in doubt with respect to his identification or interpretation of a particular feature in the sidelap area, he may temporarily omit the transfer of such annotations, and reinterpret the feature on flight 2 first. He may then compare the two interpretations, after which annotation transfer and any necessary changes may be made.

ANNOTATION OF MOSAICS

There are several ways in which mosaics are used in photogeologic studies. Accordingly, there are numerous methods of annotation employed. Some of the more frequent uses and procedures are discussed in the following paragraphs.

Mosaic Study

A mosaic, or an assembled group of mosaics, may be studied for several purposes. If a large unknown area is considered for possible investigations, the mosaics may be examined to permit the outlining of those areas within which more detailed analysis should prove most informative. For example, one may make a rapid qualitative mosaic study of a large glaciated plains area. Areas classified as apparently excellent, fair, and poor may be designated on a small-scale reference map of the area. Generalized area boundaries would be sketched on the mosaics in colored pencil and transferred by eye to the map.

In such areas as the U.S. Gulf Coast, considerable geomorphic interpretation has been done using mosaics alone. In this area of salt domes and regional fault and fracture systems, considerable information can be obtained by this method. In such work, the more obvious drainage, topographic, tonal, and vegetative features are usually sketched directly onto the mosaics. Detailed annotation is not advised, since the advantages of the stereoscopic model cannot be utilized in the tracing of the smaller and more poorly defined features. If maps are desired, the mosaic annotations may be transferred to acetate overlays. These may be printed, or they may be used in the transfer of the data to linen base maps. It would be inadvisable to annotate overlays originally were it planned to use the mosaics in the field.

Stereoscopic Study

More frequently, photogeologic mapping and interpretation entail the stereoscopic study of contact prints. Information derived from such a study is then annotated on mosaics or mosaic overlays, and may thence be transferred to final base maps.

There is no general agreement as to the manner in which mosaics should be annotated. If the annotated mosaic is to be used in the field, and if a minimum of corrections is expected, ink should be used. Pencil has the disadvantage of smearing and fading with field use, but is preferable if numerous changes, corrections, and erasures are anticipated.

In many cases the mosaics themselves are not marked. Instead, annotations are made on a transparent acetate overlay, slightly glazed on one side, which is mounted on the mosaic. This practice has many advantages. Preliminary prints of the overlay can be made at any time. In complexly folded and faulted areas, this is very helpful. It permits the photogeologist to pencil-color the print, and to detect omissions, illogical or impossible interpreted relations, to check the correctness of indicated fault movements, and to sketch in fold axes which may have been omitted in the original annotation. "Hanging" contacts, unlabeled formations and the like are also readily detected in this way.

Either colored inks or colored pencils may be used in overlay annotation. Eagle Verithin pencils are representative of the type of pencil used. Some colors print better than others. A typical color system is as follows:

#735	—Canary yellow	Quaternary deposits
#751	—Emerald green	Hydrologic features (Blue does not print well.)
#750	—Vermilion	Geologic structure (except synclinal axes)
#738½	—Light green	Synclinal axes
#746	—Sienna brown	Geologic contacts and boundaries
#747	—Black	Key beds and intraformational markers (use symbol ——k——)
#747	—Black	Cultural features

Other colors which experiments have shown to print well are:

        #735½—Lemon yellow
        #736 —Yellow ocher
        #736½—Orange ocher
        #737 —Orange
        #739½—Olive green
        #745½—Terra cotta
        #755 —Golden brown
        #756 —Dark brown

In areas of relatively well-known geology, it is usually sufficient to work with the aerial photographs and large-scale mosaics. However, in some cases an added step is advisable. The two most common situations in which this occurs are (1) large areas of virtually unknown geology, and (2) large basin, plains, or coastal areas. The additional step is the printing of small-scale mosaics, at a scale of 2½, 3, or even 4 miles to the inch. As many as sixteen or twenty of these may be assembled and glued or stapled to a medium-sized Beaverboard and faced with an acetate overlay.

Assembled small-scale mosaics cover an area of several thousand square miles. The same coverage could only be studied by hanging the corresponding large-scale mosaics on a large wall. However, using the smaller scale, the entire area can be propped against the wall at the back of the interpreter's desk, and instantly consulted whenever needed. Regional relationships can be seen at a glance. As one works, then, he can add his more significant and generalized observations to the overlay with little or no difficulty, and gradually build up a regional picture of the geology.

Such an approach is excellent in geomorphic plains and basin studies, where the regional characteristics can be perceived. The abnormal, or the anomalous, which so frequently reflect structural control, can then stand out more clearly against the normal patterns.

In detailed studies of large mountain areas, especially where the stratigraphy is unknown, small-scale mosaics are invaluable. In such areas, one must sometimes study thousands of square miles before he can establish the essentials of the stratigraphic sequence. With the entire area before him, he can slowly assemble these relations without being distracted by handling many large mosaics and trying to keep their mutual locations in mind at the same time.

In addition, crude annotations on a small-scale overlay, sometimes representing thoughts, assumptions, and speculations, as well as observations, may be made with no thought of disturbing or complicating the final large-scale annotation. The larger mosaics are saved until the basic geologic interpretation has been completed. The details may then be worked out and final large-scale mosaic annotation initiated.

It should be stressed that small-scale mosaics, while extremely useful in certain areas and under certain conditions, are unnecessary in a great many cases. They should be employed when geologic thinking alone is involved and when the photogeologist cannot turn to other sources for his information. In the more straightforward mapping projects in areas of relatively familiar geology, they would probably contribute little to the quality of the final map.

In those photogeologic projects where accuracy and detail are important, photogrammetric devices are used in the transfer of photograph data to mosaics. On highly controlled mosaics, this permits a close approach to a planimetrically correct geologic map. In addition, when care and skill are exercised in transferring such mosaic annotations to a constructed base map, the result is even more exact.

In some programs, complex and expensive stereoscopic plotting instruments are used in the transfer of data directly from the contact prints to the base map. By this process a high order of cartographic accuracy can be achieved. The product may equal, or even excel, a map made on the ground by the most experienced field topographers or geologists. As stated in the Preface, this aspect of photogeology is beyond the scope of this book, and further details must therefore be obtained from other sources.

ANNOTATION PROCEDURES: PHOTOGRAPHS TO MOSAICS

In the study of a project area, one may wish to map the following: drainage, alluvium, major roads, structure, and stratigraphy. He may annotate them all at one time, or he may study the photographs two or more times, each time concentrating on selected types of features.

There are certain advantages to the latter. During the first study, one may trace roads, drainage, stream alluvium, fans, and similar features throughout the entire area and transfer these data to the mosaics. This affords the opportunity to become somewhat acquainted with the general topography, structure, and stratigraphy. If desired, during this stage one may occasionally trace a conspicuous fault, or note such features as angular unconformities or fold axes.

When the photographs are restudied, full concentration can then be directed to the mapping and, more important, the understanding of the geology. When working in one area, the photogeologist will have some idea of what exists in adjacent areas. This can be extremely helpful when the geology is complex or relatively unknown.

The question of how mosaic annotation should progress is also important. If the geology is not difficult to map, and if no particular problems are met, it is permissible to study and annotate all the photographs covering a mosaic area, and then to transfer the entire data assemblage to the mosaic or mosaic overlay.

However, in relatively unknown areas, in complex areas, and in the case of geomorphic studies, it is far better to transfer the data from each flight, and sometimes from each photograph, as it is worked. The main reason for this is that by maintaining the mosaic "up to date," the interpreter can better imagine the geomorphic and structural relations present, and can better appreciate the significance, dimensions, and mutual positions of the features he is mapping. In geomorphic analysis, for example, one might note a particularly vague or poorly defined feature of doubtful significance. If he consults the mosaic, and sees that the feature lies along a projection of a previously mapped better-defined trend, he may thus be better able to evaluate what he is now viewing.

PART II Principles of Interpretation

INTRODUCTION

A discussion of the following three general topics constitutes this part of the book: the several basic types of photogeologic project, the many factors which determine the completeness and quality of the maps produced and the analyses made, and the numerous criteria used to identify and to interpret geologic features on aerial photographs.

The various general types of photogeologic study are presented for several reasons:

1. To acquaint the student with the many possible applications of aerial photographs in academic and commercial work

2. To help the commercial geologist appraise photogeologic contributions to exploration programs

3. To assist exploration directors in assigning personnel to a photogeologic study and in using photographs to their fullest potential

Numerous factors affecting results are listed and discussed briefly. These are important from the standpoint of economics, as well as geology. They are aspects of photogeology which should be understood and appreciated by all persons interested in photogeologic mapping and interpretation (i.e., a photogeologist, a person in charge of commercial exploration, and one who receives or uses a photogeologic map and report).

The approach of the chapter on criteria used to identify and interpret geologic features merits particular attention. Two subjects considered highly important in photogeology are structural geology and geomorphology. While frequent mention is made of structure in the following pages, no separate section has been prepared which is devoted exclusively to that subject. Geomorphology, however, is discussed in considerable detail. This is done for a purpose. In the relatively few areas where the geology is so clearly defined that the structure is obvious, it might be said that the structure is actually *seen* on the photographs. In the vast majority of cases, however, the visible geologic elements are primarily geomorphic. They consist of a variety of topographic forms and their relations. In addition, tonal patterns and variations together with variations in soil and vegetation are observed. Among other things, these elements are studied to reveal structural relationships.

There are numerous excellent structural geology textbooks, one or more of which can provide the student with a full understanding of such things as folds, faults, intrusions, extrusions, and tectonics. Similarly, a good geomorphology textbook can give a sound background for the interpretation of landforms, drainage systems, and associated features. The chapter on criteria is aimed essentially at helping the student *use* his geomorphic training to recognize, to map, and to assemble various geologic data, of which structure is one of the most significant.

In much the same way, topographic relations are used in photogeology in the identification of rock types. It is also presupposed that the student either knows the basic elements of stratigraphy and petrology or will learn such subjects elsewhere.

There are innumerable possible combinations of structure, rock type, geomorphic expression, soil, vegetation, climate, and photograph tone. It is considered more practical to stress the *nature* of the criteria used, in associating one with another, than to attempt to enumerate the particular criteria used to identify and map specific features. A fault, for example, has no single appearance. It may be obvious, or it may be completely hidden. It may be detected in many ways. Training in deductive thinking, using all possible criteria, is therefore of utmost importance. Knowing that a given structure in a given rock, in a given area, has a certain appearance is of relatively little value.

Many of the factors discussed in these chapters are illustrated in Part III.

Types of Photogeologic Study

INTRODUCTION

Aerial photographs may be used as maps. They may provide topographic and geologic data from which maps are constructed. Such data may be obtained from photographs and compiled on existing maps. A single individual or department may utilize aerial photographs in these several ways. Frequently, however, different persons perform the different tasks.

1. *Field geologists* may use aerial photographs as maps. Observation stations and geologic and topographic features may be located on the photographs. Field data and notes may be recorded on the pictures or in notebooks.

2. Accurate and detailed planimetric, topographic, and geologic maps may be constructed by *photogrammetrists*.

3. Geologic information may be obtained by *photogeologists* through the examination of stereo pairs, single photographs, or mosaics. Such data may be assembled on base maps or overlays.

The field geologist should learn to incorporate the use of aerial photographs in routine field studies and map-making projects. Whenever possible, the photogeologist should participate in the field investigation of photogeologic project areas. The principles of photogrammetry should be learned by all geologists, if only to facilitate and expedite photogeologic-photogrammetric cooperation. Some geologists and photogeologists learn to operate the more complex photogrammetric instruments, and thereby compile their own data and make their own maps. In many ways, it would be advantageous for the photogrammetrist to learn at least the elementary concepts of topography and geology.

The following pages include a summary of the field and office uses of aerial photographs by geologists. A brief discussion of photogrammetric contributions is also presented.

THE FIELD GEOLOGIST

Field geologists who use aerial photographs may be classified as follows:

1. Those who use single prints or mosaics as two-dimensional maps

2. Those who study the photographs stereoscopically and obtain, in effect, three-dimensional maps

3. Those who study the photographs stereoscopically and add some photogeologic data to their field work

Each group can obtain valuable information from the photographs. The first group usually secures the least amount of such information; the third group the most. Several observations and suggestions apply to all three categories. These will be presented before each category is discussed separately.

When aerial photographs are used as field maps, field-observed geologic and topographic features can usually be located with precision. The recognition of surrounding features permits the location of one's field position. Geologic observations and notations, recorded on the back of the photographs or in a field notebook, can thus be combined with relatively accurate geographic location. Care should be exercised in the marking of the photographs and in the taking of notes. One of many methods may be followed. If the student has not used aerial photographs in the field, he may wish to establish his own methods. The following are suggested:

1. Always carry a short pin or needle in the field. When a field observation is made, the location should be carefully marked and identified on the photographs. The pin or needle is used to prick the photograph at the precise position of the observed data. Use only enough pressure to permit the point to make an impression on, or to just penetrate, the back of the photograph. In ink, circle the back point. Each night, using a drop-bow pen, encircle the front points in small, clean circles.

2. If preferred or practicable, all observed data may be recorded on the back of the photograph. If dip and strike are measured, record the readings in note form (i.e., N 60° W, 43° NE). Rarely is a photograph oriented exactly north-south, east-west. Therefore, an attempt to plot the strike and dip on the photograph, in the field, will usually result in an error in direction.

3. A contact, dike, or fault may be seen to extend from the field station across several hills and valleys. This can be marked carefully on the photographs, in its approximate position, with colored pencil. The data recorded on the back of the photograph should be complete enough to restore such annotations should they become illegible or obliterated through use and handling of the pictures. No information or relations should be entrusted to memory.

If many notes are anticipated, a notebook should be used. Instead of recording data on the back of the photographs, it is then sufficient to assign a number to each field station. The photograph number and notebook entry number should be the same.

In addition, include in the notebook the photograph

identification numbers. This will prevent future loss of time in searching for the correct photograph to correspond with a field-notebook notation. This is especially important if many photographs are used and many notes are made. It also assists any other person who may refer to the data.

A notebook entry referring to station 76, which is located on photograph WD-703-89, might read as follows:

76:WD-703-89. Exposure of undistorted black fissile shale. Contains graptolites. Dip component 49° S 28° E . . .

In this case, an approximately oriented component symbol, with an accompanying indication of magnitude, may be sketched on the photograph face. The word "shale" or the abbreviation *sh* may also be useful.

Some field data are more reliable and accurate than others. When the field geologist compiles and edits his own data, the relative accuracy and dependability of the various data can frequently be remembered and the resulting map accordingly evaluated. However, if such material is to be used by a second geologist (photogeologist), certain precautions must be observed to ensure that the field notes and observations will always constitute an aid and not a hindrance when they are consulted. There are many ways in which geologic data may be obtained in the field. In the first instance, a well-exposed outcrop may be located and visited. The fresh unweathered bedrock may be examined, a hand sample obtained, and tentative or positive lithologic identification made. The dip and strike of bedding, jointing, lineation, or cleavage may be measured. These data may then be recorded as directly observed, reliable field information.

It is common practice, however, to make visual or binocular observations of distant surrounding geologic features from a high peak or escarpment. Regardless of the experience, ability, and confidence of the field geologist, such data are usually less reliable than those gathered at the outcrop. It is suggested that any distant observations be so identified in the notes. The information derived therefrom should be assigned a secondary category.

Finally, a geologist frequently makes observations while in transit, by motor vehicle, boat, helicopter, or conventional type of aircraft. If conditions permit, these observations are recorded and included in the field notes. The need to designate the relative unreliability of information obtained in this manner should be firmly stressed.

By providing a qualitative index to field data to be used by a photogeologist, the field geologist may significantly increase the value of his contribution to the final map and interpretation. This might be done in many ways, including the use of a different color annotation or station mark for each category, or by designating each by an appropriate letter, such as *o* for outcrop visited, *d* for distant observation, and *t* for information obtained while in transit. The method of designation is not important; the differentiation is.

Occasionally, questionable distant or transient observations are checked on the ground at a later date. If this is done, the more reliable outcrop or direct observations should replace the previous annotations and notes. If a different rock identification or structural interpretation is made, the previous observation and interpretation should be removed. This will assure the photogeologist a single, well-organized set of data. Otherwise, it is possible that in some areas contradictory field notes will occur; in such cases, the photogeologist will not know which to believe and which to discount. Such confusion must be avoided.

Photographs As Two-dimensional Field Maps

Aerial photographs can be of considerable use to the field geologist who does not or cannot study the pictures stereoscopically. Either single aerial photographs or mosaics may be used as two-dimensional reference maps.

Though planimetrically inaccurate, the photographs contain such a wealth of detail that in most cases even the untrained eye can recognize general and specific topographic, hydrologic, cultural, and vegetative features. When properly oriented, the photographs permit the location of one's field position and surrounding terrain.

Ground observations of structure, lithology, and other geologic relations can thus be plotted on the pictures and supplemented with field notes. Stratigraphic and lithologic contacts and details of structure can be plotted on the photographs and a generalized geologic map assembled.

In some areas, specific features cannot be identified on the photographs, and field stations cannot be plotted with reasonable accuracy, because the local homogeneity of the region prevents the recognition of individual ground features on the photographs. For example, precise location may be precluded in swamp areas completely overgrown by forest cover, in densely forested hilly areas characterized by fine-textured dendritic drainage, and on broad expanses of intermontane basins or undissected plains.

As previously mentioned, a field geologist frequently observes many geologic features from a distance. The use of aerial photographs as field maps may permit the sketching of the geology of a considerable area surrounding a ground station. If the photographs are not examined stereoscopically, some of the lines drawn will undoubtedly not agree with the three-dimensional geologic-topographic relations. This would be caused by the inability of the field geologist to visualize the details of the intersections of the geologic and topographic surfaces. The photogeologist who may later use the annotated photographs should consider such field-sketched geology as a generalized guide, and should correct and modify such annotations during the subsequent analysis of the pictures.

Photographs As Three-dimensional Field Maps

Though the field geologist may not undertake photogeologic studies, he should learn to see stereoscopically, first with the aid of a simple folding-lens stereoscope, which can be carried in the field, and eventually without such an instrument. It would be virtually impossible to list all the ways in which stereo vision alone can be of assistance in the field. The following are presented as illustrations; no attempt has been made to evaluate their relative importance. Stereo-vision permits:

1. Greater accuracy in locating on the photographs observation stations and such field-observed features as specific outcrops, contacts, and faults.

2. The planning of traverses and the selection of camp sites and rendezvous points.

3. A study of the terrain to estimate more accurately the time of travel between any two points. This also permits the anticipation of possible obstacles in the form of scarps, marshes, water bodies, dense-vegetation areas, "burns," and the like. If traveling downstream by canoe, for example, the field geologist will be able to know in advance the location of rapids and falls, as well as possible outcrop areas, good stopping places, and many other similar small but significant features.

4. In the case of helicopter travel, the advance selection of favorable landing places, as well as areas which should be avoided.

5. In the case of travel by a plane equipped for landing on water, the location of lakes and other water bodies of sufficient size to permit landing and take-off. Also, the selection of topography suitable for safe approach and take-off is possible when the terrain model is viewed. Good approach might well prompt the preference of a slightly smaller lake to a larger one surrounded by high and dangerous hills. A single photograph cannot furnish such comparative topographic information. A knowledge of vertical configuration assists in the recognition of the land features depicted on the map. (*By permission from Fairchild Aerial Surveys, Inc.*)

Figure 5-1. A stereogram of part of the area shown on the topographic map (Figure 5-2). Study the photographs individually, and attempt to locate the various features on the map. Then view the pictures stereoscopically. Note how the terrain model

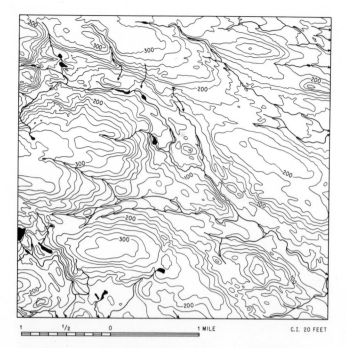

Figure 5-2. A topographic map, including the area shown on the stereogram (Figure 5-1). Outline the photograph coverage on the map; indicate the area of stereoscopic and nonstereoscopic photo coverage. What is approximate photograph scale? One of the lakes shown on the photographs does not appear on the map. Transfer this lake and the main parkway to the map.

exaggeration and model distortion is needed in judging the relative advantages or dangers of various approaches to lakes.

The above are but a few of the many stereoscopic field uses of aerial photographs. The contrast between the "flat" photograph and the stereoscopic model may be appreciated by studying Figure 5-1. The area shown on the stereogram is included on the accompanying topographic map (Figure 5-2). Before viewing the photographs stereoscopically, it is suggested that the student compare either photograph with the map and attempt to identify on the photograph several specific features shown on the map. When the photographed area has been located on the map, and the appearance of numerous objects compared, the photographs should be studied stereoscopically. The three-dimensional terrain model should then be compared with the map.

This simple exercise should suffice to demonstrate the severe limitations of the single photograph and the decided advantages of the stereoscopic model. Numerous stereograms in Part III may be studied to obtain a similar comparison.

Photogeologic Study by the Field Geologist

Despite the many applications of office photogeologic work, some geologic problems can only be solved by field mapping and data collection. The detailed study of lithologic characteristics and variations, the measurement of stratigraphic sections, and the mapping of small mineralized zones are examples.

If the field geologist undertaking such a program can supplement his ground observations with photogeologic data, he will have a decided advantage over one who uses photographs only as two- or three-dimensional field maps. Photogeologic study in the field can save considerable time, money, and effort. It can also increase the accuracy and completeness of the final geologic map.

The general advantages of field-photogeologic work are threefold:

1. Geologic information obtained in the field can be extended beyond the observation area by the immediate stereoscopic study of the photographs of surrounding areas.

2. Photogeologic identifications and interpretations can be subjected to a constant field check. Similarly, as additional field information is obtained, it can be evaluated systematically by simultaneous photograph examination.

3. Each day's traverses can be planned. Problems of access can be considered in advance. Specific features, important to the solution of the geology being mapped, can be selected for immediate investigation.

If the photographs are examined prior to the beginning of the field work, a general impression of topography, structure, and rock-unit distribution can be gained. Such features as scarps, hillsides, valleys, and road cuts may be noted. These may be important as areas of possible outcrops.

After the important rock units have been examined and identified in the field, their general distribution may be determined on the photographs. Additional possible outcrops of the units can then be located on the photographs, and field traverses directed to include these points. The photogeologic contribution can be especially helpful if these rock units are offset by faulting or are in places obscured and masked by surficial materials.

At the beginning of the field work, a general plan of investigation is usually made. By closely integrating daily field findings with field and evening photogeologic studies and appraisals, the over-all plan can be modified periodically to ensure maximum results and efficiency.

There are areas in which bedrock units can be identified and mapped on aerial photographs but cannot be detected in the field. A common case involves soil-covered rock; the photographic tone, vegetation, and textural qualities of a certain belt or area may be reliable indications that a certain rock unit is present immediately beneath the surface. Using such criteria, the field geologist who must resort to digging or trenching has the advantage of knowing where to dig to encounter the desired rock.

USES OF AERIAL PHOTOGRAPHS IN THE OFFICE

Depending on the time available, the purpose of the study and the personnel and equipment involved, photogeologic projects may consist of one of the following:

1. A rapid or detailed examination of mosaics.

2. A rapid stereoscopic study, not necessarily involving map construction or the assembly of data on a base map.

3. A more detailed study in which a photogeologic map is produced, entailing the gathering of all possible geologic information from the photographs. Such a study may or may not include coordinated field work.

4. A detailed study coordinated with a controlled photogrammetric program.

5. A comprehensive photogeomorphic study, in the search for petroleum or minerals.

6. A special project, such as an access survey, an academic or commercial research study, or a similar investigation in which greater emphasis than usual is placed on certain particular aspects of topography, vegetation, soils, transportation, hydrology, or the like.

With the possible exception of some of the extremely rapid and cursory types of study, certain preliminary steps are required prior to the undertaking of any photogeologic project. These as a whole may be called *research*. They consist of the following:

1. All available geologic maps, reports, papers, geologic cross sections, and well data, covering all or parts of the project area or of nearby areas, must be obtained and thoroughly studied. The relative reliability and completeness of a photogeologic map and analysis frequently depend on the amount of information obtained from references.

2. All available published planimetric and topographic maps of the area, as well as triangulation station and benchmark data, should be assembled. Unless the standards and requirements of the photogeologic map are to be exceptionally precise, the photographic data can usually be compiled on the available maps. If desired, individual base map sheets may first be prepared by tracing or photographically reproducing the published maps.

3. The following photographic data should be obtained: approximate scale, aerial camera focal length, height of photography, and year and month of photography. Also, the year of map publication is important, since there may be discrepancies between some of the natural and cultural features shown on the photography and on the maps.

Rapid and Detailed Mosaic Studies

One or more mosaics may be examined, either as part of a more comprehensive photogeologic study or as an individual project. Different types of information may be obtained in different areas.

The mosaics of a large area may be examined to delineate selected areas in which detailed stereoscopic studies may best be carried out. Apparent structure, outcrop area, topographic relief, economic potential, relative accessibility, or vegetation cover may be factors involved in the selection of some areas and the rejection of others. Mosaics can usually provide such comparative information.

In commercial photogeology it is frequently necessary to make extremely rapid evaluations of large areas. This may be occasioned by the recent discovery of oil or gas in a previously unexplored or untested region, with a subsequent rush for lease blocks. Another possibility, also in petroleum exploration, might be the receipt of a proposal on a farm-out or a similar land exchange. A rapid examination of the mosaics of the area may assist the exploration department in evaluating such a proposal.

Detailed mosaic studies are made in certain areas. Some are reported to have yielded significant geologic information. On the U.S. Gulf Coast, mosaic geomorphic studies of large areas have disclosed the surface expression of several fault and fracture systems. Also, in many Gulf coastal areas, salt domes frequently have either a positive or negative topographic expression, or may be located by the careful study of stream patterns or tonal and vegetative contrasts on mosaics (see Figures 12-3 and 12-5).

Two-dimensional geomorphic studies may be productive in some instances, but it is suggested that if time permits, the photogeologist should reexamine the area stereoscopically in order to render more precise his understanding of the third dimension of the area. The use of the stereoscope in such studies not only may lead to the discovery of structural anomalies which cannot be determined on the mosaics alone, but they may also permit the rejection of *anomalous-appearing* features which, when examined stereoscopically, may be found to have nonstructural explanations. Economically, this is considered to be one of the strongest arguments in favor of the use of stereoscopic photographs, since it could result in considerable saving of money through the avoidance of further ground and subsurface exploration of unproductive areas.

Some of the geologic features which are frequently apparent on mosaics are the following:

1. Major zones of tectonic weakness, such as faults.
2. Areas of intense folding and faulting.
3. Stream alluvium, alluvial fans and plains, shoreline features, glacial deposits, and sand dunes.
4. Cultural features, such as roads, railroads, agricultural areas, towns, irrigation ditches, and the like.
5. Major geomorphic relations, such as stream patterns, stream adjustments to lithology and structure, and comparisons between drainage density and other characteristics of several areas.
6. Tonal variations, such as might be produced by structure, variations in water content, soil composition and vegetation. These and others may have direct or indirect geologic significance.

In recent years, the photogeologic exploration of the glaciated plains of western Canada has produced considerable interest in the recognition and consideration of numerous linear features noted on mosaics and contact prints. These linear features, which may either be tonal or topographic in nature, are believed by some geologists to represent the surface expression of fractures in the underlying bedrock. At the present time, the significance of these features, and their satisfactory explanation, remain incomplete. The student is urged to consult several papers, published by Canadian photogeologists, dealing with this subject of *fracture analysis*. Blanchet and Mollard (see Bibliography) are two of the more prominent exponents of this line of investigation.

Rapid Stereoscopic Studies

Frequently, time does not permit the careful examination of aerial photographs in the appraisal or mapping of an area. This situation is most commonly met in commercial work, where time is usually an important factor. Numerous examples might be cited. The three following are representative of rapid commercial studies.

1. An oil company staff photogeologist may be requested to make a rapid appraisal of an area considered for leasing or farm-out. If a mosaic of the area is not available and little time is afforded for the study, a very crude photogeologic sketch map may be prepared in a day or two. In such cases, the findings and recommendations of the photogeologist may determine the expenditure of large amounts of money.

2. In relatively inaccessible areas, seismic and other geophysical operations are extremely expensive. If unforeseen difficulties are encountered, the photogeologist may be asked to examine the photographs of the area and select the most promising lines to bulldoze for seismic or other surveys. This request may come when the crews are in the field and when time is extremely important. Pregeophysical access surveys are strongly recommended in areas where such problems may be encountered.

3. The discovery of new oil production in wildcat areas invariably produces a rush for available acreage. An oil

company which has some idea of the location of favorable structures or areas in which more profitable and more rapid field investigation may be carried out has a distinct advantage. A very rapid photo study can be extremely important in the exploration and land programs of an oil company interested in such areas.

There are, of course, many other instances in which rapid stereoscopic examination of aerial photographs can be productive. The author feels that this particular aspect of photogeology is frequently too little realized and appreciated by many geologists. To be economically important, photogeologic information need not be assembled and presented on prepared maps, nor be obtained solely from careful and detailed analysis.

The responsibility for such hurried interpretations should only be assumed by or assigned to persons with long, varied, and proven experience and capabilities in the geologic interpretation of aerial photographs. Considerable harm could result from inexperience, erroneous interpretation, or poor judgment on the part of the photogeologist.

Photogeologic Reconnaissance
without Coordinated Field Work

A relatively detailed photogeologic study, with no integrated field work, may be undertaken for one of several reasons. In regions where the climate limits field studies to a few months, considerable areas may be mapped photogeologically during the inclement period without the necessity of delay. This may be a forced decision, should the information sought be required before field work is possible.

Also, since it is not uncommon to make a photogeologic study in a central office distant from the field area, it may be virtually impossible to integrate concurrent field and photogeologic information. This situation should be avoided if possible, since close cooperation between the field geologist and the photogeologist is usually extremely productive.

On numerous occasions, current requirements may be met through photogeology alone. Government agencies, for example, may wish to map large areas, the most hurried field reconnaissance of which would require several years. In such cases, *preliminary* photogeologic maps can be prepared and revision accomplished at some later date. The essential information would thus be available to the geologic profession as early as possible.

In much the same way, mining and petroleum companies may desire to map and evaluate large areas in which they are currently not active. They may intend in the foreseeable future to inaugurate exploration programs therein, or they may wish basic information should a sudden discovery transform the area into one of immediate concern. Such long-range planning has become relatively common in recent years. An excellent example is the highly competitive photogeologic investigation of vast areas in the Yukon and Northwest Territories of Canada. For several years numerous oil companies had undertaken photogeologic studies in this area without obtaining leases or organizing drilling programs. Later increased activity in the area saw them with a distinct advantage over their competitors who had not made photogeologic studies. The former companies knew what areas to lease; the latter were frequently forced to obtain available acreage with little or no idea of its potential.

How are such regional studies made? What procedures should be followed for optimum results?

Of primary importance is the geologic information which can be obtained prior to the photo study. By compiling and examining all available references, the photogeologist can determine general geography, structure, stratigraphy, and geologic history of the area in advance.

If the area is covered by a geologic map, it should be used as a guide to the photogeologic mapping. If the area is large, and available time limited, this preliminary phase may consist of selecting specific features shown on the map, examining them on the photographs, and thus building up a general impression of the appearance of the various rock types and structures to be studied.

If published maps cover only part of the project area, first attention should normally be directed to this part. This will permit familiarization with the known features, which may then be extended into the unknown areas as the study progresses.

Occasionally, the only existing literature and maps refer to areas near but outside the area to be studied. Such references should be consulted. They may provide stratigraphic or lithologic descriptions, structural patterns, historical sequence, or references to such specific facts as the way certain rock units are eroded, their topographic expression, or similar associations which can be extremely helpful within the project area. The purchase of photographic coverage beyond the project boundaries, to include the areas covered by published materials, is strongly advised.

In areas where no reference material is available, it may be necessary to create artificial stratigraphic and lithologic units, and divide the strata into mappable units of unknown specific but understandable sequential age. Crystalline rock contacts and differentiations can be mapped, using as criteria such factors as photographic tone, topographic development, fracture characteristics, and vegetation associations.

One important caution should be exercised in the use of pre-existing maps and other published information. The possibility of error should always be kept in mind. A fault, for example, based on questionable or incomplete field information, may be shown on a published map. If the photogeologic study reveals additional information which would rule out the necessity or probability of such a fault, the photogeologist must not hesitate to remove it from his compilation. Similarly, a given mapped rock unit may have been misidentified in the field, or its structural relation misinterpreted. It should be appreciated that in many cases general and regional geologic relations can be seen much better on aerial photographs than on the ground. Therefore, though published maps are extremely useful as guides, they must not be assumed to be absolutely correct in all cases. It is a human tendency, experienced by the author and reported by many other photogeologists, to place undue faith in published maps and reports, simply because they *are* published. If this tendency exists, it must be recognized and overcome when photogeologic evidence contradicts the published information.

Government agencies usually tend to publish only relatively certain and dependable field and photograph information. Questionable and uncertain elements of stratigraphy and structure, for example, are frequently omitted from government maps. One of the specific aims of the commercial photogeologist, therefore, should be the detection of possible or questionable geologic features which do not appear on government publications. The fact that a government agency has studied and mapped a given area does not necessarily mean that all its significant geologic relations have been compiled for publication. This is understandable when the aim of survey publications is recalled. Accuracy and dependability are important factors. The publication of questionable structural interpretations or of doubtful rock-unit identifications would be unwise. In most cases, considerable amounts of worthwhile information can be added by a thorough and comprehensive photogeologic restudy of such areas.

Photogeologic Studies with Coordinated Field Work

In striving for accuracy and detail, best results can usually be obtained from a well-organized and intelligently executed combined field and photogeologic study. This does not mean merely the study of photographs in the field, as discussed above, but the division of investigation, more or less in stages, into office photograph study and field-photograph study. Needless to say, numerous factors might dictate modifications of the following sequence, but if the full value of the proposed procedure is understood, the student should be better prepared to adapt his program to available time, seasonal demands, and economic conditions.

Under ideal conditions, a project area should be relatively accessible and lie in a climatic zone in which year-round field work may be undertaken. In addition, at least part of the area should be included on a published map and described in an available geologic report.

If the study is to be a comprehensive one and is not to be subject to a strict deadline, the following procedure is suggested.

Examine and analyze all available literature, including the published map. If possible, determine the essentials of structure and stratigraphy. Study the photographs of the mapped area. Using the published map as constant reference, sketch on the photographs apparent contacts, faults, and similar features. When the geology of this part of the area has been examined, study the photographs of the remainder of the area and extend the known structures and formational contacts. Rock units apparently not present in the mapped area may be encountered. Assign numbers or letters to such unidentified units.

During this phase of the study, do not attempt to solve all problems encountered or anticipated. Concentrate on establishing the location and distribution of the major elements of the geology to be mapped, and designate questionable features to be investigated in the field.

Following the initial orientation study, take the photographs and reference material into the field. Make one or more traverses across the mapped portion of the area. Examine the identified rock units and the general structures of the area. Check on the accuracy with which the structural and stratigraphic annotations have been drawn on the photographs.

A thorough reconnaissance of the entire project area is not necessary at this time. Make several traverses across the rest of the area at relatively wide intervals. Check the larger elements of the geology mapped on the photographs. Concentrate on those features which could not be identified or understood during the preliminary photo study.

Following the brief field investigation, undertake a thorough and comprehensive photogeologic study of the entire project area. Remember that regardless of how simple or complex the geology, when the map is completed, all elements of the stratigraphy, structure, and topography must fit to-gether to form a picture which may be said to "make geologic sense."

When the detailed photogeologic study is completed and the geology compiled on maps and examined and found to be coherent, understandable, and explainable, return to the field and make a final check. If, previous to going into the field again, it is found that there are still some poorly defined or questionable features, or a series of unanswered questions, single these out for detailed field investigation.

During the final field check, direct first attention to those areas or features which are believed to be incorrectly mapped or which are not clearly understood. When these have been investigated, undertake a general reconnaissance of the area, filling in as many details as required.

Following the field check, incorporate all field-obtained corrections and additions into the final map and prepare a report on the project area. If certain geologic features or relations are still questionable, or perhaps have more than one possible explanation, include on the map pertinent brief notes which will help the recipient of the map to evaluate its contents more successfully. In the final report, the uncertain and questionable geologic elements as well as the more clearly defined and accurately mapped geology should be thoroughly discussed and interpreted.

The procedure outlined above applies to what might be called the "ideal" situation, which is seldom, if ever, encountered in actual practice. Depending on the elements of time, accessibility, climate, and other controls, the suggested sequence of study as well as contributions of field and office work should be modified for each project undertaken.

A field geologist occasionally checks a map prepared or being prepared by a photogeologist. Similarly, field data may be gathered by one person, whereas the photogeologic study to follow will be done by another. If such a division of work is required, a considerable amount of valuable data can be exchanged to obtain a final map of a higher degree of accuracy and detail than either could produce individually.

The desirability of one person doing both photogeologic and field work demands further consideration. The photogeologist, through research and preliminary photographic study over a period of weeks or months, of necessity builds up an almost intimate knowledge, not only of the structure and stratigraphy of the project area, but also of the associated topography, geography, vegetation, and other elements.

In addition, during the course of many hours of intense study and analysis of the integrated picture, the photogeologist obtains subtle and poorly defined impressions of possible features whose existence cannot at this stage be demonstrated. For example, a fault may be suspected in a given area, or a circular depression or topographic dome, in an area having a linear structural trend, may be felt to suggest the presence of a buried intrusion.

It is relatively common for information originally derived from such vague impressions to be as important as, or more important than, that obtained in the more routine study. But there is one important question. How can one person, regardless of how many notes or annotations he adds to his map, possibly convey his thoughts and his thinking process to another, especially when the second person usually has far less knowledge of either the area in question, or the way in which photogeologic analysis is made? The answer is that, with rare exceptions, he cannot.

Therefore, when someone other than the photogeologist does the required field work, he is forced to restrict most of his efforts to a check of the photogeologic map alone. When the photogeologist goes into the field, he may investigate *both* the mapped features *and* those other features which have a bearing on his impressions and interpretations of less obvious and less definite geologic elements.

This need not be all. Suppose, for example, that when a photogeologist was mapping a certain well-defined structure, his attention was occasionally diverted by a series of linear features suggestive of a fault-joint system. For some reason or reasons, he may not be convinced that jointing was responsible for these features. Were another person to check the area in the field, mapped structures would be of primary importance. Even were he told of the suspected joints, and were to investigate them, his findings would in all likelihood consist of either a confirmation or refutation of their existence.

Should the photogeologist carry out his own field study, he could check the structure mapped more readily than could another, since he would best know what places to check and the significance of each observation. He could then turn to the question of a possible joint system. His findings might show that such a system does not exist. They may also disclose some other fact or facts, apparently meaningless to someone else, which might fit into photographically observed relations and lead to further postulations, investigations, disclosures and, eventually, conclusions.

To summarize, it might be stated thus: field work done by any person other than the photogeologist may well supplement the information obtained through the study of the photographs; field work done by the photogeologist experienced in field procedures *extends* the photogeologic investigation and analysis.

The fact that much photogeologic work is done by consultants for petroleum and mining companies introduces another factor for consideration. The client almost invariably continues field work after receiving a final photogeologic map and report. If only the photogeologist carries out the field checks during the photogeologic study, the client will received a product with which he is probably unfamiliar. In commercial consulting work, therefore, it is strongly urged that the client work closely with the photogeologist, especially in the field. It would also be beneficial to the client if he held several conferences with the photogeologist during the late stages of the office photograph study and report preparation. By doing so he would be in a position to evaluate the work as a whole, and to continue the investigation of specific problems, questionable interpretations, and localized features of possible economic interest.

Quantitative Photogeologic Projects

Photogrammetric instruments are used to obtain quantitative geologic data and to compile geologic information obtained during qualitative stereoscopic and field studies. Accurate planimetric and topographic maps may be constructed, and existing maps may be refined and corrected through photogrammetric procedures. The thickness of stratigraphic units may be measured, and isopachous maps prepared. The precise dimensions of intrusive bodies may be obtained. Fault displacements and fold closures may be calculated. In areas of well-exposed strata, structure contour maps may be made. Topographic profiles and structural cross sections may be constructed.

Frequently, this work is done by the geologist, who incorporates his qualitative data into a more exacting and controlled photogrammetric program. In other cases, however, where a considerable time is to be spent in measurements and quantitative compilations, a professional photogrammetrist may work closely with the geologist.

The primary value of instrumentation in photogeology is that it reduces or removes the necessity for precise field mapping. In many ways, the photogeologic-photogrammetric sequence and relation may be compared to the field-geology–plane-table-mapping relation. Frequently, the field geologist is indoctrinated into practical and commercial field methods by first serving as a plane-table mapper. The senior field man carries the surveying rod and decides the general field approach and the specific selection of rod stations. The experienced photogeologist, in a combined photogeologic-photogrammetric project, may evaluate and organize the over-all program and may either supply the photogrammetrist with specific points and areas to measure, or will direct the geologic application of photogrammetry to be carried out by the geologist using the instruments.

In order to organize and execute a plane-table survey, the senior geologist should be thoroughly versed in the procedures and mechanics of plane-table mapping. He should, therefore, have had thorough grounding and experience in the use of the alidade. Similarly, the photogeologist in charge of a combined photogeologic-photogrammetric program should, if possible, have received previous instruction and experience in the manipulation of whatever photogrammetric instrument may be used. Therefore, one of the several reasons why a geologist may be assigned to a photogrammetric instrument is the teaching or background factor.

Economics is another element which must be considered in determining the person who will undertake the photogrammetric phase of quantitative photogeology. Photogrammetry is a highly technical and specialized field. The salary of a fully experienced and competent photogrammetrist frequently exceeds that of a geologist. Therefore, depending upon the particular conditions, it may be financially advisable to assign a photogeologist to the instrument, instead of obtaining the services of a professional photogrammetrist.

Whereas geology for the most part is a nonexact science, photogrammetry demands that fullest attention be paid to details and to exact measurements. The temperament and personality characteristics of the average geologist are usually quite different from those of the average photogrammetrist. It is of considerable importance, therefore, that a geologist contemplating a career in quantitative photogeology give serious thought to the conditions under which the work will be performed. Similarly, administrative geologists who may assign personnel to such work should include proper temperament as a primary qualification. An improper choice of personnel for such functions could easily result in a rapid turnover of the geologic staff. Since considerable time is required to orient and thoroughly train individuals for the operation of the more intricate and complex photogrammetric machines, it is of both economic and operational importance that this be avoided.

Factors Affecting Results

No two photogeologic studies follow identical procedures, involve the use of identical materials, or produce identical results. There are many variable factors which determine the completeness, the quality, and the value of a given photogeologic map and accompanying report. These factors include the photography used, the area selected for study, the conditions under which the study is made, the approach followed, and the personnel involved.

OBSCURING FACTORS

Since most standard photogeologic studies are designed to compile a geologic map of lithologic units and structure, attention must be given to any element which obscures or hides underlying bedrock. The more obvious obscuring factors are as follows:

1. *Alluvium and Mantle.* Stream alluvium, alluvial fans, lacustrine deposits, stationary or moving sand, and thick mantle overburden may combine to shroud or completely obscure underlying bedrock features (see Figures 14-5 and 15-15). It should be noted, however, that geomorphic characteristics and variations in residual soil and mantle, vegetation, and photograph tone, often reflect covered rock types. Therefore, considerable geologic information may be obtained through the photogeologic study of many covered areas (see Figures 10-7, 14-7, and 12-3).

2. *Glacial Deposits.* Terminal, recessional, and ground moraines and outwash deposits are usually very distinctive in in their appearance on aerial photographs. In many instances, they mask the underlying bedrock. Careful geomorphic analysis may permit the mapping and interpretation of some bedrock geology reflected through glacial material (see Figures 8-14, 15-5, and 15-12).

3. *Forests.* In most outcrop areas which are completely devoid of vegetation, it is usually possible to carry out relatively easy and rapid bedrock identification and structural mapping (see Figure 13-17). In other areas, the presence of various types of vegetation assists in the mapping of rock units and structural features (see Figures 8-13, 11-1, 13-9, and 13-13). However, a uniform dense forest cover may effectively obscure many otherwise visible and understandable geologic features. In such cases, landform studies may be helpful in obtaining lithologic, structural, and tectonic information (see Figure 10-9).

4. *Shadows and Glare.* In many mountainous areas, it is impossible to obtain photographs in which confusing and obscuring shadows are not present. South-facing mountain slopes, when underlain by generally light-toned rock and soil, may appear as extremely white, glaring areas. Both shadows and strong glare may obscure exposed lithologic and structural relations (see Figures 15-2 and 15-5).

5. *Clouds.* In some cases, aerial photographs must be made despite the presence of some cloud cover. When such photographs are used, the clouds and their shadows constitute obstacles to the examination and mapping of the geology.

6. *Snow and Ice.* Extensive snow and ice cover usually mask the underlying geology. Occasionally, fractures and slope variations in alpine glacial ice can be used to predict the location of rock units and structures beneath the ice surface.

Small patches of snow and ice, which may occupy linear depressions along belts of nonresistant rock or fault traces, are occasionally extremely helpful in mapping rock units and determining structure.

In general, photography is planned during the warmer months, to assure maximum bedrock exposure.

7. *Lakes.* Most bodies of standing water, whether naturally or artificially produced, completely obscure underlying bedrock. In some cases, the underwater topography (indicative of rock type or structure) can be seen through the water, or is represented by variations in tone caused by currents, algae concentrations, or silt content.

The configuration of a lake may have geologic significance. For example, one linear side of an otherwise extremely irregular lake may suggest the presence of steep dip (strike) or a fault (see Figure 8-11). A linear finger of a lake may occupy a fault zone or a band of nonresistant rock (see Figure 10-5).

8. *Agriculture.* In flat and undulating plains and lowland areas under intense cultivation, topographic expression of the underlying bedrock may be obscured or altered. Agricultural selectivity may reflect geologic variations important to the understanding of the area. For example, farms may be concentrated along limestone belts. Occasionally, plowing will expose soil contrasts which are subdued or hidden where a uniform vegetative cover remains.

9. *Cliffs and Escarpments.* The face of steep cliffs and escarpments may lie in an area of shadow. Their orientation and location with respect to the camera at the time of photography are important. Excellent cliff-face outcrops may be clearly presented to the camera, or completely hidden (see Figure 6-1).

10. *Fingerprints, Scratches, Static Electricity Marks, and Patched Negatives.* Competition forces commercial com-

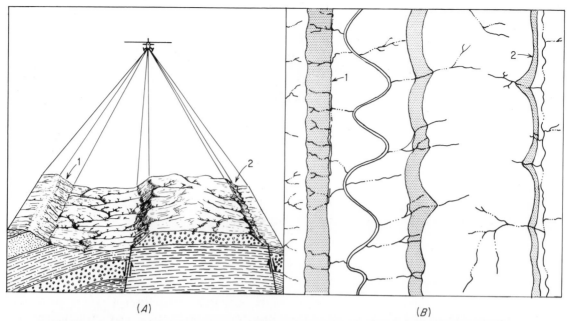

Figure 6-1. Two sketches showing the importance of orientation and location of scarps and steep slopes on an aerial photograph. (*A*) The photography of three steep slopes. (*B*) An idealized sketch of the picture of these slopes (stippled zones). Such features as slope 1, facing toward the camera (center of the photograph) are clearly exposed; those such as slope 2, facing away from the camera, are foreshortened and obscured. (*Sketches by Calvin F. Miller.*)

panies to maintain high standards of photography, handling, and printing. The quality of purchased commercial pictures is therefore usually good to excellent.

Occasionally, however, various government agencies offer photographs which show distinct or smudged fingerprints, the effects of scratches on the negatives, or evidence that the negative has been patched with material of relatively low transparency (see Figure 13-23).

11. *Angular Unconformities.* Consolidated and semiconsolidated rock materials may unconformably overlie a series of older rock units. For example, widespread lava flows effectively hide the bedrock which lies beneath them. Late Tertiary sediments frequently overlie disturbed Cretaceous and older strata (see Figures 14-13 and 14-15).

The above list, though incomplete, is representative of the many factors with which the photogeologist must work in the mapping and compilation of geological data from aerial photographs. If such obscuring or distracting features are infrequent, they are usually unimportant. If numerous, or widespread, they may constitute serious hindrances.

SCALE AND QUALITY OF PHOTOGRAPHY

Excellent-quality photographs are, of course, highly desirable. The use of clear, well-printed, tilt-free, distortion-free aerial photographs can ensure the acquisition of maximum geologic data. Accordingly, much information may be misinterpreted and misevaluated when poor photographs, including those taken with appreciable tilt, must be used.

The scale of the photographs is also very important. In general, fewer geologic details can be seen on small-scale photographs. However, one advantage of small-scale photography is that a single stereo pair may afford a regional picture to the interpreter. Such regional relations, including the larger tectonic elements and many of the more subtly expressed topographic relations, may be essential in some project areas.

The use of large-scale photography permits the delineation and analysis of many smaller features. However, the handling and examination of many large-scale photographs increase the cost and time required to study a given area. Also, the use of large-scale photographs could cause neglect of some of the regional aspects of an area.

If the photogeologist is free to determine in advance the scale of photography to be used, the following factors should be considered:

1. The time allotted for the study
2. Cost
3. The purpose of the study
4. The nature and scale of the geologic units
5. Features which must be seen and mapped

TIME AND FUNDS

The accuracy and completeness of a photogeologic study depend to a large degree on the amount of time and money which can be devoted to it.

If a given amount of money is available, it must be distributed among the purchase of photography, mosaics, and base maps, cost of research, cost of the study of the photographs, and cost of field work and final analysis. The scale of the existing photography partly determines the cost of a photogeologic project, since it involves both the purchase price and the time required to complete the study.

Factors other than financial ones may dictate the amount of time to be spent on a given study. In consulting work, a specific deadline may be established by the client. Frequently, in areas having limited field seasons, a project must be completed prior to the advent of good weather, regardless of the date the study begins.

Since the amount of information to be derived from a photogeologic study depends, at least in part, on the amount of time to be spent in the examination of the photographs and the analysis of the findings, individuals or companies should attempt to plan their photogeologic projects well in advance.

Much commercial photogeologic work, especially in the petroleum industry, is done by consulting companies. Over the past decade, the number of such companies has increased considerably. Petroleum and mining firms which contemplate the contracting of photogeologic work should consider several factors before requesting bids on a specific proposed project. If, in order to obtain such a contract, a consulting company must submit a minimum cost estimate, it must be clearly understood that in most cases a thorough and comprehensive analysis of the project area is precluded. In order to work within the prescribed economic limits, the consultant must restrict his efforts to the delineation of the most obvious geologic elements. Little or no time can be spent in the analysis of the geology mapped, or in the discovery of the more subtle and poorly expressed geologic features, which may be the most important from an economic standpoint.

If only the elementary and easily determined parts of the geologic picture are desired, it may be a sound economic policy to request competitive bids. If, however, all possible geologic information is demanded and expected, the client should realize that the selection of the lowest bid increases the possibility that an incomplete or inferior product will be obtained.

AREA SIZE

The size of a photogeologic project area may be determined by one or more factors: the purpose of the study, the nature of the geology, the cost involved, or the time available. A structure contour map of a single township may be made, using precision photogrammetric instruments. Similarly, one or more townships may be studied in the attempt to delimit a specific mineralized belt or intrusive body. In contrast, regional tectonic and geomorphic studies may involve the examination of tens of thousands of square miles.

In general, the unit cost varies as an inverse function of the size of the project area. This is primarily explained by the fact that regardless of area size, the time and cost involved in research and final analysis is approximately the same.

In the mapping of well-exposed geology, the size and shape of a project area are relatively unimportant. However, it tectonics are to be evaluated, or extensive regional plains and basin studies attempted, it should be cautioned that the selection of a small area may defeat the purpose of the study. In the interpretation of coastal, basin, and plains areas, regional comparisons and contrasts are usually important. Such comparisons cannot be made in a restricted area.

COMPILATION SCALE

The scale at which photogeologically obtained data are to be compiled determines the amount and the magnitude of the details which can be included on the final map. Prior to the designation of final map scale, such factors as structural complexity, the nature of the rock units involved, and the aim of the study should be considered. If an area is characterized by intricate fold and fault patterns, a relatively large scale should be used. If regional elements are to be mapped, a smaller scale is preferable.

Many petroleum and mining companies have standard scales at which all their geologic and other maps are compiled. The existence of such scales may dictate the scale of photogeologic maps, regardless of other considerations.

If a relatively large area is studied and compilation scale is large, it is suggested that a second, small-scale sketch map be made to permit the study and analysis of the regional components of the geology. For example, if a square area including 10,000 square miles is mapped at a scale of 1:48,000, the final map sheets will total 132 inches in width. If the major structural and stratigraphic elements are compiled on a sketch map at a scale of 8 miles to the inch, the entire geologic picture will then be included on a small map 12½ inches square. Such sketch maps are frequently invaluable in the preparation of reports and during final structural and tectonic analyses.

REFERENCE MATERIAL

The amount, variety, reliability, and age of reference material are extremely important. All possible sources of pertinent geologic data should be investigated. Such materials should be thoroughly studied and evaluated prior to the initiation of a photogeologic study. The role of research material can best be appreciated by comparing a hypothetical photogeologic program in an area where the geology is relatively well known, and a similar study of an area devoid of published or other geologic information.

In all probability, the purpose of the two studies will not be the same. In areas in which most of the geologic relations are already known, a photogeologic study is usually made to obtain certain details of structure, stratigraphy, rock-unit distribution, tectonic history, or the like. In an unmapped area, the purpose of the study will probably be to learn the general geology. In such a case the emphasis must almost of necessity be upon broad, generalized, perhaps regional, relationships. The resulting photogeologic map would be expected to require considerable refinement, correction, and addition, should later field or detailed photogeologic analyses be made.

During the study of the known area, attention may be concentrated on the specific element or elements to be investigated. In an unknown area, all factors must be considered, since not only must the data be compiled, but also assembled in such a complete fashion that an intelligible and essentially correct geologic map will be produced.

The general approach to photogeology in the United States is frequently somewhat different from that in Canada. In the United States, there are proportionately many more areas in which geologic information is available. Therefore, as a generality, much of the photogeology practiced in the United States is primarily concerned with reevaluation and refinement, while that in Canada tends to be largely of a reconnaissance nature. Frequently, this difference is reflected in the over-all attitudes and standards of procedure which have developed in the two countries.

Many photogeologic exploration programs carried out in areas other than North America are of a reconnaissance type; the principal reason for this is a lack or insufficiency of detailed geologic information. There are, of course, noteworthy exceptions to this general situation.

It should be observed that when a photogeologic project area is researched, the material sought should not be limited to surface data. If wells have been drilled in the area, the logs should be studied, as should any previously constructed stratigraphic or lithofacies maps. Through such information a photogeologically mapped surface trend, which may be indicative of a major tectonic zone, may be substantiated by noting abrupt changes in lithology, unit thickness, and other subsurface characteristics.

FIELD WORK

The desired correlation of field and photogeologic studies has been discussed in a previous chapter. It may be reiterated that a photogeologic study with no supplemental field check or field information should be expected to be less reliable and less complete than a combined project.

PURPOSE OF STUDY

Aerial photographs are studied for many reasons. They may be part of an academic research project, they may be used to compile a basic geologic map, or they may be analyzed in the search for a particular natural resource. Depending upon the purpose of a given study, the area involved may be large or small, and the map produced may be extremely detailed or very generalized. Consider the following illustration.

Suppose that a given area is to be studied by three individuals. One is a petroleum geologist, the second is a geologist with a government survey, and the third a graduate student of regional geomorphology.

The western part of the area consists of a mountain and foothills belt, characterized by complexly folded and faulted strata, maturely dissected topography, and dense forest cover. The eastern half consists of a transition zone of dissected high plateaus and, further to the east, a gradually declining, gently undulating plains area. Bedrock is clearly visible throughout all but the plains part of the region.

The primary concerns of the *petroleum geologist* are structure and stratigraphy, how they may combine to provide favorable oil or gas traps, and whether or not such traps can be located through a photograph study. Specifically, interest will be directed toward the following points:

1. *Structure.* General structure, tectonic history, anticlines or faults which might provide closure

2. *Stratigraphy.* Thickness variations, lithologies, facies changes, possible source, reservoir, and cap beds; the extrapolation of mappable units, together with predicted depth, changes in thickness and lithology, into the plains area

3. *Tectonic-Stratigraphic Relations.* The possible detection of rejuvenated tectonic trends, which could have at one time influenced stratigraphic sequence or variations

4. *Access.* Routes for geophysical crews, field parties, and movement of drilling equipment

5. *Aids to Field Parties.* Data regarding location of well-exposed sections for stratigraphic measurements, detailed structure studies, and the like.

The attention of the *government survey geologist* would be directed toward a wider range of subjects. Interest would be more on factual and less on interpreted relations. The main purpose of the study would be the construction of an accurate photogeologic map. Questionable interpretations would probably be omitted. Final map scale, or the general policy of the government agency concerned, would dictate the degree to which nonbedrock features would be studied and mapped.

The *geomorphology student* would include a consideration of the dissection of the mountains, possible evidence of Pleistocene mountain glaciation, valleys, stream gradients, erosional history, stream capture or rejuvenation, single or multiple pedimentation, peneplanation, past and present climatic changes, interrelationships among structure, lithology and certain parameters of drainage development, and many other geologic and topographic factors. In such a study, the general structure and stratigraphy of the area would probably be included. Their primary importance would be their relationship to the geomorphic development and history of the area. The adjustment of drainage lines along fault zones or shale belts would also be of interest.

A single area may be studied two or more times by the same individual or group of photogeologists. For example, a rapid mosaic study of a large area may be made to determine the regional topographic and structural relations. Such a study may also permit the delineation of smaller areas where more detailed photogeologic work might be most profitable.

A second study, involving the stereoscopic examination of the aerial photographs, may be limited to the designated smaller areas.

If important local structures or other features are located in the second phase, they may be rephotographed to obtain different scale or better-quality photography. Also, photogrammetric instruments may be used to construct topographic or structure contour maps, structural profiles, or isopachous maps of these small areas.

There are many other possible combinations of approach and results of photogeologic work, depending primarily upon the purpose to which the study is directed.

WORKING CONDITIONS

Concentration and continuity of thought are important requisites of photogeologic work. Distractions of any kind should be avoided. Proper lighting facilities are essential.

The effects of poor working conditions cannot be determined quantitatively but can well be imagined. Under optimum conditions, the photogeologist should work in his own office, should not be interrupted by colleagues, and should not be pressed by unreasonable deadlines. In brief, he should be free to think, to ponder, and to investigate the geology shown on the photographs.

PERSONNEL

No two photogeologists have identical academic backgrounds, practical experience, or temperamental characteristics. Some may be overanxious to complete a given assignment. Others may be abnormally concerned with details and hesitate to make a final compilation. Some may tend to avoid or to discount questionable or highly problematical features. Others may devote too much time to the solution of such problems. Some may view aerial photographs as a device to obtain the basic data required to compile a geologic map. Others may use photographs to aid in the analysis and interpretation of the geologic record exposed.

The fact that such variations exist is of concern to the geologist or student contemplating a career in photogeology, to the employer considering hiring a person to do photogeologic work, and to the client or executive geologist who may assign a photogeologic study to an individual or to a consulting firm.

Another important factor to consider is the number of photogeologists who should work together on a given assignment. Some types of projects permit the active participation of three or more photogeologists. Such a group or *team* may combine in the reconnaissance or routine photogeologic mapping of a large area in which the geology is relatively simple and well exposed, and in which the rock units involved are readily identified and mapped.

When a complete and comprehensive analysis and understanding of the tectonics and other geologic elements of an area are sought, the optimum number of qualified photogeologists should be two. The entire area should be studied and mapped by the first geologist, and completely restudied and criticized by the second. A one-man interpretation invites the subjective element, including preconceived ideas and a tendency to stress some factors while minimizing or overlooking others. A two-man interpretation permits the frequent and free exchange of ideas, concepts, and constructive criticisms.

Since many geologists employed in the mining and petroleum industries attended university prior to the widespread teaching of photogeology, the problem of selecting and training personnel in industry is important. When a geologist has been chosen for such work, training may follow one of two courses. The beginner may be given a brief orientation in the mechanics of aerial photographs, and then assigned to a project involving relatively obvious and easily understood geology.

The alternate approach would be to assign the individual to an experienced and well-qualified photogeologist, more or less as an apprentice. Over a minimum period of two years, they can develop a close working relationship, in which a free exchange of ideas and instruction will permit the trainee to adopt proven methods and to learn through association. If time and conditions permit, the second method is strongly suggested.

7

Identification and Interpretation: Approach and Criteria

APPROACH TO IDENTIFICATION AND INTERPRETATION

There are two basic ways of learning to identify geologic features on aerial photographs. The first is to examine many carefully chosen illustrations of *representative* structures and topographic forms. Such illustrations have been called *keys* to the recognition and identification of geologic features. The other method is to attain, through practice and instruction, the ability to deduce the identity and significance of geologic features through the study of various criteria. The author believes that the second method is preferable.

Although many of the illustrations presented here are similar to the geology which may be found in many places in the world, their structural, stratigraphic, and geomorphic details and the interrelations among them are unique. Therefore, each illustration in this book and each geologic feature the student may ever see on photographs in the future must be considered a special case. The photogeologist always deals with special cases, each of which demands its own individual interpretation.

The illustrations in Part III were chosen to permit the teaching of the correct *approach* to geologic identification and interpretation. The individual texts accompanying each stereogram were prepared with this aim in mind. To receive full benefit from Part III, the student should strive to establish and understand the reasoning behind the identification and analysis for each pair of photographs.

The basic problems of photogeologic interpretation may be summarized as follows:

1. A given feature is viewed on aerial photographs; what is it?

2. What combination of structure, history, and erosion or deposition could have produced the feature?

3. What is the geologic significance of the feature?

The general procedure to follow in answering these questions is essentially simple and straightforward, and is discussed below.

Geographic and Geologic Location

The designation of the general geographic and geologic location of a project area automatically limits the types of feature which could be present. Though in many instances the details may be lacking, in much of the world the basic geologic relations are known; the major mountain ranges have been delineated, belts of foothills defined, and basin, plains, and coastal plain regions outlined. In many areas the essential rock types are known; crystalline, sedimentary, or unconsolidated mantle. Once the area is defined, therefore, the rudiments of structure and rock types can usually be determined.

Several rather obvious examples are as follows. If an area in southwestern New Mexico is studied, sedimentary and crystalline rock units would be expected. Undrained hummocky topography in that area would not be identified as continental glaciation deposits. If an area in northern Montana were selected, circular or oval features could not be attributed to salt-dome activity. Thrust faulting would not be expected in relatively stable basin and shelf areas.

Research into Available Literature

If published data are available, the general sequence of rock units and their types can be determined prior to the photo study. Some of the major tectonic elements of the area may also be learned at this time. This will enable the photogeologist to anticipate some of the features which will be found and will be of help in their proper identification.

Published geomorphic information should be studied. If an area is known to be epeirogenically unstable, topographic features which might otherwise be assumed to reflect bedrock structure may more easily be recognized to have an erosional origin. For example, in a recently upwarped belt of complexly folded and faulted mountains, gently sloping isolated terraces or tables may be noted in the valleys. They may be gravel-capped terrace or pediment remnants. Features of identical appearance, lying in a large, generally undisturbed basin, may more probably be dip slopes on resistent sandstone units.

Climate—Past and Present

In many cases, a given rock unit will weather and be eroded differently in a humid area than in an arid area. Similar contrasts may exist between tropical or subtropical climates and arctic climates. Solifluxion, for example, is extremely common in Alaska and the Northwest Territories and the Yukon territory of northern Canada. Carbonate rocks are easily dissolved and eroded in the humid eastern

United States, while in the arid and semiarid western states they frequently stand as dominant topographic ridges and escarpments.

In addition to the above three general considerations, specific topographic form, photographic characteristics, vegetation, location, and relation to other objects are used in the identification and interpretation of features seen on aerial photographs. The following pages will include discussions of (1) shape or form, (2) tonal and textural relations, and (3) drainage. When analyzed within the framework established above, these factors are usually sufficient to permit the recognition, delineation, and analysis of the geologic features within most photogeologic project areas.

IDENTIFICATION AND INTERPRETATION CRITERIA

General

The process of identifying, mapping, correlating, and interpreting geology from aerial photographs is an extremely complex one. It requires patience, judgment, and the ability to evaluate the significance of many different types of information.

Therefore, photogeology must be approached with the full realization that geologic interpretation can only be accomplished if close attention is paid to all of the following elements: outcrop appearance and distribution, structural details, landform, drainage, vegetation, soil, and occasionally such cultural features as land utilization and population selectivity. The photogeologist must be at least conversant with the allied sciences of pedology (soils), botany, and geography.

There is an intimate interrelation among the numerous factors and elements. It is the assignment of the photogeologist to unravel the many elements, to identify each, to understand their relationships, to compile the entire accumulated data to make a map, and to interpret its geology.

Since the recognition and interpretation of geologic features involve such a diverse group of subjects, it is necessary to consider each separately, as far as possible. At times it will be noted that some are so closely associated that unavoidable overlaps will occur. It should also be pointed out that the order of presentation is not indicative of the relative importance of any one factor.

In some cases, geologic structure is reflected by the adjustment of topography to rock type and structure. Some of the more apparent examples are strike ridges, anticlinal and domal mountains, synclinal and basinal lowlands or valleys, fault or fault-line scarps, coastal plains, dike ridges, cinder cones, and lava-capped plateaus. In general, the recognition and interpretation of such features is not difficult.

In other cases, geologic structure does not coincide with the land surface. Rock units may extend across various topographic forms, intersecting them in many ways. Any number of illustrations might be given, including the well-known V outcrop of a bed or rock unit which crosses a stream valley, a similar but reverse V or U outcrop of a dipping bed which crosses a spur or ridge, the irregular trace of a low-angle thrust fault in a mountainous area, and the intricate outcrop pattern of nearly horizontal sediments in a dissected plateau area.

In the latter group, photograph tone, vegetation, soils, and texture assume a relatively greater importance, since it will be largely through such factors that beds, faults, igneous rocks, contacts, and unconformities will be recognized.

In many areas, though bedrock is either exposed or very close to the surface, details of structure cannot readily be ascertained. Maturely dissected shale and clay areas, covered by dense vegetation and drained by a fine-textured dendritic stream system, frequently present such problems. In such areas, close attention to topographic form, drainage characteristics, photographic tone, vegetation, and other visible criteria may permit tentative lithologic correlation, should an identical-appearing area be noted elsewhere, though the structure within the outcrop areas may remain unknown.

Unconsolidated materials must be identified on the basis of several criteria, including original landform, dissected or altered landform, position with respect to other topographic and geologic elements, photographic tone and texture, and relation to drainage.

Shape or Form

Numerous geologic features can be identified primarily by their shape alone. Some examples are uneroded structural domes, cinder cones, sand dunes, glacial deposits, alluvial fans, strike ridges, and plunging folds.

It is usually relatively easy to identify such unconsolidated deposits as fans, dunes, and moraines when their original form has not been altered or destroyed by erosion or covered by other materials. When modified by weathering and erosion, or mantled by other materials, their identification requires a careful study of such other factors as location, position with respect to other geologic and topographic features, their photographic tone, and general textural appearance.

Differential erosion is considered the first key to bedrock identification and interpretation on aerial photographs. In any area subjected to prolonged erosion (principally by running water), resistant rocks may be expected at or near the surface of higher topography, with less resistant rocks in lower topographic positions (i.e., sandstone ridges and shale valleys).

In relatively few instances such a topographic-lithologic correlation does not occur. For example, recent fault displacements may raise nonresistant rocks to higher positions than nearby exposed resistant rocks. If the rocks can be identified by other criteria, however, the existence of a reverse topographic-lithologic relation can, in turn, be used to assign a recent age to the faulting.

Figure 7-1 illustrates several types of topographic adjustments to differences in rock resistance. The above-mentioned exception is included.

A series of plunging (pitching) folds, involving strata of various relative resistance, is frequently represented by zigzag valleys and ridges. Where the folds do not plunge, parallel or subparallel valleys and ridges are found. The Folded Appalachians and the Ouachita Mountains are excellent examples of such structures and topography.

Volcanic necks or plugs, the resistant solidified central cores of maturely eroded volcanoes, frequently stand as sentinels overlooking the lower areas formerly occupied by the less-resistant country rock which they invaded.

In some areas, isolated mountain masses may be observed to stand above former ancient erosional surfaces or peneplanes. These isolated remnants, called *monadnocks,* frequently owe their preservation to their greater resistance to weathering and erosion. An example of the economic sig-

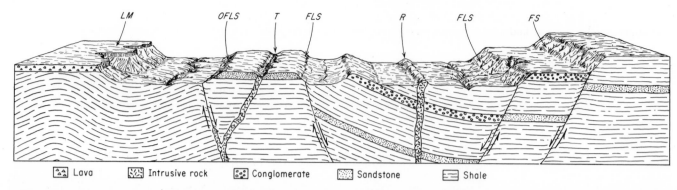

| △△ Lava | ⋎⋎ Intrusive rock | °°° Conglomerate | Sandstone | ⊟ Shale |

Figure 7-1. Composite block diagram showing several examples of correlation between rock resistance and differential erosion. LM, lava-capped mesa; FLS, fault-line scarp; OFLS, obsequent fault-line scarp; T, trench; R, ridge. FS (fault scarp) is an exception. Recent faulting has raised nonresistant shale above adjacent resistant conglomerate. Explain why intrusive rock is expressed in one place as a trench and in another as a ridge. (*Diagram by Calvin F. Miller.*)

nificance of the recognition of such features is a recent discovery of iron ore in South America. The ore concentration is restricted to monadnock remnants on an old weathered erosion surface.

Dikes may extend across an area, either as prominent wall-like ridges (see Figure 13-2) or as continuous or discontinuous trench-like depressions (see Figure 10-5). Their positive or negative expression is a function of their resistance to erosion and weathering relative to that of the surrounding country rock. Similarly, sills may produce benches along the sides of escarpments or valley walls, or, if tilted sufficiently, may exhibit a topography similar to that produced by dikes. Some veins which are composed largely of resistant minerals, such as quartz, may be traced across an area of less resistant rock by their positive topographic expression (see Figure 15-11). Conversely, veins consisting largely of nonresistant minerals may be removed easily and appear as linear depressions or trenches.

Occasionally, a photogeologist may note that a fault zone has a positive topographic expression. Such a fault zone may be confused with a dike. The relatively high topography along such fault zones is frequently explained by the fact that the zone has become silicified through underground water deposition, the concentration of silica offering greater resistance to erosion than the surrounding rock masses.

Intrusive rocks may stand topographically higher than the country rock into which they were emplaced (see Figure 13-2). If they are made of less resistant components, they may appear on aerial photographs as circular, oval, or irregular-shaped depressions (see Figure 15-13).

Contact metamorphism around the fringes of intrusive masses may produce a localized zone or aureole of more resistant or of more easily weathered and eroded rock, depending on the intrusive material and the country rock. The less resistant zone, when attacked by running water, will produce a ringlike depression surrounding the intrusive mass. In one instance known to the writer, such a circular zone of contact metamorphism and the recognition of the significance of its topographic expression led to the discovery of a previously unknown intrusive body.

Landforms are also extremely important in the recognition and mapping of numerous geologic structures. For example, a series of ridges and valleys formed by alternating resistant and nonresistant rock units may end abruptly along a linear or gently curved line. Such a line is frequently the trace of a fault (see Figure 14-7). Similarly, faulting may explain the offset of topographic features which are the surface expression of various rock units (see Figures 13-11 and 14-5).

Since fault zones and major fracture zones are frequently extensively shattered and hence more susceptible to erosion, they may be detected by noting the presence of linear valleys or lowlands. Such topographic features may be especially significant if their trend is oblique or normal to the regional topographic and structural grain. The least reliable case would be that in which the valley or lowland is parallel to the strike of outcropping beds and hence may be an expression of topographic adjustment to a nonresistant formation rather than to a zone of structural weakness.

Smaller forms or shapes may also convey valuable geologic information if properly evaluated and analyzed. Numerous undrained depressions and adjacent hummocks are typical of moraines; they are also diagnostic of karst areas. Therefore, general form alone is not always sufficient for positive identification or interpretation. A consideration of such factors as the presence or absence of outcrops, possible dip slopes, photographic tone, as well as of the regional geologic setting and history of the area, can usually afford a more accurate identification and interpretation.

Slope Asymmetry. The recognition of slope asymmetry may be considered the first refinement in the study of form, following the basic relationship of relative topographic position resulting from differential erosion. In cases of clearly defined dip slopes produced by the stripping of nonresistant beds from the upper surface of a dipping stratum (Figure 7-2), slope asymmetry need not be given great attention, since the structure is usually obvious.

However, in the more usual situation involving dipping sedimentary rocks, tabular intrusive and extrusive bodies, and bedded or tabular metamorphic rocks, it is important to compare opposite slopes along ridges, spurs, and valleys in an attempt to determine the structural attitude of the rock. Usually, if the rock unit is sufficiently well expressed topographically to prompt such a comparison, its strike is apparent; therefore, its dip is the structural element sought. In the study of slope asymmetry there are three factors which are usually helpful in the determination of dip direction.

1. Relative slope on opposite sides of a ridge, spur, or valley

2. Contrasts of interrupted slopes on opposite sides of a ridge, spur, or valley

3. Drainage characteristics on opposite sides of a ridge, spur, or valley

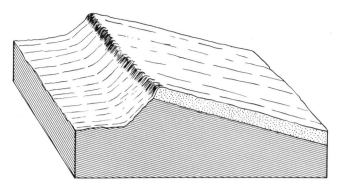

Figure 7-2. A block diagram of a low-dip asymmetric ridge. Postsandstone nonresistant strata have been stripped from the sandstone unit. (*Diagram by Calvin F. Miller.*)

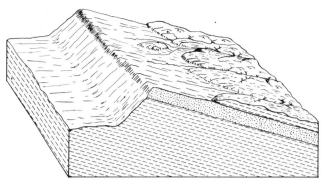

Figure 7-3. A block diagram of a low-dip asymmetric ridge. Postsandstone nonresistant strata have not been stripped entirely from the sandstone unit. (*Diagram by Calvin F. Miller.*)

These will be discussed separately below.

RELATIVE SLOPE. Along a ridge maintained or upheld by resistant dipping rock units, the slope which has the same direction as the dip is the resequent slope. The slope whose direction is opposite to dip is the obsequent slope. When dip is moderate to low (less than about 25°), the obsequent slope is usually steeper than the resequent slope (see Figure 7-3).

When dip is appreciably greater and the resequent slope truncates a succession of beds which overlie the "ridge-former," the resequent and obsequent slopes may be the same; the obsequent slope may even be less than the resequent slope. Figure 7-4 shows the equal slopes developed along a ridge of steeply dipping beds. Note that in Figure 7-4 the slopes are not interrupted by irregularities caused by the presence of beds of different resistances.

Figure 7-5 depicts ridge asymmetry reflected through an uneven cover of glacial ground moraine; the preglacial topography is modified by the overburden, but the structure is, nevertheless, apparent.

Figure 7-6 is a generalized topographic map of a series of folds involving rocks of different relative resistance. It is suggested that the student indicate dip direction throughout the area and show the fold axes, together with plunge arrows where plunge exists. Note that the ridge asymmetry at point *A* permits the determination of dip direction along the symmetric ridge at point *B*. In areas of tight folds, slope asymmetry noted along a plunging nose (i.e., at point *C*) may be the only criteria to distinguish between an anticline and syncline.

Figure 7-7 is a topographic profile across an area of gently, moderately, and steeply dipping strata. Several formations are resistant; others relatively less resistant. As an exercise, it is suggested that the student construct a geologic cross section along the side of the block, and sketch in the topography of the area in the space provided. Assume strike to be normal to the profile line.

Figure 7-8 is a geologic cross section of an area of folded and faulted sandstones and shales. The student is asked to complete a topographic profile of the area, and sketch in the topography on the top of the block. Assume strike to be normal to the cross-section line.

Slope asymmetry is not an infallible indication of dip direction. As mentioned above, along a ridge underlain by steeply dipping rocks, the resequent slope may be steeper than the obsequent slope. In addition, asymmetric ridges may be composed of massive rock bodies; the topography may be the result of different factors. For example, relatively

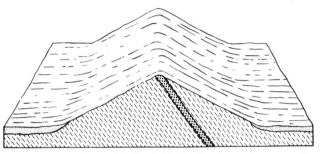

Figure 7-4. An idealized block diagram of a steep-dip symmetric ridge. Along the back slope, numerous strata have been truncated. (*Diagram by Calvin F. Miller.*)

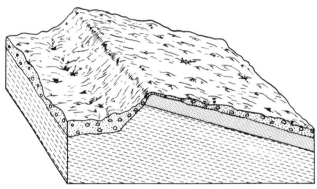

Figure 7-5. Asymmetric low-dip ridge overlain by ground moraine. The irregular cover of morainal debris obscures but does not hide the preglacial asymmetry of the ridge. (*Diagram by Calvin F. Miller.*)

recent block faulting of a previously peneplaned, homogeneous igneous rock mass may bring into existence a well-defined asymmetric landform (Figure 7-9).

Occasionally ridge and valley asymmetry, noted in areas of apparently homogeneous rock, are attributed to *Ferrel's law*. In the Northern Hemisphere, streams tend to impinge more against their right banks than against their left banks.

Also, contrasts in erosional activity on opposite sides of a ridge might produce an asymmetric profile. In Figure 7-10, there is no genetic relation between the structural attitude of the rocks and the topography. The streams draining to the east have a gentle gradient. Those draining to the west have steeper gradients. The two master streams flow at different levels. Figure 7-11 depicts one of several conditions which could exist to cause this asymmetry of ridge profile and unequal master stream incision.

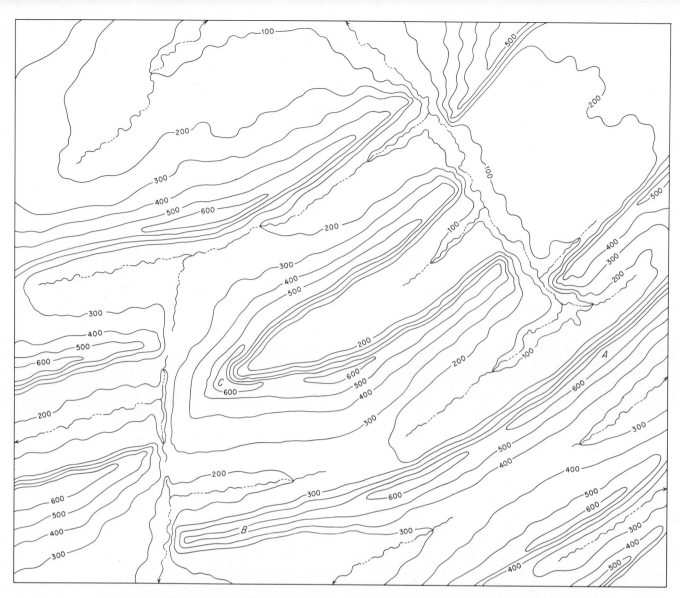

Figure 7-6. A hypothetical topographic map of an area of folded and faulted sedimentary rocks of different relative resistance. Using the criteria discussed in the text, add to the map numerous strike and dip symbols, fold axes, and fault traces. Indicate relative direction of displacement on each fault.

Figure 7-7. A topographic profile of an area underlain by gently, moderately, and steeply dipping rocks of different relative resistance. Fill in the geologic structure on the side of the block, and sketch the general topography on the top of the block. Assume structural strike to be normal to the front plane of the block. Use the designated vanishing point (VP).

VP
.

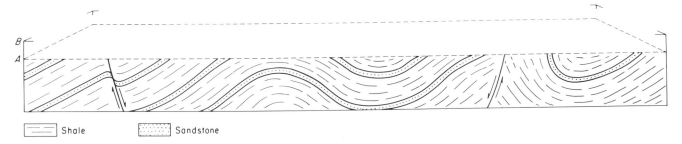

VP
•

Shale   Sandstone

Figure 7-8. A geologic cross section drawn on the front of a block. Reconstruct a differentially eroded topographic profile within the vertical interval *AB*, and then sketch the general topography on the top of the block. Use the designated vanishing point (VP). Assume structural strike to be normal to the plane of the front of the block.

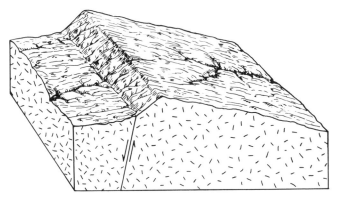

Figure 7-9. A block diagram of a recently tilted fault block of homogeneous granite. The newly raised tilted surface is part of an old peneplane. The gross form of the block resembles that of Figures 7-2 and 7-3. This figure demonstrates the principle that asymmetry does not necessarily indicate dipping strata. (*Diagram by Calvin F. Miller.*)

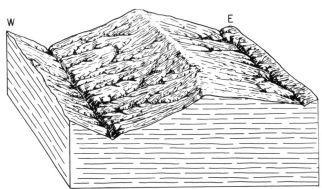

Figure 7-10. A block diagram of an asymmetric ridge resulting from active downcutting on one flank. The master stream along the west side is at a lower level than that along the east. Horizontal homogeneous strata underlie the entire area. See Figure 7-11. (*Diagram by Calvin F. Miller.*)

Figure 7-11. A sketch map showing one of several possible situations which could produce the asymmetric ridge depicted in Figure 7-10. AR, asymmetric ridge shown in Figure 7-10; SR, symmetric ridge; EC, elbow of capture; RS, rejuvenated master stream along west flank of asymmetric ridge; CS, captor stream (possibly adjusted along fault zone). Capture and rejuvenation of the western master stream, in the manner shown here, could cause active downcutting of that stream, while continued, slower, "normal" erosion, accompanied by gentle stream and slope gradients, persist elsewhere in the region. The crest of the asymmetric ridge should migrate eastward as the west-flowing tributaries of the rejuvenated master stream continue their active erosion on its west flank. The area included in Figure 7-10 is outlined by long heavy dashes.

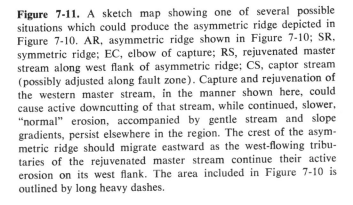

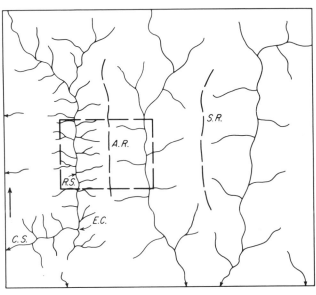

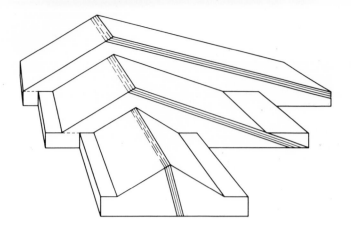

Figure 7-12. A multiple idealized block diagram showing the inverse relation between dip magnitude and ridge-crest height. It is assumed that all other factors are equal. Were a given volume of the "ridge-former" unit removed from each ridge segment, the low-dip segment would be lowered the least; the steep-dip segment the most.

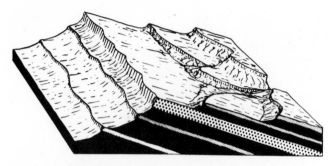

Figure 7-13. A block diagram of an asymmetric ridge formed by a moderately dipping series of beds. There are several secondary resistant units in addition to the one which maintains the ridge crest. On the obsequent slope, these units produce subparallel benches. On the back or resequent slope, incompletely removed flatiron-like remnants occur. (*Diagram by Calvin F. Miller.*)

The above exceptions call attention to two main facts:

1. No single criterion, including slope asymmetry, can always be used to arrive at the same interpretation.

2. Factors other than those directly observed may be responsible for the geologic or topographic relations included within a given photograph or project area.

As exemplified by ridge asymmetry, any criterion must be considered as a *possible* indication of certain geologic conditions. All additional criteria should be sought and evaluated before a positive interpretation is advanced. A correct interpretation of the geology depicted in Figure 7-9 might be afforded by noting jointing, general photographic tone and texture, over-all topographic and lithologic homogeneity, drainage characteristics, and the absence of stratification.

The geology shown in Figure 7-10 might be understood by observing outcrop pattern, tonal variations, vegetation, drainage, and factors other than slope.

It is occasionally possible to determine dip magnitude changes by the study of variations in crest elevation along one or more homoclinal ridges underlain by a given sequence of rocks. There is a tendency, in folded areas, for ridge-crest height to increase with decrease in dip (see Figure 7-12). Within the dip range where slope asymmetry is possible, such an inverse relation may be noted within a given project area. If this relation can be established, it may be extended to apply to symmetric, steeper-dip ridge segments. If out-

crops are scarce and the geologic relations largely obscured, such criteria could be most helpful.

CONTRASTS OF INTERRUPTED SLOPES. The appearance and topographic form of a ridge upheld by a single resistant unit are quite different from those of a ridge formed by the differential erosion of several interbedded resistant and nonresistant units.

The simple landform represented by Figure 7-3 consists generally of gentle, smoothly curved slopes descending from the ridge crest. Where numerous beds or units of contrasting resistance occur, a topography similar to that illustrated in Figure 7-13 is produced. Subsidiary or secondary resistant units, above and below the unit which forms the "backbone" of the ridge, interrupt the slopes in several ways.

In Figure 7-13, five resistant sandstone and five nonresistant shale units are shown dipping gently to the right. The middle sandstone member, which is thicker and relatively more resistant than the others, occupies the ridge crest.

Note that two benches, nearly parallel to the ridge crest and at nearly constant vertical intervals, extend along the obsequent slope of the ridge. On the resequent slope, however, the upper two sandstone units are incompletely stripped away, and are preserved as flatiron-like surfaces which lap against the gentle backslope. Their steeper faces, where present, are on the upslope side, in contrast to the downslope steep faces developed along the benches on the obsequent slope.

This contrast is often quite useful in some cases involving steeper dips. Figure 7-14 is an idealized illustration of the basic geomorphic differences produced along obsequent and resequent slopes by secondary resistant units below and above the one which maintains the ridge crest. Compare this figure with Figure 7-4.

DRAINAGE CHARACTERISTICS. Along many ridges upheld by a resistant rock such as sandstone, quartzite, limestone, or a lava flow, the lower parts of the obsequent slope are underlain by some less resistant rock such as shale, clay, or volcanic ash. As a general rule, the drainage and dissection on the two slopes of such a ridge are dissimilar, especially when dip is relatively low.

Figure 7-15 illustrates this general contrast. Down the back or resequent slope the streams are widely spaced and long, and the tributary basins are elongate. Drainage density is low. Down the front or obsequent slope, the streams are closer together and shorter, and the basins smaller. Drainage density is high.

These contrasts may be explained briefly in the following way. If topography is well adjusted to rock characteristics and structure, those nonresistant units lying above the ridge-former will have been largely or completely stripped from the resequent flank of the ridge. Those nonresistant units lying immediately below the ridge-forming unit will crop out along the obsequent slope. The greater resistance, the greater infiltration capacity, and the larger particle size of the rock and mantle exposed on much of the resequent slope will dictate the development of a relatively few longer and larger streams down that slope. Smaller tributaries could not maintain themselves in this area. The nonresistant rock on the obsequent slope, usually having a lower infiltration capacity (hence, greater runoff), and smaller particle size, is cut by more numerous smaller streams than are possible on the resequent slope.

There are, of course, many times when the special conditions discussed above will not prevail. Therefore, it should not be presupposed that Figure 7-15 depicts relationships along all such ridges.

For the sake of clarity of presentation, the above three factors of slope asymmetry have been presented separately, though in nature they usually are combined in some way. Each asymmetric ridge is made up of its own combination of the three, depending on structure, rock type, vertical or stratigraphic rock sequence and intervals, topographic relief, climate, erosion processes, the time exposed, and other factors.

A geologist who has worked with reliable detailed topographic maps or who has taken courses in their reading and interpretation will perceive that most of the material presented above applies equally well to topographic maps as to aerial photographs. The fact that such is the case is a further indication of the importance of geomorphology in the study of geology on aerial photographs. It also points to the advisability of studying topographic map interpretation as part of a basic training program in photogeology.

Tonal and Textural Relations

The use of color photography in aerial surveys, though extremely desirable in many cases, is still not common. Several photogeologic studies have been made employing color photographs; the results have been most encouraging. Repeated reports of diminishing costs indicate that eventually color photographs will become more widely available to the photogeologist.

In the vast majority of cases, however, only what is generally referred to as *black and white* photography is available. All earth colors are thus reduced to various shades of gray. Since color contrasts and similarities can only be detected through their recorded gray tones, it is imperative that careful attention be given to tonal characteristics. This is equally true in mosaic, single-photograph, or stereoscopic studies.

Closely associated with tone, but more difficult to describe and discuss, is texture. The *texture* of a feature or an area is that quality which distinguishes it from some other feature or area having the same photographic tone. Texture may be described in many ways, including smooth, rippled, mottled, irregular, and lineated. Such terms are usually qualitative and in many instances somewhat subjective, since one person may choose to describe a given texture in one way, while a second person might use a slightly different descriptive term or expression.

Textures are rarely used as the only criteria of identification or correlation. However, occasionally the principal photographic characteristics of a rock unit will be the combination of a given tone and a given texture. A second rock unit may have approximately the same tone but a slightly distinctive texture. Usually, however, tone, texture, and other criteria are used together.

Photographic tone and texture are products of numerous independent and dependent variables, some of the more significant of which are briefly discussed below.

Bedrock Color. In areas where bedrock is exposed, the hue, brilliance, and saturation of the color of a given rock unit will produce a distinctive gray photographic tone under certain light conditions.

Since many rocks weather to a different color than that of the freshly exposed outcrop, a single rock unit may photograph differently in different places. With sufficient care and practice, the photogeologist can usually overcome the problem of color and tonal contrasts produced by weathering.

Outcrop Surface. Some rocks are weathered and eroded into smooth, uniform slopes and surfaces. Others, perhaps as a result of jointing, fracturing, or bedding separations, or combinations of these, appear as blocky, irregular, lumpy, or grooved features. The more regular exposed surfaces are recorded as lighter and more uniform photographic tones. The more irregular surfaces, especially if the scale of the irregularities is small, will tend to produce darker tones and possibly irregular tonal and textural qualities. This is due to the fact that an extremely irregular surface, consisting of alternating hillocks, knobs, bumps, and projections on the one hand, and depressions, holes, and grooves on the other, affords numerous possibilities for local shadows which would effectively reduce the total amount of light which could be reflected to the camera.

Orientation of Surface. A slope or escarpment which lies in a shadow is noticeably darker than one exposed squarely to the sun's rays. Naturally, a rock unit exposed on two such surfaces would be recorded with contrasting tones.

However, whenever possible, aerial photography is undertaken when light conditions are optimum and the distracting and obscuring influences of shadows are at a minimum. Nevertheless, in many areas the topographic relief, the orientation of topographic features, and the latitude are such that some shadows will always be present. In addition, there may be certain time requirements that dictate the procurement of photography when conditions are not at their best. In either case, the photogeologist must be prepared to work with aerial photographs of areas in which shadows are present, and to learn to recognize the ways in which certain rock units appear both in shadow and in open sunlight.

Figure 7-14. A block diagram of a symmetric ridge formed by a steeply dipping series of resistant and nonresistant stratigraphic unit. Note the contrast of the obsequent and resequent slopes, caused by secondary resistant units. Compare with Figure 7-4. (*Diagram by Calvin F. Miller.*)

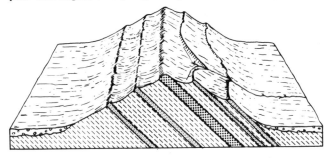

Figure 7-15. A block diagram of an asymmetric low-dip ridge, to show the contrast in drainage characteristics on the obsequent and resequent slopes. (*Diagram by Calvin F. Miller.*)

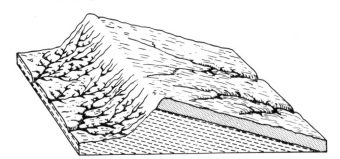

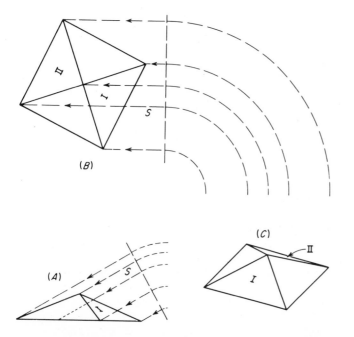

Figure 7-16. Unequal illumination of slopes; a function of slope orientation and inclination, and the position of the sun. (*A*) Side view. Lines *S* represent sun's rays. (*B*) Top view. (*C*) View of pyramid as seen from sun. Slope I receives the most intense illumination. Slope II receives the least intense illumination.

In addition to this contrast, the intensity of illumination varies considerably on exposed nonshadowed surfaces, depending on the magnitude and orientation of slope and the position of the sun (see Figure 7-16).

An indirect result of slope orientation is the effect on tone and texture produced by variable moisture conditions on different sides of a given hill, and a tendency toward a corresponding variation in vegetation.

Soils and Mantle. The term *mantle* is usually applied to any layer of unconsolidated rock material that lies on consolidated *bedrock*. Mantle may consist of particles of the underlying rock, either weathered or unweathered, and may be of any grain size or combination of grain sizes. It may also consist of materials transported from one place and deposited in another, by wind, running water, ice, or gravity.

Mantle formed *in situ* may be called *residual mantle*. That brought into an area from another area may collectively be called *transported mantle*.

Mantle which is in any way modified, altered, or weathered by chemical, physical, or biological processes or agents, is called *soil*. Soils developed in residual mantle are thought of as *residual soils*. In photogeology, those developed in transported mantle are best thought of as *transported soils*. Soils which have developed and have been moved by any agent may, for our purposes, also be called transported soils.

Numerous factors influence the development of soils and the type of soil produced in a given area. These include the parental material, topography, climate, drainage, vegetation, and time.

Transported soils or mantle may, with time, be further changed and altered, the result being the formation of what might be called *second-generation soils*. These soils would have distinct zones, the natures of which would permit more definite and accurate soil classification. They would not, however, reflect bedrock composition.

Variations in soil color, composition, and texture are often apparent on aerial photographs. Minor erosional differences, such as gullies and slope profiles, frequently indicate various soil contrasts or gradations. Since bedrock is one of the factors which determine residual soil characteristics, the differentiation of soils, by these and other criteria, may permit the differentiation of completely covered and otherwise obscured bedrock units. This is one of the advantages of photogeologic mapping over field mapping in many areas.

Vegetation is an important element in photogeologic mapping and interpretation. Even slight differences in soil, such as composition or texture, may influence vegetation in many ways. Therefore, in practice, the study of bedrock, soils, and vegetation cannot be separated.

Soils may not always reflect underlying rock or regolith contrasts. Climate, time, and general geographic conditions may combine to produce a widespread, almost uniform soil regardless of the rock material from which it was derived. The absence of soil differences, whether directly or indirectly determined on the photographs, should not automatically be assumed to indicate uniform subsoil rock type.

Moisture. The relative amount of moisture in the soil or mantle, and in some cases in the bedrock, frequently produces noticeable variations in tonal intensity on aerial photographs. The effect is sometimes direct and sometimes indirect. Relatively dry areas tend to appear a lighter gray, whereas the more nearly saturated areas tend to be darker. This is the direct effect of moisture content.

The indirect effect principally involves vegetation. In areas consistently arid or semiarid, a sparse growth of grasses, shrubs, and trees may be present. In extremely arid areas, little or no vegetation can exist. In humid areas a greater density of vegetation growth is possible. These variables produce pronounced effects in tonal register.

In addition, seasonal temperature and precipitation variations result in corresponding variations in moisture content, which will be reflected in the stage of vegetation development (i.e., lush growth versus drought-produced dry brush and trees). These variations, involving the green of the vegetation, are in turn reflected in photograph tone.

Within a more limited area, differences in near-surface moisture may be a function of differences in soil. This introduces the fourth factor in the interwoven system of bedrock, soil, and vegetation, since moisture variations could cause preferential vegetation growth in some places, or the absence of some shrubs or trees in others.

Occasionally a fault may be detected by an alignment of numerous springs. Although the springs themselves may not be seen, the concentration of certain vegetation at these points will be readily noted. Along escarpments and valley walls a stratigraphic contact, such as that between an overlying porous sandstone and an underlying dense, impermeable and impervious shale, may also be the site of a series of springs detectable at least in part by vegetation.

Vegetation. Some areas are completely devoid of vegetation. Others are heavily overgrown. Tree or shrub density may vary within a small area. Vegetative cover may be relatively uniform throughout a large region. In some areas certain varieties are restricted to or absent from certain topographic or geologic features. Usually there are noticeable seasonal changes in vegetation.

Vegetation may obscure significant geologic relations, or it may be of considerable help in the detection and mapping of geology.

The photograph tone produced by vegetation is principally determined by two basic factors: color and shadows. These in turn depend on such variables as the spacing of the individual plants or trees, the spacing of the branches, the size and density of the leaves or needles, the height of the individual plants or trees, general orientation and configuration of the slopes on which they occur, the season, and the type or types of vegetation present (i.e., coniferous versus deciduous).

Consider the following examples:

SHORT GRASS—WINTER. During the colder seasons, grass is generally a light-buff or brownish color and has a light photograph tone. The individual blades of grass do not cast appreciable shadows, since they are so closely spaced and interwoven. The total effect is that of a high degree of light reflection from the grass itself.

SHORT GRASS—SUMMER. Green grass, while not casting appreciably greater shadows than dry grass, appears considerably darker because of its more dominant color. In areas of widespread, uniform grass cover, variations in soil moisture and soil color, combined with resulting variations in density of grass color, produce observable contrasts in photograph tone.

CONIFEROUS COVER. The dark greens and blue greens of coniferous trees appear deep gray, sometimes almost black, on most aerial photographs. The shadow cast by such trees, both on the ground and on lower branches, reinforces the dark tones produced by the trees' color. The color plus the shadows result in a relatively low reflection factor.

Coniferous vegetation is conspicuous on photographs taken during the late fall, winter, and early spring seasons. They contrast with deciduous trees which are without leaves, devoid of color, and cast relatively fewer and thinner shadows.

DECIDUOUS COVER. During the seasons when deciduous vegetation is in full leaf, their shadows and color produce darker tones than during the colder seasons. In general, however, they appear somewhat lighter in tone than coniferous varieties. In spring, when the deciduous foliage is fresh and unfaded, the tone is usually darkest. With the approach of the drier period, in late summer, the tone tends to lighten somewhat. With the "turning" of the leaves in the fall, the many varieties of yellow, brown, orange, and red photograph differently, producing a mottled tone unlike either the more uniform drabness of winter or the foliage of spring and summer.

Under certain conditions, vegetation exhibits a definite geologic preference or selectivity. This may be due to topographic, soil, rock, or moisture factors or various combinations of these. In areas where a thick soil has developed, climate occasionally exerts a strong influence on the soil profile. This may largely erase or obscure the correlation between soil and parental bedrock. In such cases, vegetation changes and variations may tend to have a closer correlation with topography, moisture, and slope orientation than with bedrock.

However, in those numerous cases when the mineral content of the rock influences the composition, texture, and other characteristics of the soil, a definite correlation of vegetation and rock type can be established. Some varieties of plant and tree thrive on certain soils. Others, widespread throughout a large area, may be unable to live in certain restricted areas because of locally unfavorable soils.

In some areas, the effect of rock type on vegetation may be extremely difficult to detect under ordinary circumstances.

Albrecht [1] reports having studied photographs of a dense jungle area in South America, in which the tree cover was absolutely uniform in density, tree height, and photograph tone. Part of the area was rephotographed. The new photography clearly showed that some trees had begun to change color. These trees formed a large oval ring, which later proved to outline a broad structural dome. Apparently the oval outcrop of a particular rock unit had produced an overlying soil which promoted a slightly early change in the vegetation.

Field geologists frequently use selective vegetation growth as a key to the recognition of certain rock units. When this tool is used in the field, it is frequently restricted to such obvious contrasts as the limiting of a certain tree type to a sandstone outcrop, or the absence of certain varieties along a particular shale belt. The range of detectable vegetation contrasts, involving such subtle factors as tone and texture, is far greater in photogeologic work than in the field. During a field check, for example, it is not uncommon to notice that stratigraphic units, detected on the photographs entirely or in part by their vegetation, cannot be recognized in the field when a soil cover is present. Of course, in most such instances, soil and other tonal factors are included in the photo analysis.

Contrasts in vegetation may be noted between areas underlain by bedrock and those underlain by unconsolidated materials. In addition, various mantled areas may exhibit differences in vegetation. To a large degree, moisture content and circulation, as well as soil composition, texture, and plant type, are important in determining the photographic tones.

The magnitude and orientation of slope, which contribute to tonal quality resulting from differences in light intensity, also influence vegetation. These factors determine which plants can survive on a given slope, how densely they will grow, and what size they will attain. One commonly observed case is the contrast between the vegetation on the north and south slopes of an easterly trending ridge or spur. The north slope, though receiving less direct sunlight, tends to retain more moisture over a longer period of time and can therefore support vegetation to a greater degree than the warmer, though drier, south slope.

Since slope magnitude is frequently a function of bedrock type or structure, the following interrelations may be present in a given case: bedrock may determine slope; slope may influence soil development; bedrock may influence soil composition; soil and slope may influence vegetation; and only differences in vegetation may be noted on the aerial photographs.

Limestone sink holes are frequently floored by a concentration of silty and clayey materials leached from the carbonate rock and washed into the depressions by rills and small tributary streams. The vegetation which would adapt itself to the fine-grained clastic materials is frequently quite different from that which would occupy the surrounding carbonate slopes.

Faults and joints may permit the development or concentration of soils especially favorable to certain types of vegetation. Also, in areas of exposed bedrock, such as flat-lying limestones or sandstones in semiarid areas, fractures may offer the only possible "foothold" for trees and larger shrubs (see Figures 8-12 and 8-13). In such cases, it is not uncommon to see almost artificial-appearing lines of trees

[1] Dr. J. C. H. Albrecht, personal communication.

89

extending along an otherwise barren rock surface. In addition to the vegetation present, such fractures may also be distinguished through the tonal contrasts afforded by the soil which occupies them.

This affinity of plant life to fractures is occasionally of great importance in the correlation of rock units in areas of complex structure, even when good outcrops are widespread. Several members or formations may be similar in general appearance. It may be noted that one is fractured or jointed, and that a certain plant or group of plants is selectively associated with these bedrock features. This association may serve as a guide to the tentative identification of that particular unit elsewhere, where its stratigraphic position cannot be determined by other methods. This approach is also useful if certain vegetation characteristics identify a single unit or suite of rocks where the bedrock is partly or largely obscured by overburden.

Such criteria should not be used without full consideration of such other factors as slope and drainage characteristics, general topographic expression, and photograph tone. However, there are times when vegetation provides some of the few major clues to the solution of geologic problems.

In general, with the exception of water, ice, and cultural features, aerial photographs show three major surficial elements: bedrock, soils and mantle, and vegetation. The above discussion of vegetation can only serve to indicate to the student some of the many ways in which the recognition and understanding of plant life and its intimate association with the other factors can be of great use to the photogeologist.

Drainage

Since erosion, transportation, and deposition by running water occur in most areas, a study and understanding of stream activity and resulting landforms is essential in photogeologic analysis, regardless of the purpose of the study or project. Some of the more significant landforms resulting from differential erosion have been discussed in a previous section. In this section, the various aspects of drainage will be considered. They are:

1. Genetic classification of streams; the relation of a stream to original slope, underlying bedrock, and structure

2. The stage of development of a stream

3. Drainage patterns

4. Anomalous drainage within a given pattern

5. Detailed drainage characteristics, such as stream gradient, drainage density, basin shape and size, basin side slope, and valley head slope

6. Stage of landmass dissection

Various combinations of the above may be helpful in lithologic identification, stratigraphic correlation, structural mapping, and the determination of tectonic and geomorphic history. In the following discussion, no attempt is made to catalog all possible combinations of structure, lithology, and stream activity.

Genetic Classification. Streams are generally classified in the following manner (Figure 7-17, a block diagram, shows the relation of several stream types to bedrock structure):

Consequent
Subsequent
Resequent
Obsequent
Insequent
Superposed or superimposed
Antecedent

A *consequent stream* is one which develops on some initial topographic slope. Examples include those streams draining seaward after having formed on a recently emerged coastal plain, those which develop in irregular moraine-covered areas, and those which develop in a radial pattern down the slopes of a volcano or domal uplift. Frequently, there is a direct correlation between original slope and underlying bedrock structure. Since this is not always the case, however, it is important to stress the topographic and *not* the structural aspect of the stream's origin.

A *subsequent stream* is one which has developed a course adjusted along some line or zone of least resistance. If personality characteristics could be ascribed to streams, the subsequent stream might be said to be both lazy and efficient. It has developed headward along the line of least resistance, where it could erode with minimum difficulty and maximum effect.

The recognition and understanding of subsequent streams is frequently very important in photogeology, as will be discussed below.

Lobeck (1939) defines *resequent streams* as ". . . those which flow down the dip of the formations in the same direction as the consequent streams. But the resequent streams develop later and at a lower level on a stripped surface."

He also defines an *obsequent stream* as ". . . one which flows in a direction opposite to the dip of the formations and opposite to that of the original consequent streams of the region." Such definitions of resequent and obsequent streams demand that the consequent streams flow in a down-dip direction. As will be discussed below, the present author proposes a somewhat modified use of the terms *resequent* and *obsequent* in photogeology.

Figure 7-17. A block diagram showing the relation of bedrock and structure to genetic stream classification. Symbols are as follows: c, consequent stream; s, subsequent stream; r, resequent stream; o, obsequent stream; i, insequent stream; ?, stream of unknown genetic classification (could have been consequent on old, high surface). (*Diagram by Calvin F. Miller.*)

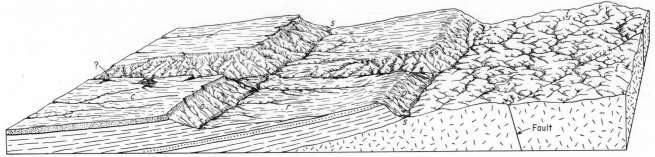

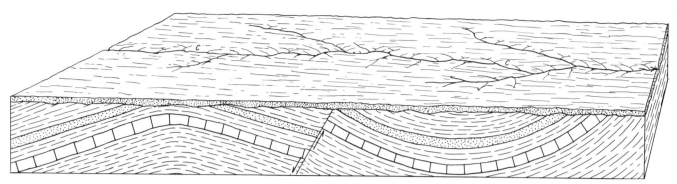

Figure 7-18. A block diagram showing an angular unconformity. A consequent stream (*c*) flows eastward down the gently sloping surface. See Figure 7-19. (*Diagram by Calvin F. Miller.*)

An *insequent stream* is one which follows a course which is apparently not controlled by any factor of original slope, structure, or rock type.

A *superposed* (*or superimposed*) *stream* is one which has formed on one surface and structure and has since cut down through an unconformity, to flow across lower rock units which have a structure discordant with that above the unconformity. The materials lying above the unconformity may either be bedrock or unconsolidated materials.

An *antecedent stream* is one which, having established a course, maintains that course despite the appearance and growth of some structural element across its path. Antecedent streams must be sufficiently powerful, or the deformation sufficiently slow, to permit the maintenance of course throughout the entire sequence of tectonic events.

Discussion of Genetic Classification. To warrant its use and consideration in photogeology, a genetic stream classification must have a practical value in discussion and report writing, and in the analysis and understanding of geology. Since a project area may be too small to permit the determination of original consequent stream direction, and the structural and geomorphic history may be too complex or too little known to permit the identification of such streams, it is suggested that the more orthodox classifiaction of streams into genetic types be reconsidered and modified to meet the everyday requirements of photogeology.

Figure 7-18 shows an angular unconformity in a recently emerged coastal area. The structure beneath the unconformity is relatively complex, whereas the materials above the unconformity dip uniformly toward the shore. A single major consequent stream is shown. Figure 7-19 shows the

resulting topography and stream adjustment to structure and lithology, following the superposition of the consequent stream and extensive erosion.

Since the stream courses and differentially eroded topography, developed on the folded sediments, bear no relation to the original slope or the original consequent stream course, it is proposed that the genetic designation of the several streams shown be dictated by their relation to the topography and structure of the underlying materials. Therefore, the streams flowing down the steep obsequent faces of the several asymmetric ridges are classified as *obsequent* streams, whether they are parallel to or opposite in direction to the original consequent stream. Similarly, streams flowing down the back or dip slopes of the ridges are classified as *resequent* streams. The continuing major stream may be referred to as a *superposed consequent* stream. The major tributaries flowing along shale belts are *subsequent* streams.

Consider Figure 7-20. Assume that the area shown lies in a region in which little is known of the ancient geomorphic development and history. The major east-flowing stream may originally have been a consequent stream, later superimposed across structure. It also could have originated as a subsequent stream, and later superimposed through an unconformity. Finally, it could have had an insequent origin, and later maintained itself as an antecedent stream while tectonic forces produced the presently observed structure. Since original consequent direction cannot be determined, it is again suggested that the sole basis for stream classification be the relation between individual stream direction and present structure. Therefore, the several streams indicated as *o* are considered obsequent streams; those marked *s* are

Figure 7-19. A block diagram of the area shown in Figure 7-18, following superposition of the major consequent stream (*c*) and extensive erosion. The tributary drainage is adjusted to the lithologies and structures formerly beneath the angular unconformity. Genetic classification is based on this adjustment and

has no relation to original consequent stream direction. Symbols are as follows: *c*, original consequent stream (superposed); *s*, subsequent stream; *r*, resequent stream; *o*, obsequent stream; and *i*, insequent stream. Label several of the undesignated streams. (*Diagram by Calvin F. Miller.*)

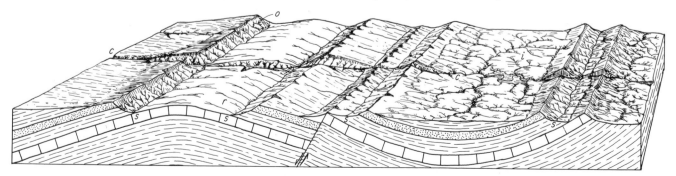

subsequent; and those designated *r* are resequent streams.

In later sections, drainage patterns and anomalous drainage features within a given pattern will be discussed. Many of the ways in which stream classification and pattern are important in photogeology will be illustrated in those sections.

Stage of Stream Development. The stages of a stream's development, as described by William Morris Davis, are comparable to those of a man's life. A stream may be said to be in youth, maturity, or old age. A detailed description and resumé of the criteria used in the classification of stream stage will not be presented here. However, the most important general characteristics of each stage will be reviewed, and the significance of stage analysis will be discussed.

INITIAL STAGE. The initial stage of a stream is usually characterized by a lack of order and organization. Falls, lakes, rapids, and variable stream gradients are typical. An original land surface, usually having irregularities of some kind and degree, is drained by the channeling of runoff into pre-existent depressions and valleylike troughs.

Initial drainage may develop on uplifted coastal plains, in glaciated plains, on young lava surfaces and volcanoes, and on pediment surfaces in areas of stream rejuvenation, for example.

YOUTHFUL STAGE. During the youthful stage, the major observable activity of a stream is that of downcutting. The stream occupies the entire valley floor. Frequently, the valley profile is V-shaped. Waterfalls and rapids persist well into this stage.

MATURE STAGE. In full maturity, a stream flows in a well-established meandering course, sweeping back and forth across a flood plain sufficiently wide to accommodate the entire meander belt. This point in development is reached gradually by the slow formation of the flood plain by lateral stream corrasion after the stream has reached what is known as a *profile of equilibrium* or the *steady state*. It has then become a fully graded stream.

Early maturity is characterized by the partial development of a flood plain. In late maturity, the flood plain is noticeably wider than the meander belt of the stream.

OLD AGE. In old age the flood plain is so extensive that the entire meander belt has enough room to follow a gross meanderlike course. The width of the flood plain is many times that of the meander belt.

REJUVENATION. At any time in a stream's development from one stage to the next, changes may occur which produce a return to the dominantly downcutting youthful stage. Thus, a fully mature stream may rapidly become incised a second time, and be forced to reenact the various stages through which it already has passed at least once.

Rejuvenated stream valleys are usually rather easily identified on aerial photographs. Since rejuvenation may have either a climatic or a geologic explanation, it is important that the photogeologist not only learn to recognize rejuvenation, but also attempt to determine its cause. Rejuvenation may be produced by one or more of the following:

1. Uplift. The uplift of the area through which the stream flows

2. Tilting. The tilting up of the headwater area or depression of the downstream area

3. Lowering of base level. The withdrawal of the sea or the draining of a lake into which the stream formerly flowed, or the rapid downcutting of a master stream which serves as local base level

4. Increase in volume of stream by capture. The sudden increase of drainage area and volume of the captor stream, by adding the headward part of the captive stream, thus increasing the downcutting ability of the captor stream

5. Increase in volume through change in climate. An increase in the annual precipitation of the area over a considerable period of time

In discussions with geologists who have had but limited academic backgrounds in the principles of geomorphology, the writer has observed a common tendency to ascribe rejuvenation almost automatically to regional uplift. In many cases, such a hasty explanation may be attributed to the fact that the chief interest of most practicing geologists in a given area is far afield from geomorphology. They may be interested in measuring a stratigraphic section, in evaluating mineral deposits, or in mapping complex thrust faults, for example. However, if rejuvenation is noted in the field or on aerial photographs, all possible alternative explanations should be considered. Pertinent data should be obtained, and a well-founded hypothesis or conclusion should be advanced.

This is advisable from an economic as well as an academic standpoint. For example, demonstration of epeirogenic uplift may appreciably increase the potential of an area as a petroleum province. Conversely, a nonstructural explanation for regional rejuvenation may greatly decrease the possibilities of oil and gas in the area. Determining a climatic cause for rejuvenation could therefore result in the saving of money, by the avoidance of further exploration.

AGGRADATION. The aggradation of some stream valleys represents the opposite of rejuvenation and may be explained

Figure 7-20. A block diagram of a maturely eroded area of moderately complex structure. The tributary streams can be classified with respect to structure. The master east-flowing stream is of unknown origin. It may have been superposed from a former, higher surface. It may have been antecedent, having maintained its course during structural deformation. The letters denote the genetic classifications of several of the tributary streams. Others may be designated by the student. (*Diagram by Calvin F. Miller.*)

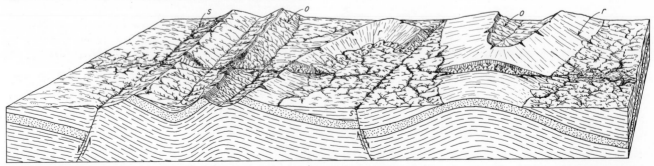

by the reverse of the causes listed above. Thus the depression of an area, the tilting downward of the headward area, the rise of base level, the decrease in stream volume by capture, and the change to a more arid climate may be in part or totally responsible for the aggradation of a given stream valley.

VARIATIONS IN STAGE ALONG A STREAM COURSE. Valuable lithologic and structural information may be obtained through a careful study of the stage characteristics along major stream courses. For example, it may be noted that along one segment, a given stream may occupy a mature valley, and that downstream it flows in a more restricted youthful valley. When such changes in valley characteristics are noted, their explanations should be sought (see Figure 7-21).

One of the more common causes for such valley variations is the occurrence of different lithologies along the course of the stream. While flowing in a belt of shale, clay, or unconsolidated materials, the stream will be enabled to develop a mature profile and a well-established flood plain. If it then enters an area of sandstone, limestone, or resistant crystalline rock, it will be forced to restrict its activity to downcutting, and its valley will maintain youthful characteristics.

The structural relations between the different types of rock, as expressed geomorphically by variations in valley development, should be investigated. For example, a resistant rock unit may be crossed by a major stream as a result of superposition, or through the rising of a structural block across the course of the river. Conversely, the occurrence of dip in a series of alternating resistant and nonresistant rock units could expose resistant rock across the stream's course.

In areas where the bedrock is not well exposed, and where the use of geomorphic criteria is especially important, a consideration of such things as the above may have major structural, tectonic, and economic significance. For example, variations in stream stage may be the only apparent evidence of the presence of a low dome or anticline across a drainage line.

ANALYSIS OF STAGE OF STREAM DEVELOPMENT IN A LARGE AREA. When a large area is studied, it is advisable to devote some attention to the stages of development of all large streams of comparable magnitude and drainage area. If they all flow across similar rock types and have approximately the same discharge, it should be anticipated that they would reflect similar geomorphic histories. Occasionally, however, otherwise similar stream systems within a large area may be noted to be in different stages. Some may show evidence of rejuvenation, while others may have undergone a constant, uniform development or even anomalous-appearing aggradation. The noting of such contrasts could lead to the investigation of possible epeirogenic warping in the area, since climatic and other factors would be assumed to be constant.

In such cases, however, the decision to explain such features by epeirogenic warping, without thoroughly investigating all other possible causes, would be ill-advised. It could be, for example, that within a general area aggradation of some streams may be caused by the encountering of resistant rocks not discernible on the photographs, while the rejuvenation of other streams could be explained by local lowering of base level through the drainage of a lake or through the encountering of extremely nonresistant rock units immediately downstream from the zone of rejuvenation.

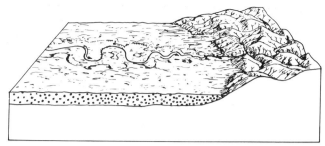

Figure 7-21. A block diagram illustrating abrupt change in stream stage from one segment to another. Upstream (left segment), the stream is in maturity. Downstream it enters a youthful valley. Numerous structural and lithologic combinations could produce the topographic relations shown here. As a suggested exercise, the student should trace the outline of the block face, and sketch various geologic cross sections which could explain the topography. (*Diagram by Calvin F. Miller.*)

It is not possible to predict or anticipate what the many variations in stage of a single stream or numerous streams may indicate. However, it should be stressed that valuable geologic information may be detected through a thorough analysis and evaluation of such geomorphic criteria.

The interpretation of stream aggradation and rejuvenation, of erosional history, and of variations in stage development, can only be made after an entire area has been carefully studied stereoscopically. Since stream configuration and drainage patterns are not necessarily involved, two-dimensional mosaic studies are usually of little or no value. In addition, persons undertaking such analyses should be highly trained and experienced in the principles of geomorphology.

Drainage Patterns. A drainage pattern may be defined as the planimetric arrangement of several streams which are usually adjusted to certain topographic, structural, or lithologic controls. The streams which comprise a pattern may be of any genetic type: insequent, consequent, subsequent, resequent, or obsequent. Frequently, the noting of a stream pattern in an area is helpful in the identification and interpretation of geologic features and structures. Similarly, the analysis and determination of genetic type is of great importance in the evaluation of the meaning of a stream pattern. The several drainage patterns are as follows.

DENDRITIC DRAINAGE PATTERN. The courses of insequent streams are apparently not controlled by such factors as regional slope, structural trends, or rock differences. In areas principally drained by insequent streams, a lack of preferred orientation and spacing results in a gross pattern which resembles the complex branching of a tree (Figure 7-22). The stream courses are usually irregular and bending, and tributaries may flow into the larger streams from any angle. In general, however, since the major streams follow a general incline or grade, most tributaries tend to enter at an acute angle to the direction of flow of the master stream.

Numerous conditions favor the formation of dendritic drainage systems; they all have one common element—homogeneity. In areas of dendritic stream patterns, the material subject to erosion may be bedrock or unconsolidated deposits; it may be sedimentary, igneous, or metamorphic, and the structure may be simple or complex.

In most areas of unconsolidated sands, clays, silts, or gravels, the direction of headward stream erosion is apparently a matter of chance. There is no line of structural weakness, and no steeply dipping, nonresistant stratigraphic interval along which a stream can cut more rapidly than

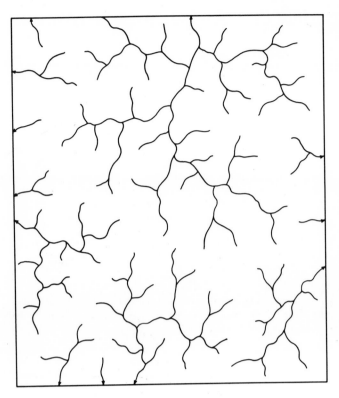

Figure 7-22. Dendritic drainage pattern.

elsewhere. Similarly, there are no resistant units which will form ridges. Hence, there can be no predetermined oriented slopes on which either obsequent or resequent tributaries can develop.

The structure of crystalline rocks is important. There must be no lines or belts of greater or less resistance than that present throughout the rest of the mass. Regardless of how complex the folding in a highly metamorphosed se-

Figure 7-23. Rectangular drainage pattern.

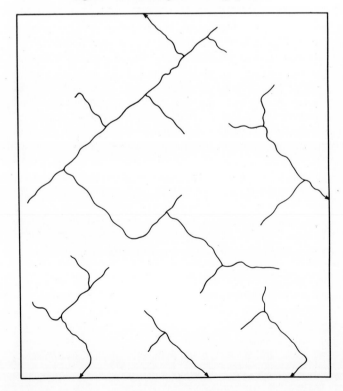

quence of rocks, for example, a dendritic stream system can develop if there are no nonresistant fault or shear zones, and no pronounced variations in resistance in the rock units exposed to erosion.

In literature, reference is often made to the development of dendritic drainage patterns in areas of horizontal and nearly horizontal sedimentary rocks. There are cases, however, in which homogeneous sedimentary units, though disturbed and contorted, may also be drained by streams arranged in a dendritic pattern.

Where there has been folding and faulting, special conditions must exist to permit the development of uncontrolled drainage. Rock resistance over the entire exposed area must be virtually uniform. Also, any faults or fractures present must be sealed to such a degree that they neither constitute significant lines of less resistance nor have a resistance exceeding that of the surrounding rock. Areas underlain by shales occasionally exhibit dendritic drainage despite structural complexity.

The more resistant sedimentary rocks, such as sandstones, quartzites, conglomerates and, in arid and semiarid climates, limestones, are frequently interbedded with less resistant units. In areas of folded or faulted interbedded sediments, a dendritic drainage system would not be expected.

In areas of flat-lying strata, a general absence of faults and joints is sufficient to permit dendritic stream development, regardless of the lithology of the rocks exposed. Thus conglomerates, sandstones, shales, limestone, clays, and many other types of strata may be present.

In most instances it is not necessary to rely on drainage pattern alone to identify rock type or structure. Tonal qualities, topography, surface texture, and other factors assist in the proper identification of such masses as granite, metamorphosed sediments, and massive horizontal sandstones.

RECTANGULAR DRAINAGE PATTERN. Rectangular drainage patterns (Figure 7-23) usually develop along intersecting fault or joint systems. The adjusted streams or stream segments which define the pattern are all subsequent streams. Areas in which such a pattern may occur include those underlain by large bodies of homogeneous crystalline rock, and regional plateaus underlain by horizontal or gently dipping resistant sedimentary rocks. Small-scale, restricted patterns are commonly present in highly jointed sandstones exposed in arid and semiarid areas.

Joint and fault systems rarely intersect at exactly 90°. The term *rectangular* is therefore usually extended to include large acute intersections. Pronounced variance from the rectangular form is more appropriately called an *angular drainage pattern* (Figure 7-24).

Commonly in both rectangular and angular drainage patterns, adjustment along one set of joints or faults is more pronounced than along the other.

A combination of dendritic and rectangular drainage patterns may occur in a single area, as in the case of an essentially homogeneous mass scored at relatively wide intervals by major faults or joints. The large streams form a rectangular pattern, while the intervening blocks are dissected by insequent tributaries which constitute local or isolated dendritic patterns (Figure 7-25).

TRELLIS DRAINAGE PATTERN. Trellis patterns derive their name from their resemblance to a vine, with its many short branches, as it clings to a trellis (Figure 7-26). This pattern is produced in areas in which structural complexities or differences in rock resistance have directed stream development and location along a single major trend, with smaller tributaries largely at right angles to the main units.

Parallel folds in strata of various resistance, parallel block faults, folded imbricate zones and similar structures 'are usually drained by streams forming this pattern. The scale of the pattern may vary considerably, from miniature trellis drainage, developed along small tight folds in thin-bedded sandstones or shales, to great regional patterns, such as are present along the Appalachian Mountains in the eastern United States and the Front Range of the Rockies in British Columbia and Alberta, Canada. In the Appalachians, large folds and faults are present. In the Canadian Rockies, block faults and thrust faults are important structural elements.

The large streams which follow the dominant trend are usually subsequent streams, while their tributaries are usually resequent and obsequent streams.

A nonstructural origin of trellis drainage may be found in areas which have been subjected to Pleistocene glaciation, usually of the continental type. Parallel low ridges and depressions, constituting an elongate *drumlin,* or drumlinoid topography, may be drained by parallel streams which follow consequent courses along the original lowlands. In such areas the small tributaries which drain down the gentle flanks of the low divides are also consequent streams. In some cases, parallel abandoned beach ridges and intervening depressions may also be drained by a similar pattern of consequent streams.

Since streams of different origins may combine to form a trellis pattern, it is important to determine genetic classification before attempting a structural or lithologic explanation for the presence of such a pattern. This can usually be done by considering such other direct criteria as the presence or absence of outcrop, ridge asymmetry, and tonal relations. Also, such indirect criteria as the location and position of the drained area, with respect to surrounding topography and structure, and the past geomorphic history of the area, should be considered.

RADIAL DRAINAGE PATTERN. Most circular or oval topographically high areas are drained by streams which radiate outward from the central part, and flow down the flanks in all directions (Figure 7-27). Such radially drained topographic features may be underlain by horizontal strata, by dipping strata, by anticlinal or synclinal folds, by faults, by crystalline or sedimentary rocks, or by unconsolidated residual or deposited materials. Radial drainage alone cannot be assumed to indicate any particular structure.

However, many structural domes rise as topographic domes. Radial consequent drainage develops around their flanks. Volcanoes also display radial drainage.

Breached or eroded domes may have a central depression, if the rocks exposed in the core are relatively nonresistant. Around the inner lowland an inward-facing scarp or highland rim may be present, representing the remnant of overlying resistant rock removed from the central area by erosion. Inward-flowing obsequent streams, flowing down the obsequent face of such rimrocks, form a radial pattern known as *centripetal drainage* (Figure 7-28).

Structural and other topographic basins may also be drained by centripetal patterns of streams. If such a basin is an original landform, the streams are consequent streams. If it is developed at a lower stratigraphic level than the original, the streams are resequent streams.

Eroded domes frequently have a central dome, surrounded by a ringlike depression. Such topography results from the removal of the overlying beds and the exposure of a resistant

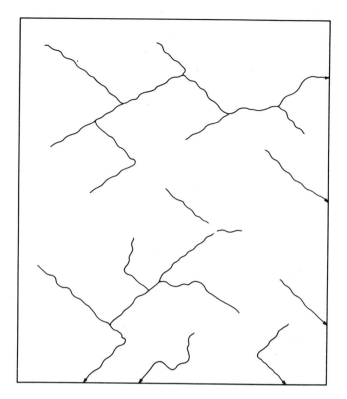

Figure 7-24. Angular drainage pattern.

unit in the central core. This lower, older resistant rock is drained radially by resequent streams.

ANNULAR DRAINAGE PATTERN. Maturely dissected domes and basins are frequently expressed topographically by a series of concentric circular or arcuate ridges and lowlands. The lowlands, which are developed on nonresistant beds, are usually occupied by subsequent streams. These streams, if sufficiently well defined and restricted to the nonresistant

Figure 7-25. Gross rectangular drainage pattern, with local dendritic drainage developed within the large blocks.

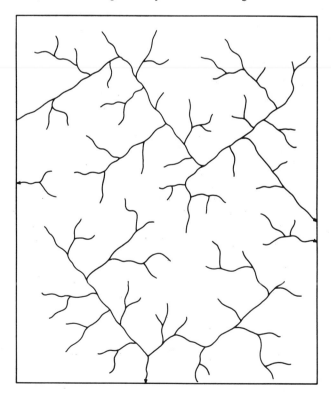

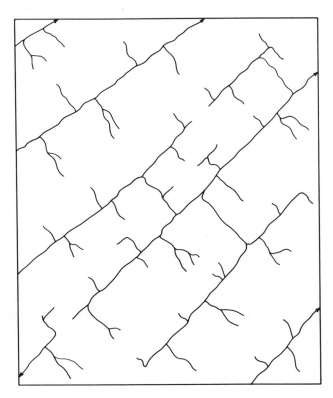

Figure 7-26. Trellis drainage pattern.

belts, form what is called an *annular drainage pattern*. Such a pattern may be expressed by a few long arcuate streams or by a combination of short segments of numerous tributary streams (Figure 7-29).

In some areas a single stream may swerve around the fringe of a dome and alone constitute a conspicuous drainage feature. Maturely eroded gentle structural basins may also be "avoided" in a similar way. Such "bowing-out" of a single stream or of several streams, therefore, must not

Figure 7-27. Radial drainage pattern.

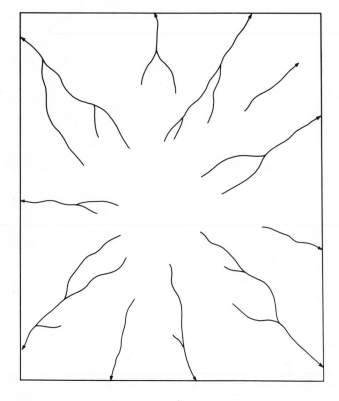

automatically be assumed to indicate positive structure. This will be discussed below in connection with anomalous drainage.

Annular drainage frequently occurs in association with radial patterns around well-dissected domes and domal anticlines. In fact, resequent or obsequent radial and centripetal drainage is usually tributary to subsequent annular drainage. The latter may in turn be tributary to one or more larger original consequent radial streams.

PARALLEL DRAINAGE PATTERNS. Extensive unidirectional slopes, such as those along a broad coastal plain or an elongate linear homoclinal ridge upheld by gently dipping resistant strata or other tabular rock, are often drained by relatively uniformly spaced parallel or subparallel streams.

When such streams constitute the principal drainage of an area, they may be referred to as forming a *parallel drainage pattern*. However, if the essential pattern of a region is trellis, for example, the parallel or subparallel resequent or obsequent tributaries to a major subsequent stream could not be singled out as a parallel pattern, but should be considered as an integral part of the larger trellis pattern.

GENERAL REMARKS. It should be noted that there could be some element of inconsistency occasioned by the fact that some patterns require numerous streams, while others may be defined by one or two. For example, for drainage to be classified as dendritic, trellis, radial, or parallel, a relatively large number of streams are involved, and their mutual arrangement, spacing, and orientation must be considered.

However, in some instances, a single stream may follow a course which can appropriately be termed *rectangular*.

More commonly, the arcuate or semicircular course of a single stream may well classify it as an *annular stream segment*.

Anomalous Drainage. In numerous geologic publications, reference is made to drainage anomalies. Since the interpretation of aerial photographs and mosaics frequently entails the analysis of drainage, the subject of drainage anomalies must assume an important position in the present discussion.

Consider first a working definition of the terms *anomalous* and *anomaly*. Broadly speaking, a stream or drainage anomaly is one or more characteristics of a stream or stream system which do not coincide with or fit the dominant or prevalent drainage characteristics of an area as a whole. The word *anomalous* may thus be used to designate such different-appearing drainage. Such terms as *drainage anomaly* and *anomalous drainage* do not necessarily denote any significant structural or stratigraphic relationship.

Drainage anomalies may or may not involve planimetric stream shape, arrangement, or direction. They may include such elements as valley depth and width, flood-plain characteristics, the presence or absence of stream terraces, and many other features and relations which cannot be shown on a planimetric map.

Drainage anomalies may be divided into two basic categories:

1. There are streams or stream segments which appear incongruent with respect to a regional pattern or erosional history, but for which a logical, relatively reliable geologic explanation may be found. For example, in a maturely dissected hilly area, drained by a dendritic pattern of streams, the presence of one or more streams aligned in a particular direction may be classified as anomalous according to the above definition. Through careful study of other criteria, it might be established that these streams are subsequent along major fault lines. Their location and linearity are thus ex-

plained. Since they are unlike their neighbors, however, the linear streams retain the designation of anomalous.

2. There are streams which similarly attract attention by being different in some way, but for which no demonstrable explanation can be found. The recognition of the anomalous character of such streams, coupled with the development of soundly based postulations of their cause, constitutes an important branch of photogeology. Since the factors responsible for such drainage development cannot be ascertained by other observations, it follows that the streams themselves are the only evident indication of the causal factors. Therefore, the primary requisites in such drainage analysis are: (*a*) the ability to differentiate such streams and (*b*) a broad geologic and geomorphic background, on which to base scientifically sound hypotheses relative to geologic conditions which *could* have produced the observed geomorphic relations.

The interrelationships between streams and the landmass into which they cut usually preclude the separation of the two factors in topographic and geomorphic analysis. Therefore, topographic anomalies, which technically may or may not be considered to be true drainage anomalies, should be included in the present discussion. There are many such features, including "anomalously" undrained areas in a generally well-dissected region, a maturely dissected landmass close to areas of less advanced dissection, and linear arrangements of knobs, depressions, and points of floodplain constriction or abrupt widening.

In photogeology, drainage anomalies serve two functions. In areas where the geology is well exposed and clearly expressed, they act as signposts which attract attention to certain geologic relationships. In such cases, further photograph study may reveal critical structural or lithologic data, by which the factors which have influenced the drainage can be identified and interpreted. This approach is applicable in areas of dissected bedrock, involving virtually any combinations of rock type and structure.

The second function arises in the interpretation of photographs of areas in which little or no direct geologic interpretation is possible and in which the geomorphic approach is employed. In such areas as low coastal plains, large deltas, vegetation- or mantle-covered basins, and vast glaciated plains, the regional drainage analysis permits the establishment of the norm or regional patterns and other drainage characteristics in relation to which some streams may appear to be anomalous.

At the present time, extensive photogeologic studies are being carried out in such areas as the U.S. Gulf Coast, the Mississippi Delta area, and throughout the glaciated plains of western Canada and adjacent states. In the Gulf areas, drainage is known to reflect two structural types: (1) regional fault and fracture systems and (2) salt domes. The fault systems in some areas are so well expressed by drainage adjustments that within parts of these areas it may be more appropriate to designate fault-controlled linear stream segments as subsequent rather than as anomalous. Those streams which encircle or otherwise indicate known salt structures require the designation of anomalous, since they are isolated departures from the regional norm. Similar streams which suggest the influence of domes or faults elsewhere should all be classified as anomalous streams.

In the glaciated areas of western Canada, several types of petroleum traps are present, including reefs, faults, and stratigraphic traps. Unfortunately, geomorphic analysis is greatly hindered by variable glacial deposits, which range in

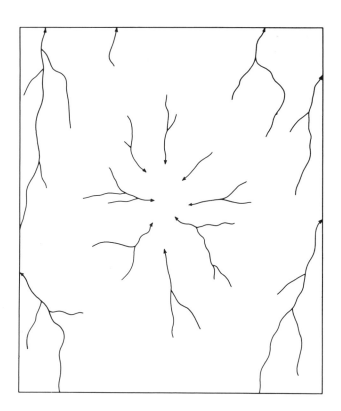

Figure 7-28. Centripetal drainage pattern.

thickness from negligible to several hundred feet, and in composition from fine silts to coarse gravels. In such areas, caution must be exercised both in a photogeologic study and in the evaluation of its findings.

Some preglacial erosional features, which were reflections of underlying structure, have in all probability been com-

Figure 7-29. Annular drainage pattern, with associated radial drainage pattern. Annular drainage may consist of one or two large stream segments (such as segment *A*) or several small tributaries (such as tributaries *B*).

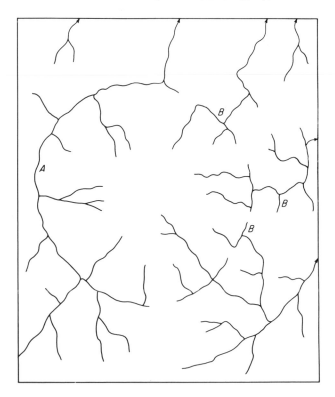

pletely masked by the Pleistocene deposits. Nevertheless, many others have been incompletely obscured; these may be detected at the present time. Also, it is possible that in some areas completely masked pre-Pleistocene topography has been revealed as a result of the compaction of the glacial deposits. For example, thick ground moraine which fills a pre-Pleistocene valley could settle more than the thin veneer overlying higher preglacial terrain, resulting in gentle sags, in the present surface, above the former valleys.

The elastic rebound of areas once subjected to continental glaciation is extremely important in the photogeologic analysis of such areas. The author has seen instances in which crustal depression by glacial ice was apparently accompanied by some differential movements along old fault trends. In postglacial time, elastic rebound was apparently also accompanied by differential displacements along some of these faults. A painstaking stereoscopic study of moraine and outwash-covered plains areas, therefore, may reveal slight topographic discordances which could have been produced by this differential elastic rebound process, and which could in turn lead to the location of old and possibly important fault zones.

Glaciated areas should, therefore, be approached with neither complete optimism nor complete pessimism. There is much valuable geologic information to be obtained from aerial photographs of many glaciated areas. The problem is far more difficult and complex than that of the study of unglaciated areas, and greater time and painstaking effort are required. The possibility of locating long-existing tectonic trends in these areas where seismic and other exploration methods experience great difficulties is of the highest importance.

Occasionally, anomalous drainage features are of such a magnitude that they can only be recognized and evaluated on a regional basis. Some may be rather obvious, while others are extremely vague and poorly defined. Since anomalous drainage can only be so classified because of its relation and comparison to many surrounding streams, it should be stressed that no specific criteria can be presented here which will apply in all situations. In fact, that which would be considered anomalous in one area might well be completely normal elsewhere.

The following are some of the more frequently found types of stream anomalies. Some of their possible bedrock causes are listed. Most of the anomalies, however, may also have explanations that do not involve bedrock type or structure.

1. Linear drainage lines may denote the presence of faults, joints, fractures, or less resistant linear outcrop belts.

2. Arcuate stream courses may indicate domal upwarps or, less frequently, basins.

3. Radial drainage, as previously noted, may form on domal structures. It may also occur around the flanks of hills formed by differentially eroded broad synclines and structural basins.

4. Abrupt changes in the drainage density, and other three-dimensional erosional factors, from one part of an area to another, may be caused by differences in lithology which are not otherwise indicated.

5. Abrupt differences in the stage of stream development from one part of an area to another may be caused by different types of bedrock, by structure, or by recent epeirogenic warping.

6. Numerous stream captures are suggestive of recent crustal movement, though the possibility of nonstructural causes must not be overlooked.

7. Variations in flood-plain characteristics, such as width, entrenchment, and the presence or absence of terraces, may be a reflection of underlying structure or lithologic changes. For example, in Gulf coastal areas, an anomalous widening of a natural levee along a distributary is suggestive of the presence of a salt dome immediately below (see Figures 12-4 and 12-5).

8. Abnormally linear arrangements of springs, sink holes, or other less well-defined depressions, may indicate fractures or faults at some depth, if not at the surface.

9. The presence of a waterfall or rapids along the course of a single stream may indicate the outcrop of a resistant bed. A linear arrangement of such features, involving many streams, could testify to the presence of a fault, especially in areas of low dip or homogeneous rock of any structure.

The above are but a few of the innumerable possible drainage anomalies which might be encountered in a photogeologic study. It is noteworthy that most, if not all, are such that they might well pass unnoticed in the field.

In studying drainage features, several points must be kept in mind at all times. For discussion purposes, again consider a glaciated plains area. Such an area is chosen primarily because its interpretation is more difficult than most others; hence, it offers more pitfalls.

Anomalous drainage is frequently subsequent or controlled drainage. Some drainage anomalies, when fully investigated, are found to have no relation to structural or lithologic control. Therefore, it is of the greatest importance, not only to differentiate anomalous drainage from regionally conformable or normal drainage, but also to attempt to classify the anomalous streams genetically.

For example, imagine two abnormally straight streams in a glaciated plains area. One of these is a surficial stream flowing entirely on the upland surface. The other, a tributary to a major incised river, has cut hundreds of feet into bedrock through the glacial debris cover. What might be the geologic explanation for these streams, and, more important, in what ways may they be different?

The surficial stream may be a consequent stream following a glacially produced linear trend, such as occurs in drumlinoid topography. It may follow a partially filled pre-Pleistocene subsequent valley. It may drain a gentle lowland produced by the differential compaction of thick glacial debris in a filled preglacial subsequent valley. Assuming that no nearby topographic evidence tends to substantiate either of these alternatives, it must be concluded that this stream, though possibly controlled structurally, is at best a doubtful subsequent stream.

The entrenched stream may be a superposed glacially controlled consequent stream, or it may be a subsequent tributary which, early in its development, cut through the glacial material and extended itself, through headward erosion in bedrock, along a less resistant zone. The probability of a subsequent, controlled origin is greater in this instance than in the case of the surficial stream. In neither case can a definite cause and effect statement be made; but a differential relative evaluation is possible.

The above example is representative of the approach which must be followed in a photogeologic study involving drainage analysis. In most cases, at least two alternative explanations may be possible. Therefore, final conclusions must be avoided and relative qualitative interpretations proposed.

Virtually all geomorphic studies must be subject to field check. The primary value of the photo study is the delineation of possible and probable structurally controlled anomalies. Usually the analysis cannot, and should not, include a final single interpretation and evaluation of such features.

Detailed Erosional Characteristics. The basic concepts of landform analysis and description have been clearly established by such geomorphologists as Davis, Gilbert, Johnson, and Lobeck. They and others have stressed the primary roles played by bedrock, erosion agent, and time. In recent years, geomorphologists have begun to study landforms from the standpoint of quantitative as well as qualitative relationships.

In principle, the quantitative geomorphic approach consists of the measuring and statistical analysis of various parameters which combine to constitute a given landscape. Among these are slope, drainage density, basin size and shape, and what is termed the *hypsometric factor.* Limited space precludes a detailed treatment of the subject in this volume. However, some of the more important landscape elements being investigated by quantitative methods will be briefly discussed, since their understanding is occasionally of great value to the photogeologist.

During the course of drainage development, several factors determine the ultimate type, density, and other characteristics of the stream systems of an area. The more significant of these are rock type, structure, climate, and vegetation.

Resistant rocks, such as sandstones, quartzites, and conglomerates, prevent the development of many small tributaries. Areas underlain by such rock units are usually drained by a relatively few widely spaced, large tributary streams. Soluble rocks, such as limestones and dolomites, in humid and semihumid climates, accommodate within themselves a large portion of the precipitation and permit less surface runoff in the form of streams. Areas underlain by such rocks are, therefore, frequently characterized by low drainage density and large tributaries. Conversely, such rocks as shales and clays, being dense and impermeable, have a far greater surface runoff and allow the formation and maintenance of many closely spaced small finger-tip tributaries.

Distinct contrasts in rock type are clearly reflected in the minor drainage characteristics. A plateau underlain by extremely resistant quartzites is easily distinguished from one underlain by either porous limestones or dense clays. With continued study of a given area over a period of months or years, the photogeologist gradually learns to note less obvious differences in drainage. These permit a refinement of lithologic identification to the point where a distinction can be made between shales, sandy shales, and shaly sandstones. Such differences may not be uniform over great areas, since various climatic, topographic, soil, and vegetation factors produce variations which must be taken into account. Within any one relatively restricted area, however, certain recognition criteria, which are very helpful in lithologic identification, can be established.

Occasionally, such criteria may be useful in structural as well as lithologic identification and interpretation. For example, in heavily wooded areas, where bedrock is largely or completely obscured, it may be possible to determine changes in dip magnitude by noting a corresponding change in the width of a belt having certain drainage characteristics. Also, it may be possible to locate a fault by noting the juxtaposition of two drainage textures which elsewhere are separated by a constant horizontal (stratigraphic) distance or interval.

In general, this type of interpretation requires far more imagination and concentration than is necessary in areas of exposed outcrop. It is an extremely valuable tool in areas where the more direct methods of photogeologic mapping are not possible.

Stage of Landmass Dissection. A landmass, like a stream, may be said to pass through several stages of development from initial form, through youth and maturity, to old age. As may well be imagined, relatively few landmasses actually have an initial form. For example, block mountains rise gradually and sporadically, while the uplifted area is constantly being attacked by weathering and erosion. Some noteworthy landforms which do have initial stages include recently drained lake floors, rapidly uplifted coastal areas, volcanic forms, and glaciated areas (about to be drained by running water).

The *initial stage* of dissection of any area may be considered that stage in which drainage is just beginning to develop or has recently developed. Much of the initial block surface remains undissected and undrained.

The *youthful stage* is characterized by active stream development and dissection, though most of the original surface remains.

The *mature stage* may be described as consisting of slopes, resulting from the almost complete dissection of the original landmass. Little or no original upland surface remains.

In the *old-age stage,* a large number of the interfluvial spurs and divides have been removed by erosion and much of the lower topography is adjusted to a new base level. The original upland surface is reflected only by a relatively few remaining hills or outliers which rise above the new well-developed lower surface.

In the photogeologic study of relatively large areas, close attention should be paid to the stage of landmass dissection. It may be possible to detect variations in stage from one part of an area to the other. Such contrasts or variations may be structurally significant if they cannot be explained by such factors as the direction of flow of regional drainage, relative location of particular landmasses, or bedrock characteristics. When a nonstructural explanation cannot be demonstrated, such geologic events as crustal warping or relatively recent faulting should be considered.

It is not possible to illustrate this aspect of photogeologic study and research, since for the most part the elements involved are of a regional nature. Occasionally, however, the criteria may be distinguished within a relatively small area. One particularly striking example of rejuvenation of drainage along the flank of a mountain mass is to be seen in Figures 8-5 and 8-6. Other somewhat similar examples, though not specifically designated as such, will be found in Part III.

CONCLUSION

Working closely with an experienced photogeologist on an apprenticeship basis, a qualified geologist can learn photogeologic techniques and become relatively proficient in photogeologic interpretation in about two years. Under such a training program, his three-dimensional geologic thinking, his understanding of time, tectonics, structural details, erosional processes, and numerous other aspects of geology will be improved and developed to a high degree. He will learn that when he undertakes a photogeologic

99

study, he must understand and appreciate the types of problems to be expected in different areas and the limitations imposed by such factors as time or photograph scale to the solution of such problems. In short, he will have, as a background to which he can turn at any time, the concepts presented in Parts I and II of this book, and many others which he will have encountered during his apprenticeship.

A geologist who is not and does not intend to become a professional photogeologist can, after an extremely brief orientation, become quite proficient in mapping rock units and structures in areas of exposed and clearly expressed bedrock. The area shown in Figure 8-4, for example, should offer little difficulty to the average geologist. Several other photo illustrations in Part III can simply be examined and mapped, more or less as a matter of routine, by anyone with a background in basic geology.

As long as such factors as vertical exaggeration and stereo-image distortion are understood, most geologists should be capable of using aerial photographs to map dips and strikes, faults, fold axes, stratigraphic contacts, and igneous rock boundaries in most areas of exposed bedrock. For this reason, this book does not attempt to teach routine strike-dip photogeologic mapping.

Professional photogeologists and those geologists who map obvious geology on photographs constitute two groups who use aerial photographs in geology. Probably most students and practicing geologists who take the time to read this book will fall into some category intermediate between the two. These are the readers who do not intend to become photogeologists but desire to learn to obtain as much geological information as possible through photograph study.

Throughout the world there are vast areas, where photogeology can be undertaken, in which the bedrock is not completely exposed nor evidence of its presence entirely lacking. In these areas the rock, though perhaps covered by mantle or vegetation, is expressed on the surface by slope, shape, tone, texture, and erosional characteristics. It is, essentially, geomorphically expressed. Through a compre-

hensive analysis of observed geomorphic criteria, the photogeologic mapper and interpreter can derive his data and his understanding of the geology present in such areas. For this reason, Chapter 7 has evolved into a discussion of photogeomorphology.

The commercial geologist who uses aerial photographs in mapping an area should have two principal aims: to make as complete and accurate a map as possible, and to learn more about the geology of the area than others who may have mapped and studied it for competitive companies. *Since all obvious geologic structures, features, and relations will be mapped by all qualified geologists who study a particular area, it follows that the advantage will go to the person or company that can derive the most information from the areas where the geology is poorly expressed and less exposed. The key to gaining greater structural and stratigraphic information from such areas is the application of sound geomorphic principles.*

Since geomorphic principles are important in the photogeologic interpretation of those extensive areas where structure and stratigraphy are not obvious, the following three summary conclusions must be stressed:

1. Three-dimensional photo study is essential. Mosaic and two-dimensional photo studies can provide incomplete information and impressions, but a thorough interpretation or evaluation is possible only when the entire project area is studied stereoscopically.

2. In photogeologic studies of basin, plains, and coastal plain areas, a drainage or erosional anomaly must not be assumed to denote a structural anomaly until such an interpretation is more or less forced by the elimination, through geomorphic analysis, of all possible nonstructural explanations.

3. The caliber of a photogeologic interpretation is primarily determined by the academic background of the photogeologist and his understanding of, and ability to use, the principles of classical and, in some cases, quantitative geomorphology.

PART III Illustrations and Exercises

INTRODUCTION

The following stereograms show many geologic features in a wide variety of topographic, climatic, and geologic settings. Some areas shown are devoid of vegetation. Others are heavily forest-covered. Some are extensively mantled by alluvial and colluvial materials. Others consist primarily of exposed bedrock. In some, the geologic structure is extremely simple. In others, it is so complex that it cannot be deciphered and mapped correctly or in detail. Consolidated and unconsolidated sedimentary units are included, as are metamorphic and intrusive and extrusive igneous rocks.

Perhaps the single most important fact which the student must bear in mind while reading this part of the text, and while studying the aerial photographs and maps, is that no collection of photographs, however extensive, can possibly include all variations and combinations of rock type, structure, topography, climate, vegetation, and soils. The purpose of this part of the book is to introduce to the student many of the basic *problems* of identification and interpretation, while including as many different situations and combinations of factors as space permits.

8

Division of Illustrations into Categories

The stereograms have been assembled into several necessarily arbitrary categories. The categories fall into two groups—geomorphic and geologic. The four geomorphic categories are based on the role of geomorphology in rock identification and in geologic interpretation. The three geologic categories are based on the relative ease or difficulty with which rock units are differentiated and identified, structures are determined, geologic maps are compiled, and an over-all interpretation is made.

In some areas, a single type of geomorphic or geologic problem may exist. In others, two or more may be present.

GEOMORPHOLOGY

In previous chapters, considerable attention has been given to the significance of geomorphology in photogeologic mapping and interpretation. Geomorphic criteria may be used in several ways. To permit the greater appreciation of the role of geomorphic principles in photogeology, the following categories are introduced and illustrated. Chapters 9, 10, 11, and 12 consist of collections of stereograms which further illustrate each category.

General or Elementary Geomorphology

Numerous accumulations of materials and many erosional features can be identified primarily on the basis of form alone. Among such features are sand dunes, stream valleys, shorelines, volcanic cones, glacial moraines, and alpine glacial erosional features. The application of geomorphic criteria in such instances is relatively straightforward and simple.

In Figure 8-1, a stereogram of an extensive area of sand dunes, form is the principal element used in *identification*. Differences in form from one part of the area to another permit a general *interpretation* that variations in soil moisture exist in the area.

Direct or Supplemental Geomorphology

The term *supplemental* or *supplementary* may be used to apply to something which is *added* to complete a thing, to supply a deficiency, or to reinforce or extend a whole. The key word is *added*. In contrast, the term *complemental* or *complementary* may refer to something which is actually *needed* to complete a given thing. The difference between these two words, *added* and *needed*, constitutes the difference between supplemental and complemental geomorphology.

Direct, or supplemental, geomorphology refers to the use of geomorphic criteria to assist the photogeologist in rock identification and in the interpretation of such factors as structure and tectonic history. It is used *directly* in association with such other criteria as vegetation, photographic tone, and the relative positions and elevations of two or more rock units.

Supplemental geomorphology is almost automatically employed by all photogeologists, whether they are seeking to differentiate between a shale belt and an adjacent sandstone formation or between a granite mass and an intruded, though obscured, basaltic dike. Such factors as relative resistance to erosion and those characteristics of the rock which influence drainage density and other minor geomorphic forms are considered in a study of supplemental geomorphology.

Figure 8-4, which is a stereogram of an area in the Colorado Front Range foothills belt, is an excellent example of the type of area in which direct or supplemental geomorphology can be applied. Some of the geologic relations can be determined immediately by outcrop pattern and the dip of exposed strata. Lithologic differences are detected and interpreted when slopes, drainage patterns, and other geomorphic factors are studied.

Indirect or Complemental Geomorphology

The observation of relatively recent changes in the *geomorphic history* of an area may be of great assistance to the photogeologist. For example, in the study of a large region, it may be possible to detect stream aggradation in one area and recent stream rejuvenation in another. If such variations in drainage conditions cannot be explained by normal geomorphic processes and reasoning, a tectonic or epeirogenic explanation may be advanced and further investigated.

Complemental geomorphology and supplemental geomorphology, therefore, are entirely different in scope and in purpose. Figure 8-5, which is a stereogram of a mountain front, illustrates both supplemental and complemental geomorphology. The use of supplemental criteria is helpful in the tracing of key beds and in the detection of some structure. The use of complemental criteria, however, introduces into the structural interpretation the possibility of extremely recent major normal or high-angle reverse faulting. Figure 8-6, an oblique photograph of the same general area, brings out strikingly the possibility of such a recent structural movement, which could not be indicated by such things as dip and strike, relative rock resistance, or differences in lithology.

During the course of a photogeologic study, supplemental geomorphology is used far more and to much greater immediate purpose than is complemental geomorphology. The primary reason for this is that in many project areas there are no indications of such events as recent crustal warping or recent fault rejuvenation.

It is of the utmost importance, however, that from the very beginning the student of photogeology learn to be on the search for indications, suggestions, or subtle hints that there is more in the recorded history of the area he is mapping than can be detected within the realm of dips, strikes, fault displacements, and those other elements which constitute photogeologic mapping.

Independent Geomorphology

There are many areas of the world, where petroleum or minerals are sought, within which there are no mappable outcrops and no easily discernible structures. A few examples of such areas are the extensive glaciated plains of western Canada, the Gulf coastal area of the southern United States, the extensive intermontane basins of the southwestern United States, and the jungle-covered basin and lowland areas of South America.

In such areas, the photogeologist cannot deal with such factors as strike ridges, differential erosion, and rock or soil contrasts. Considerable information may sometimes be obtained, however, through a careful examination of the topography and of the recorded geomorphic history of the area.

In many cases, the surface bedrock consists entirely of unconsolidated and semiconsolidated late Tertiary, Quaternary, and even Recent deposits, usually alluvium or other mantling materials.

There exists within the geologic profession a tendency to subdivide regions into two categories: (1) outcrop-structure areas, and (2) nonoutcrop-"geomorphic" areas. These two may be exemplified by the exposed folds of Wyoming on the one hand and by the extensive delta of the Mississippi River on the other.

The fact which must be stressed, however, is that in many regions grossly considered to be outcrop-structure areas there exist numerous large and small expanses which are locally covered by alluvium, pediment capping, outwash, and ground or terminal morainal materials.

If such masked or covered areas exist within a general region of structural disturbance, in which it is possible to map formations and to delineate structures elsewhere, both the covered and the outcrop areas should be studied with the utmost of care. It may be possible to detect some geomorphic evidence for differential warping, faulting, or other tectonic disturbances which may not be indicated by bedrock relations within the outcrop area alone.

Included in the category of *independent geomorphology* are such elements as drainage characteristics, slopes, and topographic anomalies. Figure 8-9 is a stereogram of a small area in the glaciated plains of Alberta, Canada. The major stream follows a course which may be designated as *anomalous*. Such a feature is one of several, represented by those included in Chapter 12, which constitute the study of independent geomorphology.

GEOLOGY—STRUCTURE AND LITHOLOGY

Chapters 13, 14, and 15 consist of collections of stereograms (and associated figures and texts) of areas in which the geology is relatively easy to identify and to map (Chapter 13), moderately difficult to determine (Chapter 14), and extremely difficult to map and to understand (Chapter 15).

Such a differentiation into three categories is, of course, comparatively subjective. Some of the features included within the photographs designated as difficult to interpret are extremely obvious and self-evident. Some of the individual features included with the group of photographs designated as relatively easy to map cannot be identified and interpreted.

This brings out one extremely important element of photogeologic mapping and interpretation; an area which appears to be easy to map may include unsuspected problems. These may be completely overlooked if it is assumed that there are no such problems and that a complete geologic interpretation can be obtained from a rapid study. Regardless of where the area may be, or how simple the geology may *seem*, it is a sound practice to take sufficient time to ensure a complete and accurate map and analysis. Occasionally, a vaguely defined or largely obscured feature may prove to be the key to an important concept which could be overlooked during a rapid or routine examination of the photographs. *No area is so simple that it can be glanced at and considered completely mapped and understood!*

As a gross generality the more outcrop exposed or expressed topographically, and the less obscured by overburden, vegetation, and similar factors, the easier is the interpretation of the geology and the compilation of a reasonably complete map.

Figures 8-11, 8-13, and 8-14 are representative of the relatively easy, intermediate, and difficult in photogeologic identification, rock differentiation, and mapping.

Since each classification can embrace innumerable combinations of topography, geology, climate, and the other elements, it is impossible to describe the classifications in further detail or to ascribe to them particular common characteristics.

SUGGESTIONS FOR THE READER

Different individuals should derive different information and benefits from a study of the illustrations in this part of the book. The photographs include a considerable variety of topographic, geologic, and geomorphic features.

The student of elementary geology and physical geography should direct his attention toward specific photographs and specific features to further his understanding of terrain, erosion, deposition, and geologic structure.

Students of advanced courses in structural geology, geomorphology, general geology, and field geology should find the many illustrations and the principles they demonstrate to be of considerable value.

Students of photogeology should study each stereogram thoroughly, should carefully read the accompanying text, and should attempt to solve all problems and to answer all questions in connection with each illustration. Many of the exercises involve annotation. If the exercises are to be used for class purposes, it is suggested that transparent cellulose acetate be placed over the photographs and that all annotations be made on the acetate, which can be submitted to the instructor.

The ability to read and to interpret topographic and geologic maps is greatly enhanced by a thorough and intimate knowledge of the ways in which geology and topography are related. Therefore, the principles of photogeologic mapping and interpretation may be extremely valuable and helpful when applied to practical and theoretical map reading and interpretation.

The oil or mining company staff geologist should attempt to apply the principles presented here to his own particular problems and projects.

Senior exploration personnel should become acquainted with photogeologic mapping and, even more important, with the *limitations* and *problems* of photogeology as well as with the advantages and economy which photogeologic studies can bring to an exploration program or to a regional research project.

The photographs and maps compiled and discussed in Part III are designed to illustrate principles of identification and interpretation. The location of the areas shown and the details of stratigraphy and history are not important in most cases. The erosional characteristics of a shale belt are equally important to the photogeologist in Italy or Pakistan as they are to the photogeologist in Wyoming or Alabama or anywhere else.

For the benefit of those advanced students or professional geologists who wish to obtain copies of the original photographs used, or who wish to assemble complete geologic data on particular areas shown, the Appendix has been prepared. It includes the exact or approximate geographic locations and reference to the sources of most of the maps and photographs.

Unless specifically stated otherwise, in all of the texts which accompany the maps, mosaics, and stereoscopic photo illustrations, compass directions are given with respect to figure orientation and not with reference to true north. For all maps, *north* is therefore toward the top of the page. For all stereoscopic pairs, *north* is toward the top of the page. For all stereo triplets, *north* is toward the top of the figure when it is oriented to permit the reading of the figure title.

Since the orientation of a slope or a feature may frequently influence photograph tone, vegetation, soils, and erosional characteristics, true north direction is indicated on most of the figures by an arrow.

Figure 8-1. *Example: General or Elementary Geomorphology.* Stereogram of an area of sand dunes. (*Courtesy of U.S. Dept. of Agriculture, Soil Conservation Service.*)

EXAMPLE: GENERAL OR ELEMENTARY GEOMORPHOLOGY

This is an area of sand dunes. Most obvious are the small barchans in the center of the area. Their horseshoe outlines and steep southeast slopes indicate prevailing northwest winds (about N 30° W).

In the north, numerous barchans combine to form transverse dunes. Slope asymmetry exists here also.

In the south, the dark areas indicate more moisture and vegetation. The hairpin dunes are caused by northwest winds and the anchoring or hindering effect of vegetation. Here only the higher parts of the dunes advance. Southeast slopes are steeper than the northwest slopes.

The dark northeast-trending sand-free area appears to be a remnant of a shallow undrained intermontane lake (possibly in a bolson).

The entire area appears to slope to the west. At the time the photographs were made, the optical axis of the camera was appreciably tilted.

105

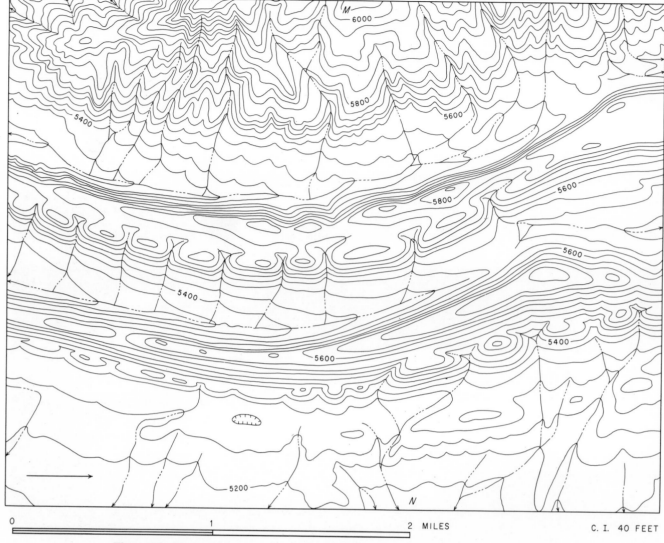

Figure 8-2. Topographic map of an area of dipping strata and underlying crystalline rocks.

Figure 8-3. Geologic map of an area of dipping strata and underlying crystalline rocks. IS, Idaho Springs series; PF, Fountain formation; PI, Ingleside formation; PS, Satanka shale; PLY, Lyons sandstone; ᖇLK, Lykins formation; JE, Jelm-Entrada formations; JM, Morrison formation; KD, Dakota group; KB, Benton group; KN, Niobrara group; KP, Pierre formation; ss, sandstones; sh, shales; slt, siltstones; ls, limestones. (*By permission from C. Maynard Boos, Margaret Fuller Boos, and the Carter Oil Company.*)

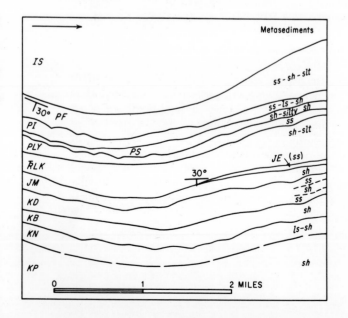

EXAMPLE: SUPPLEMENTAL GEOMORPHOLOGY

This area offers an excellent opportunity to use geomorphic criteria to obtain geologic information. North of stream *a* the topography is relatively homogeneous. As shown in Figure 8-3, this northern area is underlain by metasedimentary rock.

South of stream *a* the topography consists of a series of strike ridges and strike (subsequent) valleys, lowlands, and saddles. Dip is to the south.

Differential erosion of the exposed strata is the major key to bedrock identification. Belts *A*, *C*, *E*, *G*, *I*, and *K* are underlain by nonresistant beds, which may be assumed to be shaly or silty (see Figure 8-3).

The resistant rocks stand as ridges, to form belts *B*, *D*, *F*, and *H* and the several lower spines in area *J*. Coarse-grained clastics and, in relatively arid areas, carbonate rock, are more resistant to erosion and weathering than are shales and siltstones (see Figure 8-3).

Several excellent dip slopes occur in this area, indicating that in each case the resistant dip-slope stratum is directly overlain by extremely nonresistant, easily stripped materials.

At points 1 and 2, careful study will reveal small faults trending obliquely to strike.

EXERCISES

1. Note the white bands and lines in area *L*. What might they be? What might be their general composition?

2. The geologic map shows regional dip to be about 30°. Estimate apparent dip at several places. Determine an approximate average vertical exaggeration for the stereogram.

3. Using Figure 8-3 as a guide, draw stratigraphic contacts on the photographs.

4. Draw a topographic profile along line *MN* on Figure 8-2.

5. Transfer line *MN* to one of the photographs and, using the observed vertically exaggerated stereo model for topographic control, add a geologic cross section to the profile.

6. Transfer all geologic data from the photographs to Figure 8-2.

Figure 8-4. *Example: Supplemental Geomorphology.* Stereogram of a homocline of south-dipping sedimentary rocks underlain by pre-Cambrian metasedimentary rocks. (*Courtesy of U.S. Dept. of Agriculture, Commodity Stabilization Service.*)

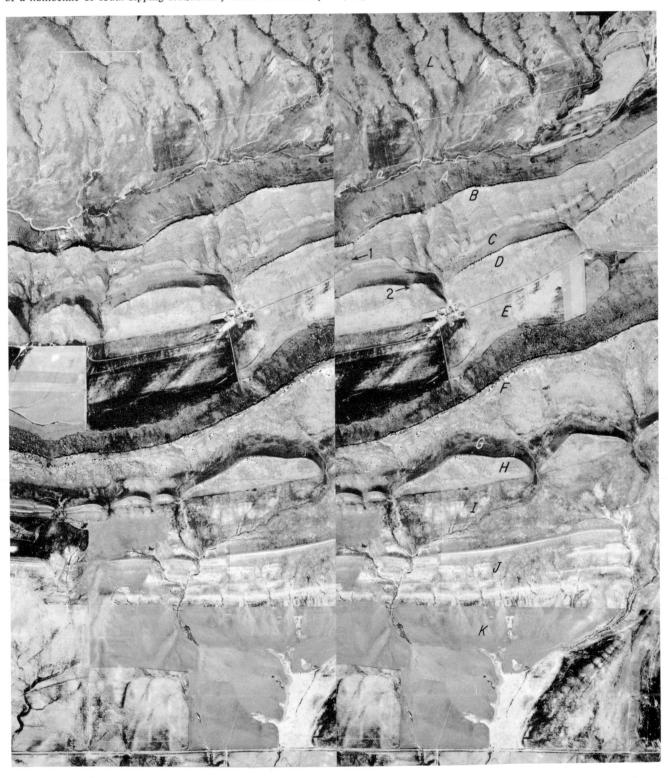

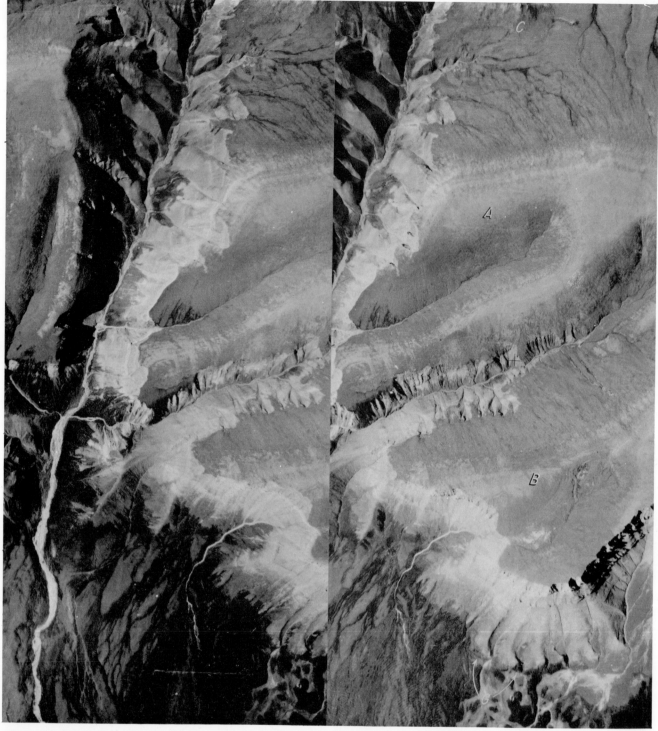

Figure 8-5. *Example: Complemental Geomorphology.* Stereogram of a mountain front, showing differential erosion of bedrock and major stream rejuvenation. (*Courtesy of Royal Canadian Air Force.*)

EXAMPLE: COMPLEMENTAL GEOMORPHOLOGY

This is an area which is in a cycle of erosional rejuvenation. In the mountains are large areas of mature, differentially eroded uplands [i.e., areas *A, B,* and *C* (Figure 8-5) and areas *D, E,* and *F* (Figure 8-6)]. Along the mountain front the gentle and moderate slopes and stream gradients are being destroyed by the headward erosion of canyons and the retreat of steep scarps and cliffs.

At points *G* (Figure 8-5) there is a series of small but obvious knicks (a discontinuous low topographic scarp) at the base of the mountain front. This strongly suggests an unconsumed fault scarp or scarplet, such as occur along the eastern base of the Sierra Nevada Range in the United States. This feature can also be seen in the left middleground of Figure 8-6.

A structural interpretation may be advanced, based on these geomorphic observations. The entire mountain mass may have been subjected to relatively recent block faulting. As viewed in Figure 8-6, and diagrammatically shown in Figure 8-7, the western block could have dropped down while the eastern area was considerably raised. The almost entirely preserved old erosional surface of the mountain mass suggests that this movement occurred in recent time.

Figure 8-6. Oblique photograph of mountain front shown in Figure 8-5. (*Courtesy of Royal Canadian Air Force.*)

Figure 8-7. Sketch of geomorphic relations critical to *complemental geomorphic* interpretation of area shown in Figures 8-5 and 8-6. *a*, adjusted stream gradient; *r*, rejuvenated stream gradient; *p*, projected stream gradient (extending preserved part of adjusted gradient); *s*, scarp; *k*, knick or scarplet at base of main scarp; *deot*, differentially eroded old topography.

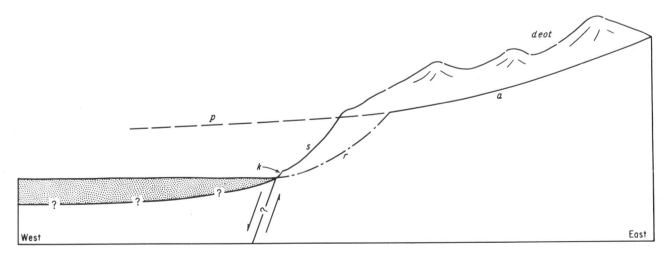

0   1   2   3 MILES   C.I. 50 FEET

• OIL WELL   + SECTION CORNER

Figure 8-8. Topographic map of the area shown in Figure 8-9. This map was made in 1922. Its original scale is 1 inch to 3 miles. Note oil-well distribution.

EXAMPLE: INDEPENDENT GEOMORPHOLOGY

Most of this area can be described as youthfully dissected moraine-covered plains. The river which crosses the southwest corner of the area is in early maturity; its flood plain is relatively narrow. It has cut through the glacial material and deep into nearly horizontal thin-bedded sediments. Study Figure 8-9. The large tributary system in the central and northern parts of the area has also cut into bedrock. Note the beginning of badlands in area *A*. The irregular north-trending mass along belt *B* is a broken slump block which has slid down into the stream valley from the west valley wall.

Across the valley, at point *C*, the contact between the intricately fluted dark morainal material and the medium- to light-toned bedrock is clearly expressed.

Typical undulating, hummocky, poorly drained ground moraine topography is noted in area *D*. Note several dried lakes in this area.

At several places, the major tributary appears to flow "uphill" toward the west. This impression is produced by tilt in the photographs. Dip is extremely low. Tilt renders dip determination impossible, unless instrumentation is used. A photogeologic study of this area, therefore, must concentrate on geomorphic factors.

The course of major tributary *E* is anomalous. Were there no drilling in the area, the photogeologist would call attention to this feature and suggest further investigation, perhaps a seismic or slim-hole survey or the drilling of an exploratory test well. Point *F*, west of the middle of the south-flowing eastern stream segment and opposite the middle of the swing at the south end, would be a logical location for such a well. In most cases, however, the drilling of geomorphic anomalies, without other evidence or investigation, is unwise and at best a poor gamble.

A comparison of the erosional pattern and the area of oil production (see Figure 8-8) suggests a cause-and-effect

relation between structure and erosional development. However, such a relation may or may not exist.

Consider the following factors which quite possibly *could* have contributed to the positioning of the tributary's course.

1. Preglacial topography—a function of structure, lithology and erosional history.

2. Glacial ice erosion—scour by ice.

3. Glacial water erosion and deposition—outwash deposits, melt-water stream erosion, damming by ice and moraine, and the like.

4. Ground or recessional moraine deposition—thickness and composition variations in morainal debris, caused by such nonbedrock factors as rate of melting, load variations, differences in thickness of stagnant ice, and runoff load transportation and sorting.

5. The life history of the defining tributary. Did it form (*a*) as a consequent stream on a surface of morainal material, (*b*) as a result of lake drainage or stream capture, or (*c*) as a bedrock-cutting short tributary to the master river, which then extended itself headward along some bedrock-controlled subsequent course?

In summary, only the following can be said, with assurance, about this feature.

1. It is an anomalous stream.

2. It coincides, essentially, with the trend of oil production, as defined by numerous wells.

3. The general area of production would have been studied, had this feature been noted during a photogeologic study of the area prior to drilling.

EXERCISE

Using as control the three section corners shown on Figure 8-8, transfer the well locations to the photographs. Outline the area of known production on the photographs.

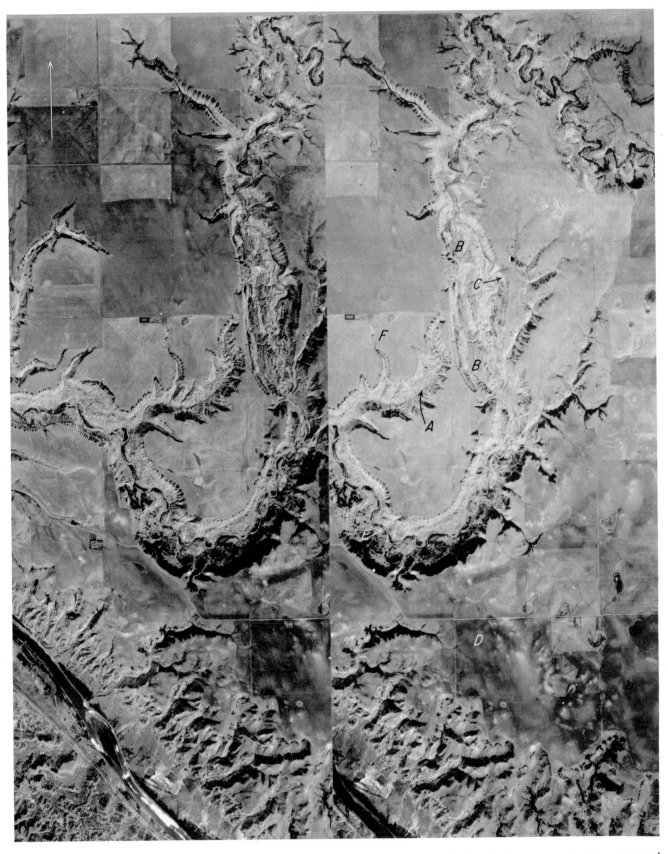

Figure 8-9. *Example: Independent Geomorphology.* Stereogram of a drainage anomaly in a glaciated plains area. (*Reproduced* *by courtesy of the Technical Division of the Department of Lands and Forests, Edmonton, Alberta.*)

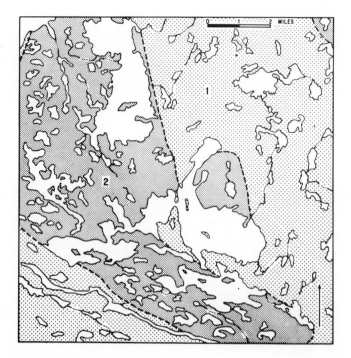

Figure 8-10. Geologic map of an area of metasedimentary rocks and granite intrusives. Area shown in Figure 8-11 is included in map area. 1, schist derived from greywacke, slate, and other sediments; 2, granite, granodiorite, and allied rocks.

EXAMPLE: AREA OF ROUTINE OR EASY PHOTOGEOLOGIC MAPPING

This is an area of pre-Cambrian rocks, located in the northern part of the Canadian Shield. Continental ice sheets have overridden the area and have removed most of the overburden and weathered bedrock. The scale of the geologic map is small. The area covered by the photographs lies in the central part of the map area.

Without viewing the photographs stereoscopically, it is possible to outline two general rock types on the basis of photograph tone alone. The darker-gray area (area *A*), in the northeast, is part of rock type 1 (metamorphic) shown on the map. The light-toned rocks (area *B*), in the southwest, are of type 2 (granitic).

When the photographs are studied stereoscopically, the granitic rocks appear more resistant than the metamorphic rocks. The intrusive masses stand as higher, more irregular hills, generally somewhat above the lower, more modified topography formed in the metamorphic rock areas.

Note the gray area *C*, within the area shown on the map as entirely underlain by granitic rocks. This is a large inclusion of metamorphic rocks, separated from the main metamorphic area to the northeast.

There are several sets of straight and arcuate lines and bands in this area. Some, such as feature *D*, appear as narrow dark lines. Others, such as feature *E*, are discontinuous white lines. Some have positive topographic expressions (washboard), as at area *F*. Others are less resistant than the surrounding rock and appear as linear trenchlike depressions (feature *G*).

Some of these features are faults and fractures. Some are dikes. Some are alternating resistant and nonresistant beds in the metamorphic series.

The most obvious are the discontinuous, thin, linear and irregular granitic intrusions in the metasediments. The sharp tonal contrast leaves little doubt as to the identification and nature of these white materials surrounded by dark-gray bedrock. Feature *E* is one of these dikes. They are possibly pegmatitic.

Note that dike *H* and depression *G* lie along a northeasterly projection of the dark, soil- and vegetation-covered, wider zone *I* in the granite area. Zone *I* could be one of two things. It could be a fault zone, along which brecciation has reduced rock resistance, permitting the removal of material and the formation of a relatively wide trench or ditch. It could also be a basic dike. Basaltic dikes which intrude acidic rock may produce a similar topographic relation. Feature *J*, south of and *en echelon* to zone *I*, could also have the same two possible explanations.

The washboard topography of area *F* is probably caused by the differential erosion of metasediments of different relative resistances to weathering and erosion.

Note the linear east side of lake *K*. This is probably fault-controlled. This probable fault line can be extended in a northwesterly direction, as a discontinuous, and in places *en echelon*, series of lines and zones. It is sharply defined at point *L* by vegetation and tonal contrasts. It can be seen at point *M* as the linear side of a lake, and at point *N* it appears as a linear swamp- or muskeg-filled depression. At points *O* it appears to be occupied by intruded granitic materials.

The north-facing scarp *P* probably overlooks a scoured fault zone. The linear lowland *Q* also appears to lie along a fault zone. Feature *Q* is an extension of feature *J*. In this area, therefore, it is considered that most of the dark lines and bands, in the granite mass, are more probably fault lines and zones, and less probably basic dikes.

Within both the granitic and metamorphic outcrop areas are numerous large and small faults and fractures and numerous other acidic dikes.

EXERCISES

1. In red, trace all fault and fracture lines.
2. In blue, trace all acidic dikes and other intrusive bodies.
3. In purple, trace the contacts between areas *A* and *B*, and between areas *B* and *C*.

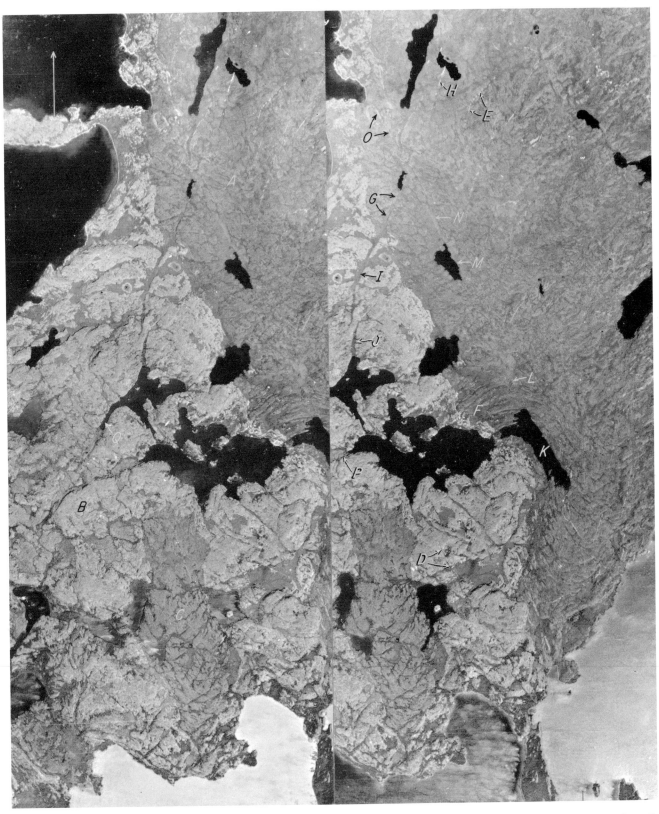

Figure 8-11. *Example: Area of routine or easy photogeologic mapping.* Stereogram of an area of intruded metamorphosed rocks. Dark-gray areas are metamorphosed sediments. Light areas are granitic intrusive rocks. (*Courtesy Royal Canadian Air Force.*)

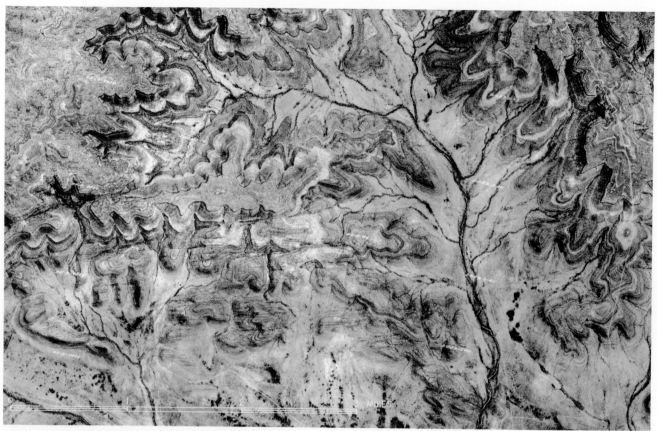

Figure 8-12. Mosaic of an area of jointed and faulted low-dipping sediments in a semiarid region. Figure 8-13 covers part of the southwest of the mosaic area. (*By permission from Edgar Tobin Aerial Surveys.*)

EXAMPLE: AREA OF MODERATELY DIFFICULT PHOTOGEOLOGIC MAPPING

A series of marine limestones, marls, and shales is reported to crop out in this area. The climate is semiarid. Carbonate rocks would be expected to be more resistant than shaly strata in this area.

Throughout most of the mosaic area (Figure 8-12), the outstanding element is the extremely irregular pattern of light and dark outcrop bands, characteristic of the advanced dissection of flat-lying strata. The larger drainage systems form a dendritic pattern.

In the southwestern part of the mosaic area, however, a strong easterly-trending set of joints is superimposed on the other pattern. The stereogram (Figure 8-13) shows the details in this part of the area.

In the jointed area, numerous tributary streams are adjusted to subsequent courses along lines of structural weakness. Elsewhere the drainage appears to be insequent.

Lattman and Olive (1955) report that in this region there is a positive correlation between general dip direction and the solution widening of selected joint sets. Here the obvious joint set has an easterly trend. Though not apparent, there is also a regional northward-trending joint set in this area. Some of the larger southward-oriented stream segments shown on the mosaic may be adjusted along this second set of joints.

According to Lattman and Olive, underground water migrates along regional dip and actively dissolves bedrock along joints which have a similar orientation. Joints which cross regional dip would not offer similar opportunity to solution. In this area, therefore, gentle easterly or westerly dip would be suspected, on the basis of joint solution only.

A joint is rarely so well defined that it can actually be seen on a medium- or small-scale photograph. The lines and zones seen on the mosaic and stereogram are not joints but rather narrow bands of denser vegetation, deeper soils, and possibly concentrations of greater moisture, developed along solution-widened joints (and faults).

The aerial camera was tilted at the time the photographs were made. This is indicated by the strong apparent westward gradient of stream *A* and the gentle westward *apparent* slope of surface *B*, which probably actually either slopes to the east or is nearly horizontal. Regional dip cannot be determined by the stereoscopic study of the limited area shown in Figure 8-13.

In Figure 8-13 some locally steeper dips, probably caused by block faulting, may be noted, as at point *C*. In area *D* the concentration of joints as well as the absence of appreciable relief and traceable bedding afford an impression of nearly vertical east-striking beds.

EXERCISES

1. In orange, trace all joint lines and zones.
2. In red, trace faults, indicating relative displacement where possible.
3. Show local dips and strikes where they can be detected.
4. Indicate by *s* all subsequent streams on the stereogram and on the mosaic.

Figure 8-13. *Example: Area of moderately difficult photogeologic mapping.* A dissected low plateau, underlain by highly jointed and faulted low-dipping strata. (*By permission from Edgar Tobin Aerial Surveys.*)

115

EXAMPLE: AREA OF DIFFICULT PHOTOGEO-LOGIC MAPPING

This is an area of sparse outcrop. Much of the bedrock is covered by variable thickness of glacial debris. The bedrock is further obscured by a widespread forest cover.

The structure of the northern highland (area *A*) is apparent. Reliable dips at points *B*, *C*, and *D* define a gentle northwest-plunging syncline.

The area south of the upland is characterized by: (1) dense tree growth, (2) east-trending topographic, vegetative, and tonal alignments, and (3) topographic asymmetries.

If it be assumed that, for the most part, tree height is uniform, the *topography* of the tree-top slopes may be used to interpret structure and to obtain some idea of variations in lithology in this area.

The east-trending lines must first be studied and identified. At point *E* such a line is defined by trees. At point *F* one is defined by both trees and a linear shallow stream valley. At point *G* a deep gash and an adjacent sharp ridge are aligned along the same general trend.

These are glacial lineations, caused principally by gouging and grinding along local lines of weakness and by uneven, remolded glacial ground deposits of variable composition and thickness. Insufficient area is shown here to permit the

Figure 8-14. *Example: Area of difficult photogeologic mapping.* A stereogram of gently folded sedimentary strata in a forested glaciated area. (*Courtesy of Royal Canadian Air Force.*)

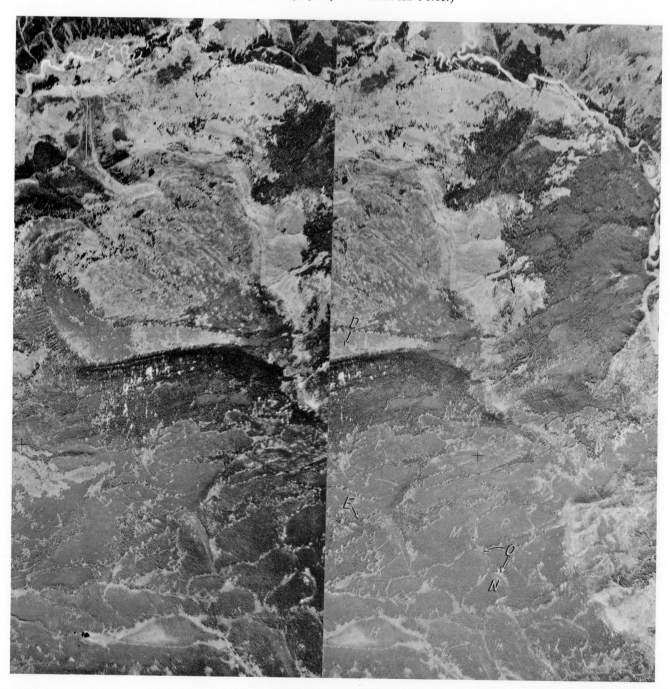

conclusive determination of the direction of ice movement (eastward or westward).

Feature H is a filled undrained glacial depression, probably originally a postglacial lake. Note the contrast in tone and height between the vegetation in this depression and the forest to the south, east, and north. The local vegetation here suggests that the depression is swampy or filled with muskeg (this area is in west-central Canada). The thickness of glacial materials is probably greater at H and to the southwest than it is in the area immediately to the east and northeast.

Features I and J are well-defined asymmetric ridges. The gentle west slopes and the steep east scarps may be interpreted as resequent and obsequent slopes along a local ridge upheld by differentially eroded resistant west-dipping strata. The white, treeless line at point K is probably a sandstone or limestone outcrop or a barren slope of thin soil or mantle immediately underlain by a resistant bed.

Asymmetric ridge L may be a southward continuation of the stratigraphic units present at features I and J. Westerly dip is also suggested here.

Slopes M and N are strongly suggestive of dip slopes on a stratum stratigraphically below a shaly section which underlies the ridge-formers of features I, J, and L. The sharp linear depression of feature O is probably caused by a thin shale which lies below the dip-slope unit of slopes M and N. This shale is in turn underlain by another resistant bed, as suggested by the apparent dip slope at point P.

North of point P, dip appears to be toward the northwest.

At points M and P dip is to the west. At point N dip is to the southwest. A westward-plunging anticlinal nose is therefore defined in this area which is virtually devoid of traceable outcrops, obscured by forest growth, and further confused by the pronounced easterly-trending glacial lineations.

EXERCISES

1. In solid green lines, trace all possible exposed beds around the synclinal upland A.

2. In dashed green lines, trace the several stratigraphic marker or key beds in the southern area.

3. There is a bench at point Q. Can an approximate correlation be made between the beds at this point and one or more of those in the tree-covered area to the south and southwest?

4. Indicate all possible dips and strikes within the stereoscopic area, estimate apparent dip magnitudes, and, using an assumed vertical exaggeration of 2.75, reduce the apparent dip values to true values.

5. Add fold axes to the annotated photograph.

6. Draw a west-east exaggerated topographic profile across the stereogram, passing through letter M.

7. Add a geologic cross section to the profile.

8. Using the assumed vertical exaggeration, reduce the profile and cross section to true scale.

9. Draw a similar exaggerated profile and cross section north-south across the entire stereogram, through point I.

10. Reduce this profile and cross section to true scale.

11. Draw a block diagram of the stereogram area, as viewed from the west.

General or Elementary
Geomorphology

INTRODUCTION

In most of the following illustrations, one or more geologic features can be identified by their forms or shapes and by their locations with respect to nearby features. Two features which might at first appear to be exceptions to the above general statement are included.

The first *apparent* exception is shown in Figure 9-8. It is a sinuous flat-topped ridge consisting of a lava flow which originally flowed down a stream valley. Erosion has removed the higher areas which surrounded the valley. The lava is so resistant that with continued erosion of the surrounding less resistant rock an inversion of the topography has occurred (obsequent topography). The former valley-floor lava fill is, nevertheless, so well preserved that little imagination is required to mentally reconstruct the topography which once existed and to visualize the filling of the valley by a tongue of basic molten material.

The second *apparent* exception is shown in Figure 9-12. This figure is a stereo triplet of an area of irregular hills, ridges, and horizontal ledges in a semiarid area. At first it might appear that several angular unconformities have been uncovered by extensive, prolonged erosion. On more careful examination, however, the horizontal benches are seen to be former lake shorelines (Pleistocene Lake Bonneville).

In much the same way, past events are recorded in Figure 9-17. The mountains in this area have been subjected to alpine glaciation, as well as to erosion by running water. The ice has disappeared, leaving such erosional evidence as tarns and abandoned troughs. Also, deposits of glacial origin (moraines) can be identified.

A single arêtelike divide is not conclusive proof of previous glaciation. A small isolated terminal moraine may so resemble a landslide, an earth flow, or a rock glacier that positive identification is impossible; but when numerous different features occur in the same small area and *fit* together into a coherent and well-integrated whole, the correct identification of each is more assured, since it is backed up or reinforced by the others.

The same is true of unglaciated mountain valleys. Many stream-cut valleys have segments which resemble glacial troughs. In such cases, rounded spurs, integrated drainage and accordant stream junctions, and an absence of other features normally associated with ice erosion permit the correct interpretation of the origin of the valley, *despite* its troughlike cross section.

In areas where *general geomorphology* can be applied, therefore, the important principle is that the whole, and not just a small part, must be considered simultaneously. The whole, of course, consists of many small parts.

Accumulations of unconsolidated sediments frequently have easily recognizable forms or shapes. The most obvious are alluvial fans, deltas, talus cones, sand dunes, and some morainal deposits.

Gravel-capped pediment slopes may be misidentified as alluvial aprons of much greater thickness. When pediments are dissected, the bedrock exposed beneath the capping gravel, and *not* the upper surface form, provides the key to identification.

Some consolidated rock accumulations have consistent and easily recognized shapes. Volcanic features such as calderas, cinder cones, and lava flows are included in this group. Some caldera-like craters are not of volcanic origin, however. In eastern Canada the Chubb Crater, believed to be a meteor crater, is an example. The geographic location of such a feature, as well as its form, must be considered. Is it near other volcanic features, or is it isolated?

While studying the following stereograms the student will note that in some cases features can be identified on the basis of their general geomorphic form alone. In others, the use of other criteria not strictly in this classification, combined with shape, size, and location, permit reliable identification.

Many features and relations similar to those in this chapter will occur in some of the illustrations used in succeeding chapters. This will be true despite the fact that the photographs included in the succeeding chapters were selected to show other types of areas, features, and relations and to demonstrate other identification problems and interpretation approaches.

The opposite situation also exists. Several of the illustrations included in this chapter include features whose identification requires careful study of factors other than form.

Figure 9-1. Stereogram of an alluvial fan at the base of a high fault scarp in an arid area. Note the clearly defined fault line (feature *A*), the intricate dissection of the mountains, and the high area of alluvium (area *B*). (*By permission from Fairchild Aerial Surveys, Inc.*)

Figure 9-2. Stereogram of an alluvial fan in a semiarctic area. Note the polygons in areas *A* and *B*. Their distribution and shape are controlled by bar and swale undulations. (*Courtesy of Royal Canadian Air Force.*)

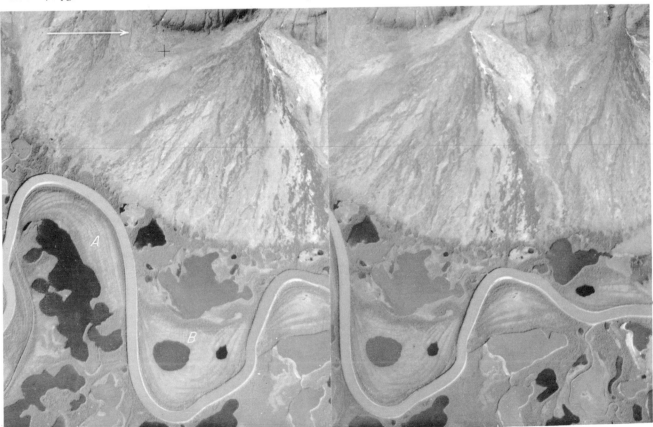

Figure 9-3. Stereo triplet of cinder cones and lava flows, in an arid area of gently dipping strata. Four-lens photographs. (*Courtesy of U.S. Dept. of Agriculture, Soil Conservation Service.*)

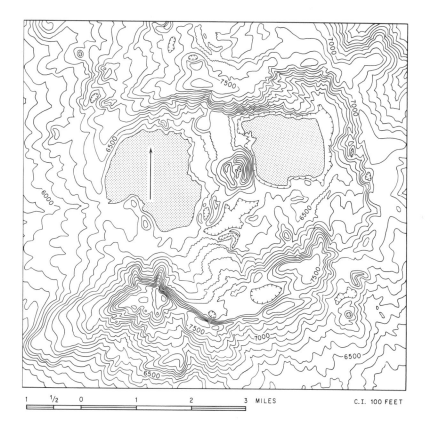

Figure 9-4. Topographic map of a caldera and postexplosion volcanic features. This map includes the areas shown in Figures 9-5 and 9-6.

| 1 | ½ | 0 | 1 | 2 | 3 | MILES |

C.I. 100 FEET

VOLCANIC FEATURES: CINDER CONES AND LAVA FLOWS

Relatively recent volcanic features are usually easy to identify, principally because of their distinctive forms.

This series of three stereo triplets (Figures 9-3, 9-5, and 9-6) is representative of such volcanic forms. Figure 9-3 shows an area located in an arid climatic zone. Figures 9-5 and 9-6 show volcanic features in a more humid forested area.

In Figure 9-3, two features are obvious: the cinder cone (feature A) and the lava flow (feature B). The breached oval hill (feature C), of which about half can be viewed stereoscopically, is somewhat more difficult to identify. The contrast between the whitish and light-gray rocks (area D) and the darker-gray area (area E) also requires explanation.

Area E is irregular and in places hummocky. It has undergone considerable erosion, as evidenced by several extensive alluviated areas (such as features F). At numerous points dark outcrops occur within area E. At points G, rocks of area E are seen to lie on those of area D. The dark lava (area B) lies on and adjacent to outcrops of area E.

Area E consists primarily of older volcanic materials. Area D is not volcanic. It consists of gently north- and northwest-dipping sedimentary rocks, probably limestones and some interbedded shales.

Note the ropy top surface of the lava flow (area B). The lava material apparently solidified first along the edges (i.e., along zones H and I), permitting the continuing outpouring to be funneled on between leveelike ridges. At several points the "levees" were breached, with local lateral outflows forming small, short-lived distributaries (i.e., features J and K).

Feature C is an older breached volcanic cone. The linearity of the eroded part suggests that this cone lies along a fault zone, probably owes its existence to such a zone of weakness which permitted the molten material to rise here, and then suffered slight dislocation after formation as a result of minor fault rejuvenation. Feature C is probably of the earlier volcanic stage which produced the older volcanic materials distributed throughout area E.

Figure 9-5 shows an area which lies within and near the north side of the large caldera shown in Figure 9-4. Figures 9-5 and 9-6 have the same orientation as Figure 9-4. In the following discussion, directions will be given with reference to true north and not "page" north.

Feature A is a cinder cone (post eruption) which has emitted a small lava flow (feature B) and other extrusives (i.e., area C). Feature D is another lava flow, derived from north (to the right) of the area shown. This flow is younger than flows B and C. It is more perfectly preserved and has far less tree cover than the older surfaces.

Figure 9-6 shows an area within and at the south side of the caldera. The high scarps at points A and B are segments of the inner walls of the caldera. Area C is a recent lava flow. Its source area or vent was at point D. The highly fractured circular mound at this point appears to be the solidified core which, during the late stage of extrusion, was lifted bodily by the extreme pressures from beneath. Several spatter cones (features E) occur on the surface of lava flow C.

Note that in area F this flow has partially filled a circular depression. The depression may have been a small caldera, produced by the eruption of one of several small cones within the older, large caldera.

In area G the several bands of contrasting tone, surface texture, and vegetation growth suggest either a series of different flows from vent D, or more probably, the relatively uninterrupted extrusion of several types of material from this source.

121

Figure 9-5. Stereo triplet of a breached cinder cone and lava flows. This area is included in Figure 9-4. Photographs and map have some orientation. (*Courtesy of U.S. Dept. of Agriculture, Forest Service.*)

Figure 9-6. Stereo triplet of a lava flow and source area, within caldera. This area is included in Figure 9-4. Photographs and map have some orientation. (*Courtesy of U.S. Dept. of Agriculture, Forest Service.*)

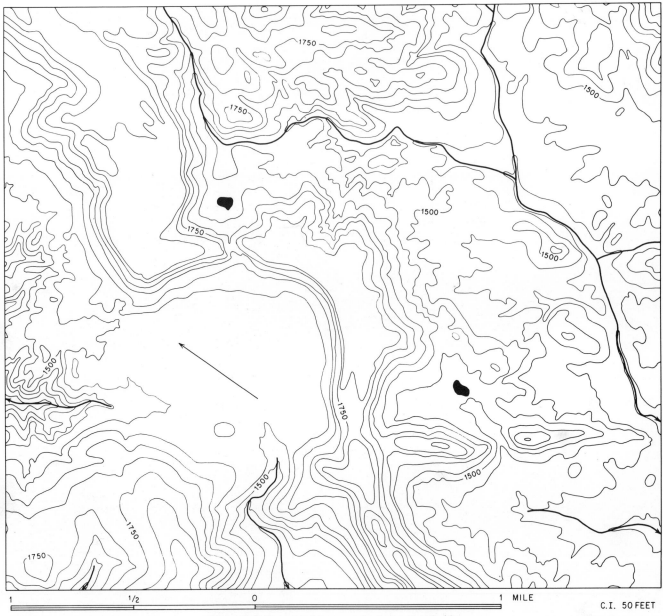

Figure 9-7. Topographic map of a lava-capped ridge.

OBSEQUENT TOPOGRAPHY: LAVA-CAPPED RIDGE

The most obvious feature in this area is the flat, dark-gray upland surface (surfaces *A* and *B*). This surface is formed on an easily outlined rock unit, reported to be a Miocene lava flow. Lighter-gray benches (features *C*, *D*, and *E*) are probably formed on older flows.

The serpentine outline of the lavas suggests that their present distribution closely approximates their original distribution, and that when laid down, they followed the sinuous lowland of a stream valley.

The bedrock beneath the lavas is not the same throughout the entire area. This is especially evident in the south, where areas *F* contrast with areas *G*. The flat-floored lowland *H* is mantled by alluvial debris.

In areas *F* the soils are dark, and the slopes are gentle and uniform. In areas *G* the soils (and probably the underlying bedrock) are lighter, and in general the slopes are steeper. The rocks in areas *G* are apparently less resistant than those in areas *F*. (How does the resistance of the lava capping contribute to this conclusion?)

Lava surface *B* is higher than surface *A*, though the 50-foot contours of Figure 9-7 do not indicate an offset. Note the several parallel depressions in surface *B*, accentuated by lines of trees. These are probably minor fault lines. Line *IJ* is probably a fault trace, post-lava-flow movement having been up on the south and down on the north.

Fault *IJ* may be an old major fault, since it separates the dark rocks of areas *F* from the lighter and somewhat less resistant rocks of areas *G*. The displacement of the lavas, if an interpretation of post-lava-flow faulting is correct, would represent a fairly recent rejuvenation of relatively minor magnitude along the older, major fault zone. Note that the mine at point *K* and the pit at point *L* are located along fault *IJ*.

This area is in the Sierra Nevada Mountains. What economic minerals might be obtained from this area? What materials might underlie the central strip of the capping lavas (i.e., the lavas at letters *A* and *B*)?

124

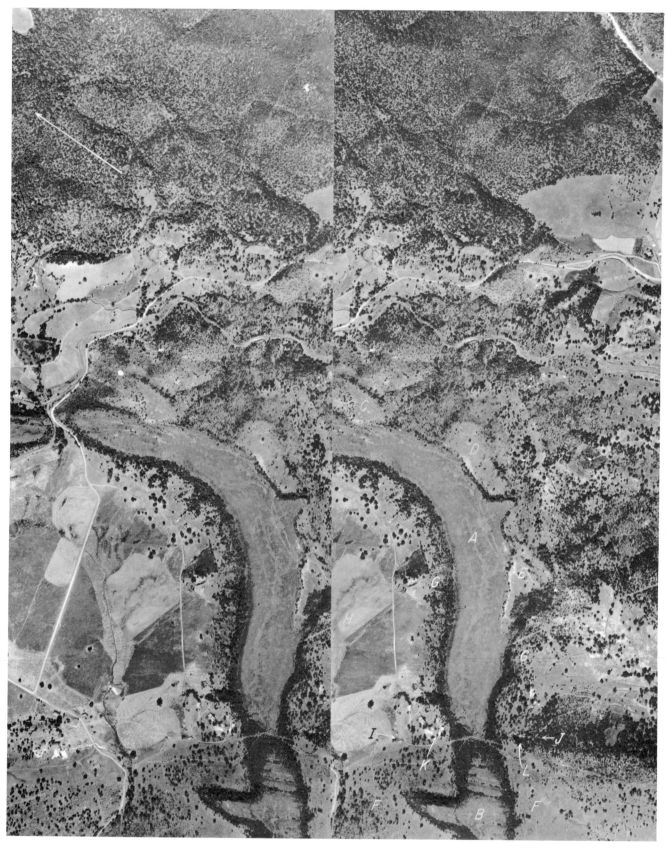

Figure 9-8. Stereogram of a lava-capped ridge. Topography is reversed; former valley-filling lava flow now stands as a sinuous flat-topped ridge. (*By permission from Fairchild Aerial Surveys, Inc.*)

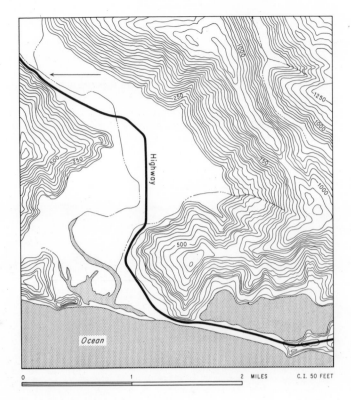

Figure 9-9. Topographic map of a submature shoreline of submergence.

SUBMATURE SHORELINE OF SUBMERGENCE

The underlying bedrock in this area is reported to consist of metamorphosed sediments.

The general region has been peneplaned, uplifted, dissected, and, finally, partially submerged. The submergence of the irregular topography that had been produced by extensive erosion and dissection of the area created a shoreline consisting of numerous embayments and promontories similar to that shown in Figure 9-10A, a generalized block diagram of such a region prior to wave attack and shoreline modification.

Figure 9-10. Initial (A) and submature (C) stages in the erosion of an irregular shoreline of submergence. (*Diagrams by Calvin F. Miller.*)

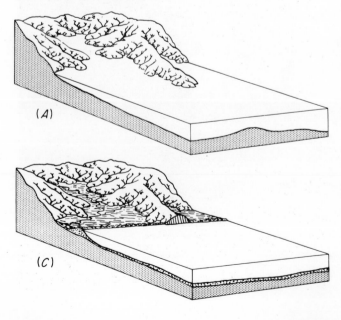

The seaward ends of the promontories were attacked by waves and currents and eventually eroded backward to their present positions. During this process the detrital material derived from this erosion accumulated across the embayments to form continuous bay-mouth bars. The present topography, shown on the photographs and on the topographic map and depicted in Figure 9-10C, consists of the old topography (area A), a truncated spur (feature B), a sealed-off embayment (area C), and a sealed-off and filled embayment (feature D).

With the exception of the sea cliff and probable road cuts, no outcrops are apparent within the area shown on the photographs. Abundant vegetation and rounded slopes suggest a relatively well-developed soil and mantle cover over the entire area.

Attention is called to the following relations and features:

1. The sharp contrast between the vegetation on the seaward (area E) and the landward slopes (area F).

2. The flat area in the northwest corner of the stereogram (area G).

3. The linearity of feature H, which consists of a north-facing escarpment and, to the east, a stream valley.

4. The numerous white lines (features I) which cross the bay-mouth bar (feature J). These are small depressions which somewhat resemble beheaded or abandoned gullies or stream valleys.

EXERCISES

1. Construct a block diagram showing the youthful stage (Figure 9-10B), which would be intermediate between the two stages shown in Figure 9-10.

2. The seaward shoreline of the bay-mouth bar (feature J) is relatively linear. The bayward (north) shoreline is interrupted by numerous small promontories, each located at the end of one of the white lines previously mentioned (features I). Explain the white features and their corresponding inland shoreline irregu-

larities and postulate a connection between these features and the probable chemical composition of the lagoon (area *C*) immediately to the north.

3. In the flat area (area *G*) in the northwest corner of the photographs a concentration of trees forms a large number 3 (feature *K*). What is the nature of area *G*, and what is indicated by the configuration of feature *K*?

4. If prevailing onshore winds are assumed and the vegetation observed throughout the area is natural, what is the probable explanation of the contrast between seaward (area *E*) and landward (area *F*) tree growth?

5. Feature *H* may be the topographic expression of bedrock control. What structural feature or features could produce the observed topography along this line?

6. What would be a possible lithologic or stratigraphic explanation of feature *H*?

7. Map scale is indicated by a scale bar. What is the approximate scale of the photographs?

8. After the photographs were taken, a highway was constructed along the shoreline at the foot of the sea cliff (see Figure 9-9). What engineering problems may have been encountered in the construction of this highway?

Figure 9-11. Stereogram of a submature shoreline of submergence. (*By permission from Fairchild Aerial Surveys, Inc.*)

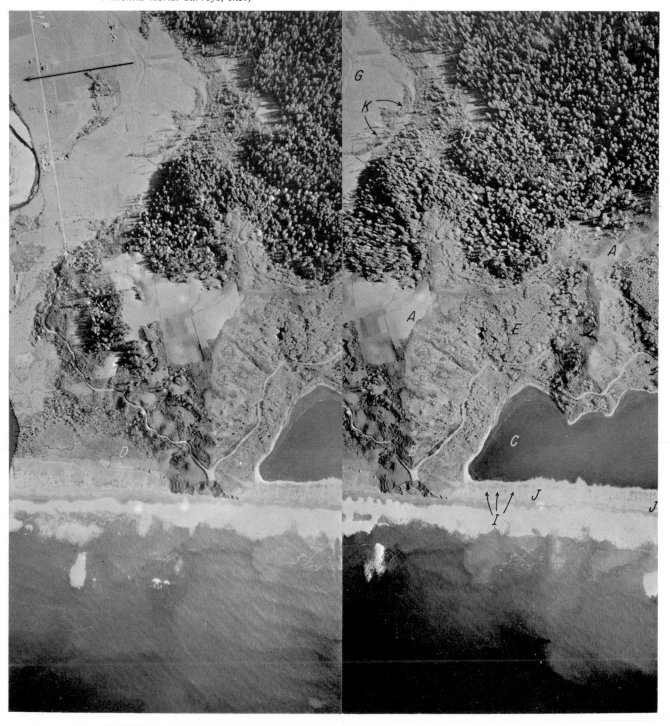

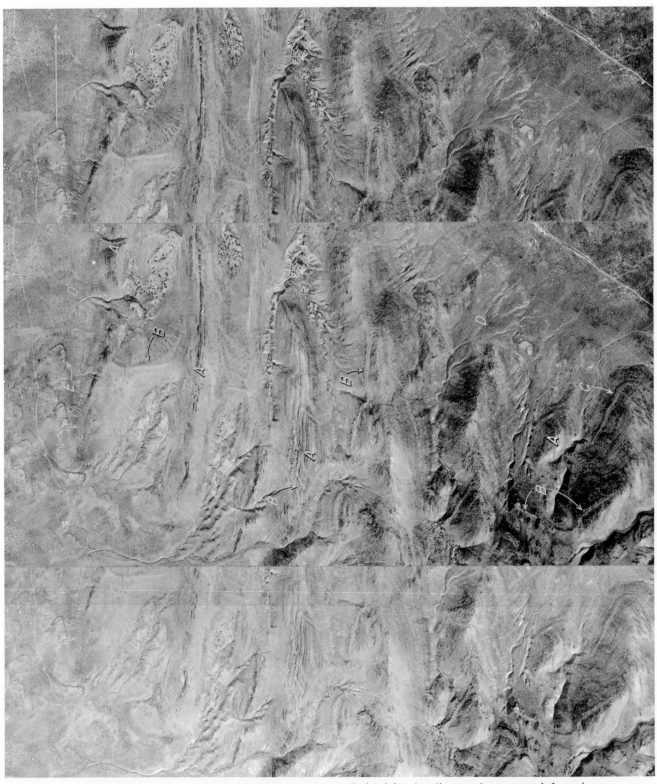

Figure 9-12. Stereo triplet of complex structure, glacial lake shorelines, and recent sand dunes in an arid area. (*Courtesy of U.S. Dept. of Agriculture, Commodity Stabilization Service,*)

ABANDONED PLEISTOCENE LAKE SHORELINES

An interesting geologic history is recorded in this area. Sedimentary strata were subjected to extensive deformation and erosion. The area was then submerged (in a Pleistocene lake) and finally uncovered by the draining or evaporation of the lake waters. Relatively dry winds now cross the area.

Note these specific features (letters correspond with photograph annotations):

A. Outcrops of steeply dipping, jointed, and locally faulted strata (probably carbonates)

B. High abandoned shorelines and bars

C. Low abandoned shoreline

D. Recent alluvial fans

E. Sand dunes (partially stabilized by vegetation)

In areas where the geology is not so clearly shown, features *B* and *C* might be misidentified, possibly as representing parts of one or more unconformities.

128

MUDFLOW

This is a large mudflow in a mountainous area of thick extrusive volcanic rocks.

The mudflow (feature A) poured into the lowland from the mountains (to the east of the area shown). Note the irregular, hummocky surface in the lower parts of the flow and the long downstream tongue of flow material (feature B).

The lake (feature C) was formed by the damming of the main valley. The steep walls and flat floor of the main valley suggest that it was once occupied by an alpine glacier.

Note the resistant jointed volcanic beds (features D), the steep alluvial cones (features E) formed by tributary stream deposits, and the narrow valley (feature F) cut by the stream which drains the lake.

The mudflow resembles a lava flow in general form. Its extremely light photographic tone contrasts sharply with the usually dark tone of lavas (see Figure 9-3, 9-5, 9-6, and 9-8 for comparison).

Figure 9-13. Stereogram of a large mudflow. (*Courtesy of U.S. Dept. of Agriculture, Forest Service.*)

Figure 9-14. Stereogram of solifluction in a subarctic area. (*Courtesy of Royal Canadian Air Force.*)

SOLIFLUCTION

Extensive solifluction occurs in areas of long winters, heavy snowfall, permafrost, and extremely wet spring thaws.

In the area shown, the structure is obvious. It consists of gentle west dip. The oval mesa (feature *A*) is underlain by a sequence of resistant rocks. The surrounding lowland (area *B*) is underlain by older, less resistant strata.

In the broad sloping apron area, outcrops are rare. Vegetation and tonal bands (feature *C*) and local scarps (features *D*) indicate near-surface bedrock traces.

Many of the radiating dark lines (i.e., features *E*) are not well-defined stream valleys. They are lines of concentrated soil creep and flow (solifluction).

The white lines on the east flank of the mesa are outcrops of resistant light-colored beds. At point *F*, where the surface material has flowed downhill, these lines are clearly distorted.

The parallel soil bands (feature *G*) on the mesa upland follow the dip slope to the west. Where they pass over the steeper slope (slope *H*) they resemble extremely fluid basic lava.

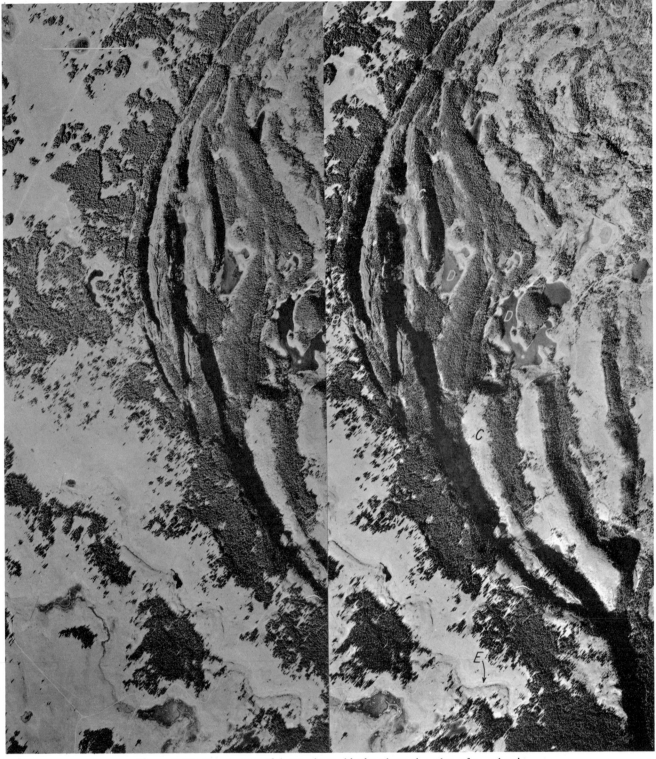

Figure 9-15. Stereogram of large slump blocks along the edge of a volcanic plateau. (*Courtesy of U.S. Dept. of Agriculture, Soil Conservation Service.*)

SLUMP BLOCKS

In the restricted area shown here, no bedrock identification or direct geologic interpretation is possible. Geologic references indicate that in this general area Tertiary volcanic rocks overlie a sequence of shales.

The upland surface (area *A*) is upheld by the nearly horizontal volcanic beds. Basal sapping in the underlying shales has created a zone of instability along the bordering scarp. This has resulted in widespread rupture of the volcanic beds (see trace *B*) and repeated large-scale slumping (area *C*).

Rotation of the several slump blocks, with associated local landslides or rockslides, has created a series of undrained lakes (features *D*).

Note stream course *E*. It is steeply "inclined" toward the right. This impression of slope is caused by tilt of the photographs.

Figure 9-16. Topographic map of a glaciated mountain area. North slopes have been glaciated; south slopes have not been glaciated.

1   ½   0   1   2   3   4 MILES   C.I. 200 FEET

ASYMMETRIC ALPINE GLACIATION

This area permits the study of two different aspects of geology: (1) the topography formed by alpine glacial erosion and deposition and (2) complex structure in a mountainous area.

In the central valley, note the following features (letters correspond with annotations on Figure 9-17):

A. Amphitheater-like valley headwall

B. Lakes

C. Drained lakes, now dry or almost dry

D. Absence of channel of stream which could have cut the valley

E. Notches within valley floor

F. Extremely irregular light-toned area

All these features attest to the former existence of an individual alpine glacier in this valley. Feature *A* is the headward part of the cirque. The lakes (features *B* and *C*) are tarns. The broad valley floor was produced by ice scour which destroyed the original V-shaped stream-cut valley profile. Postglacial drainage establishment and erosion have cut the local notches (features *E*). Feature *F* is the terminal moraine.

Feature *G*, a smooth, masked, rounded surface, may be outwash-covered bedrock, as may be feature *H*. Another possible explanation for surface *G* may be proposed. The outer edge of the terminal moraine *F* is well defined (feature F_1). It can be traced upstream to point F_2, where it occurs as a lateral moraine, apparently resting on surface *G*. Much of the material underlying surface *G* could be of preglacial age. A gravel-capped erosional (pediment) surface, now largely destroyed by stream erosion, could have existed here, later to be gouged away by the tongue of ice. The older pediment gravels could be capped by a thin layer of outwash.

Valley *I*, to the east, shows several characteristics of alpine or valley glaciation. Here, however, the ice was ap-

parently far more restricted in distribution, probably not extending farther downstream than area *J*, an irregular morainelike area.

Study valleys *K* and *L* on the photographs. Note especially their well-defined stream channels and pronounced V-shaped valley profiles. Though snow and ice may have occupied these valleys during the glaciation of the valleys to the north, valleys *K* and *L* did not contain large moving and growing glaciers. As shown on the map, valleys *M*, *N*, and *O*, to the west of the stereoscopic area, are also apparently stream-cut valleys.

In many partially glaciated mountain areas, glaciers frequently develop on north and east mountain flanks, and are absent or less well developed on south and west flanks. The area shown here is typical of asymmetric glaciation.

The structure of the area is complex. In such a small area correlation of rock units (here sedimentary strata) is virtually impossible, and strike faults cannot be detected. However, tight folding is readily noted.

At point *P* strike is northeast, and dip is steep to the northwest.

At point *Q*, where strike is northeast, dip is nearly vertical.

The outcrop traces at point *R* indicate very low dip.

At point *S*, strike is east to west and dip is steep to the north.

At point *T*, strike is east to west and dip is nearly vertical.

EXERCISES

1. Outline terminal moraine *F*.
2. Indicate dips *P* through *T* on the photographs.
3. Add all other observable dips to the photographs.
4. Trace key or marker beds (i.e., several at point *T* can be traced westward across the valley, into a tight fold). Vegetation can be helpful in some areas, as can photograph tone and relative rock resistance.

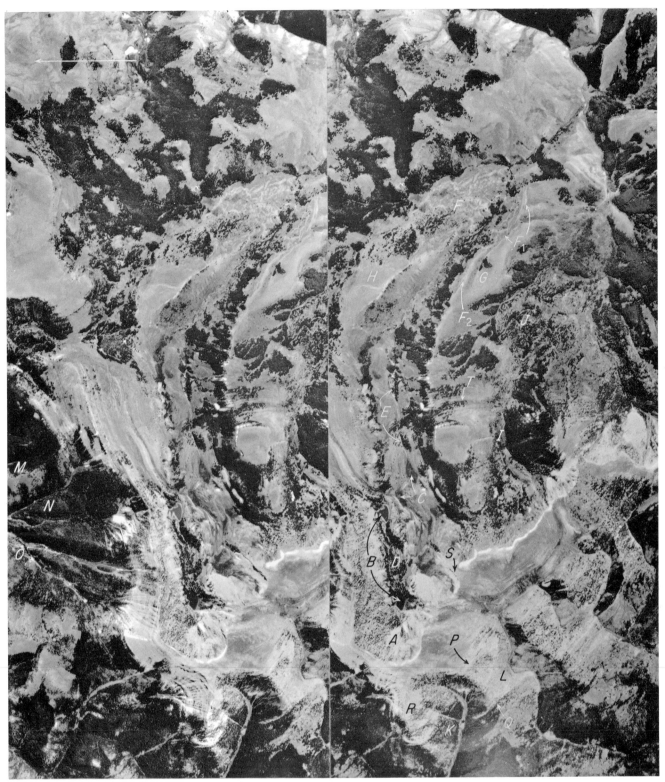

Figure 9-17. Stereogram of a glaciated mountain area. (*By permission from Fairchild Aerial Surveys, Inc.*)

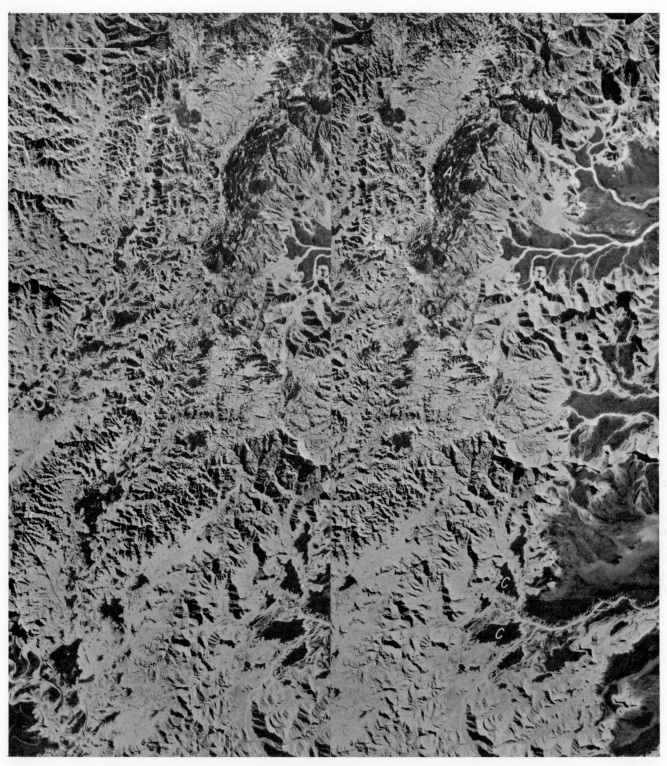

Figure. 9-18. Stereogram of a badland area, showing a network of clastic dikes. (*Courtesy of U.S. Dept. of Agriculture, Commodity Stabilization Service.*)

CLASTIC DIKES

This is an area of low-dipping, high-clay-content sedimentary rocks which have been maturely dissected. The general absence of vegetation throughout much of the area indicates an arid or semiarid climate.

The intricate network of intersecting small straight, narrow ridges is an outstanding feature of the upland surface. These are clastic dikes; joint fillings which are more resistant to erosion than the bedrock surrounding them. Differential erosion has etched them out.

Dark area *A* is an area of slumping. Slumping is also suggested at point *B*.

Note that the dikes occur, or at least can only be detected readily, in the upper part of the exposed stratigraphic section.

Surfaces *C* resemble stripped low-dipping resistant beds. What is another possible explanation for these and other similar-appearing surfaces in the area?

Figure 9-19. Stereogram of dike ridges and pediment remnants. (*Courtesy of U.S. Dept. of Agriculture, Forest Service.*)

DIKE RIDGES AND PEDIMENT REMNANTS

This is part of a swarm of intrusive dikes in a semihumid area. Compare the topography here with that produced in the clastic-dike area of Figure 9-18.

The intrusive dikes shown here are more resistant to erosion than the surrounding country rock. As a result of differential erosion, they now stand as narrow long ridges, in places as walls or spines.

Note surface *A* and surface *B*. Surface *B* is an erosional plain developed in the present erosional cycle by drainage ad-

justed to the existing base level. Surface *A* appears to be a remnant of a gravel-capped older erosional plain (a pediment remnant). At points *C* and *D* the truncation of a dike and its unconformable relation to the gravel capping can be seen.

The apparent offset of the dike at point *E* may have been caused by postintrusion faulting, or by the filling of joints or faults earlier arranged in the pattern now formed by the intrusive rock.

The right photograph is a poor print. A ghost, or vague duplicate image, suggests movement of print or negative during printing.

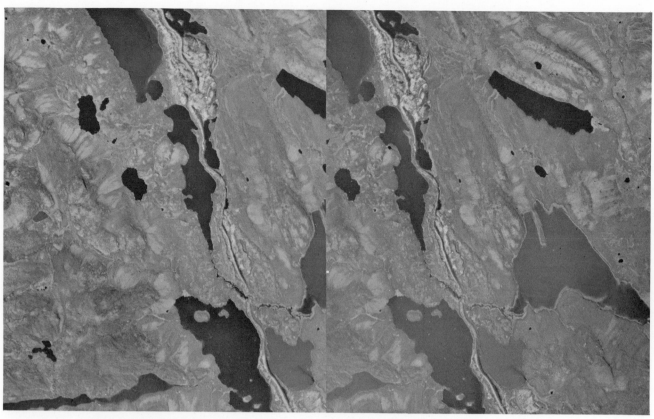

Figure 9-20. Stereogram of an esker in a subacrtic area of ground moraine, muskeg, and poorly integrated surface drainage. (*Courtesy of Royal Canadian Air Force.*)

Figure 9-21. Stereogram of eskers in a semihumid, cold area of muskeg, swamp, forests, and thick ground moraine. (*Reproduced by courtesy of the Technical Division of the Department of Lands and Forests, Edmonton, Alberta.*)

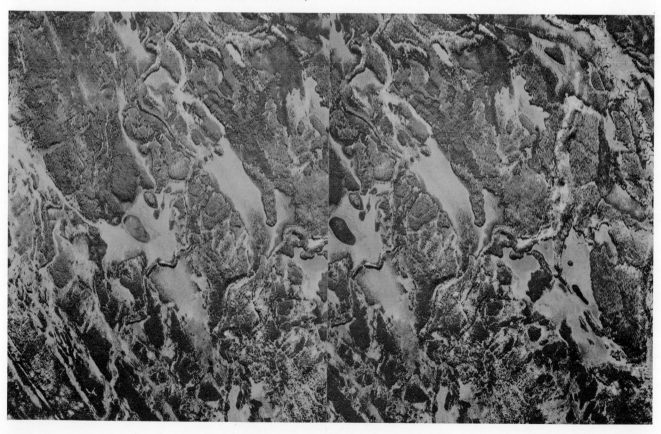

10

Direct or Supplemental Geomorphology

INTRODUCTION

One of the most important and frequently used elements in photogeologic mapping is *direct* or *supplemental geomorphology*. It is so intimately interrelated with such other factors as vegetation, photograph tone, and outcrop pattern that after a geologist has studied photographs for as little as a few weeks, he almost unconsciously includes this tool in the solution of all routine photogeologic mapping and identification problems.

The following seven stereograms were selected to illustrate the general application of this type of geomorphology. Most of the photographs used in the later chapters include features which could have been selected to show the same principles.

It is suggested that, before studying the stereograms of Chapters 11 through 15, the student concentrate on those on the following thirteen pages. As succeeding stereograms are examined, he will soon notice that he too will begin to apply direct or supplemental geomorphology to them, whether or not he is specifically instructed to do so in the text.

The first phase use of supplemental geomorphology consists of the study of the relative resistance to erosion of two or more rock units. In many instances, this comparison provides the initial step in the determination of lithology or composition of the surface rock units.

Detailed erosion characteristics, such as drainage density and the magnitude and relative uniformity of slopes, can be used as further indications of gross lithology, as well as of whether the rocks are thin-bedded or massive, jointed or unjointed, flat-lying or inclined.

Faults, of course, are frequently indicated by differential erosion and selective (subsequent) stream adjustment. Sharply defined linear or gently curved scarps, breaks in erosion or dissection characteristics, alignments of solution depressions, and many other combinations of topographic features are used in the detection of fault traces.

In Figure 10-5 relatively nonresistant basic dikes cross resistant granites and metamorphosed sediments which are of intermediate resistance. In some places where the dikes outcrop, differential erosion and weathering have etched out details of columnar jointing, oriented at right angles to the strike of the dike walls. In many other places the dike material is completely masked by muskeg, recent sedimentary debris, or by bodies of standing water. The dikes can nevertheless be mapped with considerable accuracy and assurance. The mapping of topographically expressed but covered or hidden bedrock units is an important part of *supplemental geomorphology*.

In the mapping of large areas, facies changes may be detected and interpreted through the careful and thorough application of *supplemental geomorphology*. A shale belt, for example, may underlie a smooth uniform obsequent ridge flank. When traced along strike or identified in distant outcrop areas, it may be expressed as a series of small but noticeable steps or benches produced by the presence of interbeds of more resistant rock, such as thin sandstones.

Another observation in a case where uniform slopes continue to exist may be that the shale belt becomes more resistant as a gross unit. This would suggest a gradual increase from shale to silty or sandy shale. In arid or semi-arid areas it could also indicate a change to a limey shale or a shaly limestone.

The possible conditions and combinations of relations among lithology, topography, structure, and climate are infinite. Each area as well as each outcrop and local topographic feature within an area must be studied, analyzed, and evaluated in its own setting.

Variations in flood-plain characteristics are frequent clues or keys to the presence of different rock types along the course of a stream. This has been discussed in a previous chapter and will not be treated in detail here, except for the following caution. Factors *other than bedrock differences* can cause variations in the width of the flood plain of a mature stream and in the valley form along a younger stream. A common factor is a variation in the amount, composition, and average particle size of detritus entering the valley as tributary load, slump, slide material, and creep. Such variations depend on the types of bedrock in nearby uplands and distant areas drained by tributary streams, on local relief, and on numerous other factors.

A valley constriction, therefore, need not indicate the presence of resistant rock across the stream course. It could be caused by a talus cone, an alluvial fan or cone deposited by a tributary, or imperceptible slumping.

The principles given in this chapter comprise an essential tool of photogeologic mapping and interpretation projects.

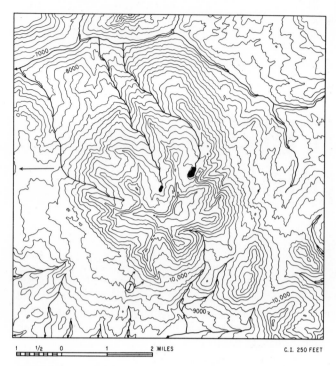

Figure 10-1. Topographic map of a maturely dissected glaciated mountain. Compare this map with Figure 9-16, which shows a partially (asymmetrically) glaciated mountain.

ALPINE GLACIATION OF A MOUNTAIN OF INTRUSIVE ACIDIC ROCK

Both *supplemental* and *elementary geomorphology* are well illustrated in this area.

This mountain mass, composed of an intruded acidic stock, has undergone widespread alpine glaciation.

Most of the preglacial topography has been destroyed by ice erosion. Some old surfaces remain, however (see Figure 10-3). Surfaces *A* and *B* were either formed by weathering and erosion by running water, or (especially in the case of surface *A*) may have been uncovered by the removal of adjacent country rock by erosion.

The following features can be recognized: arêtes (feature *C*), matterhorns (feature *D*), cols (features *E*), tarns (features *F*), and lateral moraines (feature *G*).

Landslides and other gravity mass movements, such as rock glaciers, are widespread postglacial features in the glacial troughs (i.e., feature *H*).

Differential erosion is an important factor in the mapping and identification of bedrock units in this area. Note the abrupt topographic break in slope (steep above, more gentle below) along line *I* in the south, and along line *J* in the north. Topographic break *I* is shown very clearly in Figure 10-1. Feature *J* is more a break in slope characteristics than in gross slope magnitude; it is obvious on the photographs but does not appear on Figure 10-1.

Refer to Figure 10-2. Lines *I* and *J* (on the photographs) correspond with the mapped southwest and northeast borders of this part of the stock (*Ti*).

The shrouded but mappable scarp *K* (on the photographs) is formed along the trace of the Lower Tertiary conglomerate (*Tsl*, Figure 10-2).

The steplike, tree-striped slope *L* is formed by the erosion of the Upper Cretaceous continental sediments of various relative resistances (*Ksu*).

Figure 10-2. Geologic map of the general area surrounding the glaciated mountain shown in Figures 10-1 and 10-3. Original map scale was 1 inch to 8 miles. *Ksl,* Lower Cretaceous sediments (shale); *Ksu,* Upper Cretaceous sediments (continental beds); *Tsl,* Lower Tertiary sediments (conglomerate); *Tsu,* Upper Tertiary sediments (shale and sandstone); *Tb,* breccia; *Ti,* intrusive (acidic); *Tv,* volcanics undivided; *x,* mountain peak.

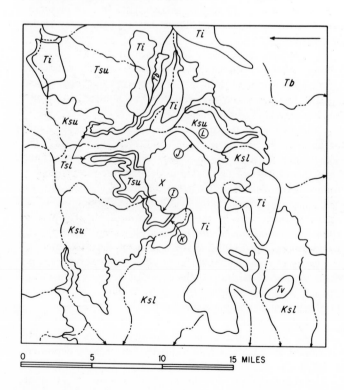

EXERCISES

1. On the photographs, outline surfaces *A, B,* and any others which appear to have escaped ice erosion.

2. Outline on the photographs masses of unconsolidated recent materials, such as talus, alluvial fans, and rock glaciers.

3. By some numbering or lettering system, indicate and identify all glacial features within the stereo-model area (i.e., arêtes, cols).

4. On Figure 10-1, trace the contact between *Ti* and adjacent rocks.

5. Locate topographic break *K* on Figure 10-1. Extend feature *Tsl* westward across this map.

Figure 10-3. Stereogram of the maturely glaciated mountain shown in Figure 10-1 and included in the area shown in Figure 10-2. Compare with Figure 9-17, which shows a partially gla-ciated mountain. (*Courtesy of U.S. Dept. of Agriculture, Forest Service.*)

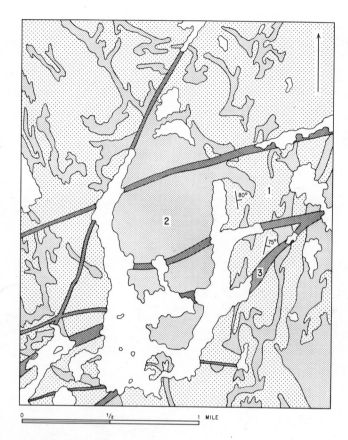

Figure 10-4. Geologic map of an area of metamorphosed sediments intruded by acidic rocks, and both later intruded by basic dikes. (1) metamorphosed sediments; (2) acidic rocks; (3) basic dikes.

METAMORPHOSED SEDIMENTS, ACIDIC AND BASIC INTRUSIVE ROCKS

This is an area of sharp topographic and tonal contrasts. These two factors make possible detailed photogeologic mapping, rock identification, and the interpretation of geologic history.

The lowland areas and irregular depressions are filled with lakes (i.e., area A) and swamp or muskeg materials (i.e., feature B). Most of the area, however, consists of exposed bedrock.

This area is on the Canadian Shield. Residual soils and mantle are sparse and poorly developed, since in Pleistocene time the area was scoured and gouged by overriding ice sheets. The present topography is the result of preglacial differential stream erosion and of glacial ice erosion.

Note the large oval light-toned area C. The rocks here are highly jointed. Relative resistance is high, since this and other white areas (i.e., features D and E) stand topographically higher than the surrounding darker areas. Note the many other small linear and irregular white outcrops (i.e., features F and G). These are obviously intrusive rocks, since they do not have a constant conformable relation with the rocks in the darker areas. Area C is an oval stock. Features D, E, F, G, and the many other light-toned rocks are dikes and smaller irregular intrusive masses. The light tone denotes a general acidic composition, possibly granite or granodiorite.

The field-measured dips shown on the map suggest that the numerous north-trending acidic intrusions (i.e., feature F) are along bedding planes. The numerous parallel northeast-trending dark lines (i.e., lines H and I) are therefore probably members of a regional joint or fracture series.

The several easterly- and northeasterly-trending dark bands (i.e., bands J and K) cross both the metamorphosed sediments and the granitic intrusive rocks. In most places these

lines are characterized by low, often trenchlike topography.

At point L one of the northeasterly-trending bands is occupied by a finger of a lake. At point M it consists of a muskeg-filled linear depression. At point N it is a sharply defined trench bordered by granitic rock, and at point O it is a linear lake-filled depression. At no place along this feature can the bedrock be observed.

Consider dark band PQR, however. At points P and R, dark, jointed bedrock is exposed. The joints are normal to the trend of the band. The intruded nature of the body is apparent. This is a columnar-jointed basic dike, younger than the metamorphosed sediments and the acidic intrusive rocks.

The general geologic history is therefore reviewed as follows:

1. Deposition of sediments
2. Orogeny, producing complex structures and metamorphism of the strata
3. Intrusion of acidic materials
4. Intrusion of basic dikes
5. Prolonged erosion and probably peneplanation
6. Continental glaciation
7. Some erosion, transportation, and deposition by running water (note partial filling of lake at point S)

Most of the lakes are undrained. Some may be dammed by unconsolidated glacial debris or by muskeg or swamp materials. Many, however, occupy depressions in the bedrock surface. These depressions could not have been carved by running water. They are best explained by preferential ice scour.

The outstanding lake is the horseshoe-shaped lake A which surrounds stock C. This aureole of low erosional resistance may be explained by contact metamorphism or by a concentration of fractures and joints in the country rock surrounding the intruded rock mass. Lake arms L, O, and Q result from the scour of relatively nonresistant basic dike bedrock.

140

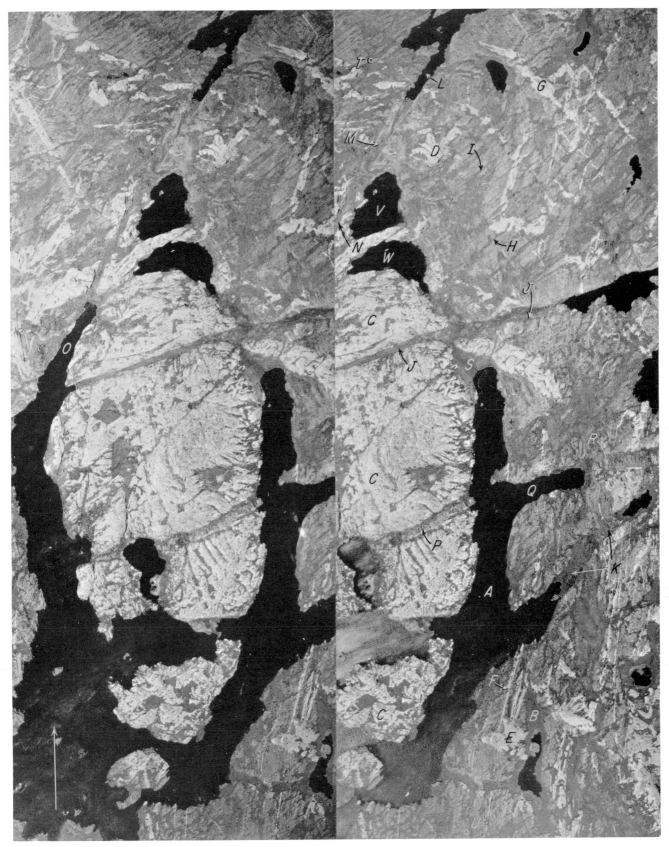

Figure 10-5. Stereogram of an area of metamorphosed sediments (gray areas) intruded by acidic rocks (white areas) and later intruded by basic dikes (darker-gray lines and bands). (*Courtesy of Royal Canadian Air Force.*)

EXERCISES

1. Many of the smaller acidic intrusives are not shown on Figure 10-4. Trace the unmapped acidic rocks on the photographs and transfer them to the map.

2. Draw a topographic profile and geologic cross section along line *TU*. Indicate rock type in covered areas (i.e., under lakes *V* and *W*), as well as in areas of exposed bedrock.

Figure 10-6. Topographic map of an anticlinal lowland, in a humid temperate climate zone.

ANTICLINAL LOWLAND

This is an area of folded limestones, shales, and sandstones. Two formations are exposed on the photographs: a lower carbonate unit and an upper unit consisting of interbedded shales and sandstones.

Note the following features:

1. The several depression contours in the central lowland area of the map

2. The well-integrated drainage in the hills north and south of the central lowland, as shown on the map and on the photographs

3. The smooth slopes and uniform photographic tones in the middle and upper slopes of the north and south hills (i.e., features *A*, *B*, and *C*)

4. The many small white outcrops in the lowland (i.e., features *D, E,* and *F*)

These features indicate the presence of solution depressions (in limestones) in the lowland, noncarbonate strata in the hills, and the general contact (i.e., at points *G* and *H*) between the carbonates and the shale-sandstone unit.

The following features permit the determination of the structure in this area:

1. The asymmetry of ridge *I;* steep south slope and gentle uniform north slope (north dip slope)

2. The asymmetry of ridge *J;* gentle though uneven south slope and steep north slope (south dip)

3. Arrangement of white outcrops at point *K;* discontinuous outcrops of south-dipping limestones

4. Erosional asymmetry of ridge *L*, with smooth dip-slope–

Figure 10-7. Stereogram of an anticlinal lowland, in a humid temperate climate zone. (*Courtesy of Tennessee Valley Authority.*)

appearing south facets (feature *M*) and widely spaced streams (streams *N*) on the south slope, and more intricate dissection (area *O*) of the north flank (obsequent flank).

The erosional asymmetry of ridge *L* may be seen on the map as well as on the photographs. A similar asymmetry does not exist along the north ridge (ridge *P*), which is shown on the map but which lies largely beyond the coverage of the photographs.

The reason for the relative symmetry of ridge *P* can be determined by studying the northwest corner of the map. Note two depression contours in this area. These contours indicate limestone at or near the surface of the northwest low area.

Note also the streams flowing northward, down the north flank of ridge *P*. They are similar to the obsequent streams

which drain the north flank (area *O*) of ridge *L*. South-dipping shales, underlain by limestones, are therefore assumed to extend along the north side of ridge *P*.

Ridge *P*, then, is probably a synclinal ridge. This ridge is shown more completely, and its structure more clearly demonstrated, in Figures 10-8 and 10-9.

EXERCISES

1. Draw a topographic profile along line *QR*, the ends of which are indicated on the map.

2. Indicate strikes and dips on the photographs. Trace the contact at the top of the limestone unit.

3. Add a geologic cross section to topographic profile *QR*.

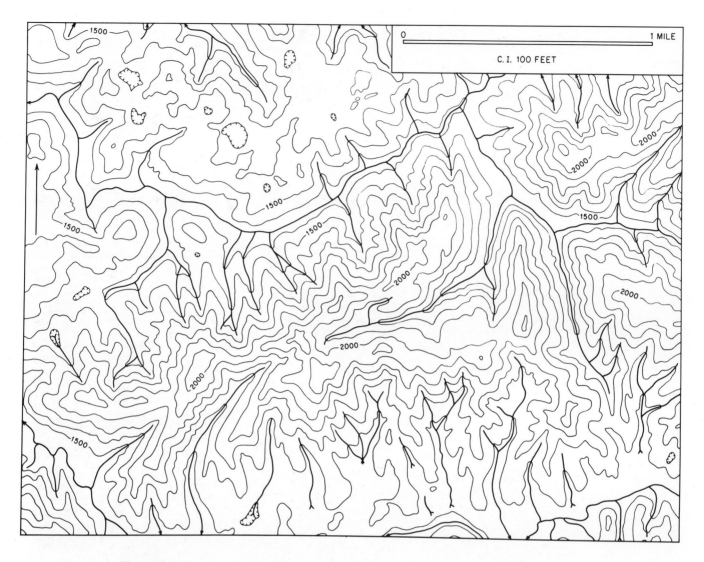

Figure 10-8. Topographic map of a synclinal upland flanked by limestone lowlands. This area is in a humid temperate climate zone.

SYNCLINAL UPLAND

This is an area in which the structure is readily determined, despite a relative absence of outcrop. Topographic form is the main element in the understanding and interpretation of the geology.

Limestones, shales, and sandstones are known to occur in this general area. The map shows several depression contours in the lowland areas. These may be assumed to be limestone-solution depressions or sink holes.

Along the large northeast-trending upland, part of which (ridges *P*) is shown on the photographs, drainage is well developed and well integrated. The bedrock is noncarbonate. Shales and interbedded sandstones constitute the stratigraphic sequence forming this upland.

From north to south across the stereo model, note the following:

1. Clearly defined modified dip slopes (south dip) at point *A*.

2. The tonal break *B*, which is the contact between underlying darker beds and overlying lighter beds. The trace of this horizon also defines south dip here.

3. The general northeast-trending topographic grain in the hilly area lying between streams *C* and *D*. This grain reflects the strike in this area.

4. The apparent homoclinal south dip in the area between streams *C* and *D*. An excellent dip slope is preserved as surface *E*.

5. The numerous small sink holes in this lowland area. These do not appear on the map because of contour interval. Explain.

6. The contrast in topographic relief, slopes, tone, and drainage characteristics on the north and south sides of the valley of stream *D*. The stratigraphic contact at the top of the limestones is at or near point *F*.

7. Stream *G*, which flows along regional strike. North of stream *G* dip is to the south.

8. The sink holes in area *H*.

9. The north dip detectable at point I.

10. The impression of gentle north dip at point *J*.

Stream *G* is a subsequent stream. From the arrangement of dips, it appears that this stream flows along a northeast-plunging synclinal axis. The extreme linearity of the stream along segment *K*, however, suggests the possibility of strike fault control along or near the axis.

Compare asymmetric ridges *JL* and *MN*. The south flanks

144

Figure 10-9. Stereogram of a synclinal upland and surrounding limestone lowlands. This area is in a humid temperate climate zone. (*Courtesy of Tennessee Valley Authority.*)

of both ridges appear to be the steeper, suggesting north dip. The south flank of ridge *JL* is scored by many tributary streams; the north flank has few streams. The opposite is true along the flanks of ridge *MN*. Drainage density along its north flank is greater than along its south flank.

This demonstrates the need to consider all available cri-

teria in photogeologic mapping. The use of gross ridge asymmetry alone affords the impression of north dip along ridge *MN*, whereas the drainage characteristics attest to south dip.

Dips along the south flank of the syncline are gentler than those along the north flank.

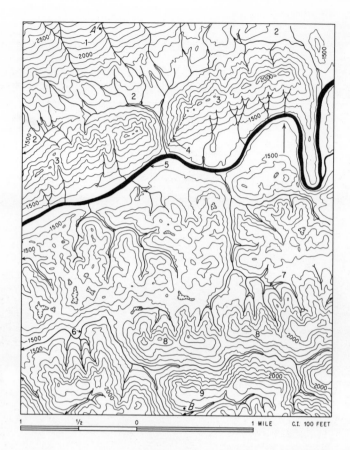

Figure 10-10. Topographic map of a maturely dissected homocline of carbonate and noncarbonate rocks in a humid temperate area.

MATURELY DISSECTED HOMOCLINE

The structure in at least most of this area is extremely simple, consisting of homoclinally south-dipping strata. Available references identify all the bedrock as sedimentary. Though some outcrops can be seen on the photographs, a general structural interpretation and lithologic identification and differentiation can be made on the basis of topography alone. Consider the terrain depicted on the map.

Slope 1 is quite uniform and is drained by relatively few, large subparallel streams. Two possible structures could produce such a slope: a fault, perhaps along the base, or a modified south dip slope developed on resistant strata.

Lowland 2, which is followed by four subsequent stream segments, is underlain by a wide belt of nonresistant rocks. An extremely wide fault zone or a sequence of steeply dipping nonresistant strata, such as shales, could be eroded in this way.

Ridge 3 is nearly symmetric at its western end but is asymmetric in its central and eastern parts. Its north flank is far more intricately dissected than its south flank (see Figure 7-15). Note line 4, formed by the abrupt bending of several contour lines. This line is probably the topographic expression of a resistant south-dipping bed, that on which the south flank (dip slope) of the ridge is developed. The north slope is characteristic of dissected obsequent slopes.

From stream 5 south to streams 6 and 7, the area consists of rolling hills, gentle slopes, and undrained depressions. Such topography is common in carbonate bedrock areas under humid climatic conditions. In arid and semiarid areas, these rocks would form high ridges and steep scarps. There is no reliable indication of dip in this central area.

The upland area south of streams 6 and 7 is principally underlain by noncarbonate rocks. The general topographic grain in this area probably results from a slightly more easterly strike than that in the areas to the north.

South dip is shown at several places in the upland area. Erosional asymmetry is noted along ridge 8. Slope asymmetry and drainage density differences are well defined along ridge 9. In this area, south slopes are less uniform than the south flank of ridge 3. Therefore, it would be less advisable to assume dip-slope or near-dip-slope conditions here.

The topography of the entire map area suggests the following structural and stratigraphic relations:

1. South-southeast dip throughout most of the area.

2. Resistant rocks beneath slope 1.

3. Shales or similar rocks beneath lowland 2.

4. A single resistant bed (outcropping along line 4) which maintains the crest and underlies part or all of the south flank of ridge 3.

5. Nonresistant, probably shaly rocks exposed along the north flank of ridge 3.

6. Carbonate strata throughout most, if not all, of the central lowland area.

7. Relatively resistant strata in the south upland. The rocks in this area may consist of interbedded resistant and nonresistant layered rock.

EXERCISES

1. Study the photographs and concentrate on locating and evaluating topographic criteria which will permit a further understanding of the geology.

2. Annotate strikes and dips on the photographs, trace exposed key beds, trace topographically expressed key beds, and sketch in approximate stratigraphic contacts.

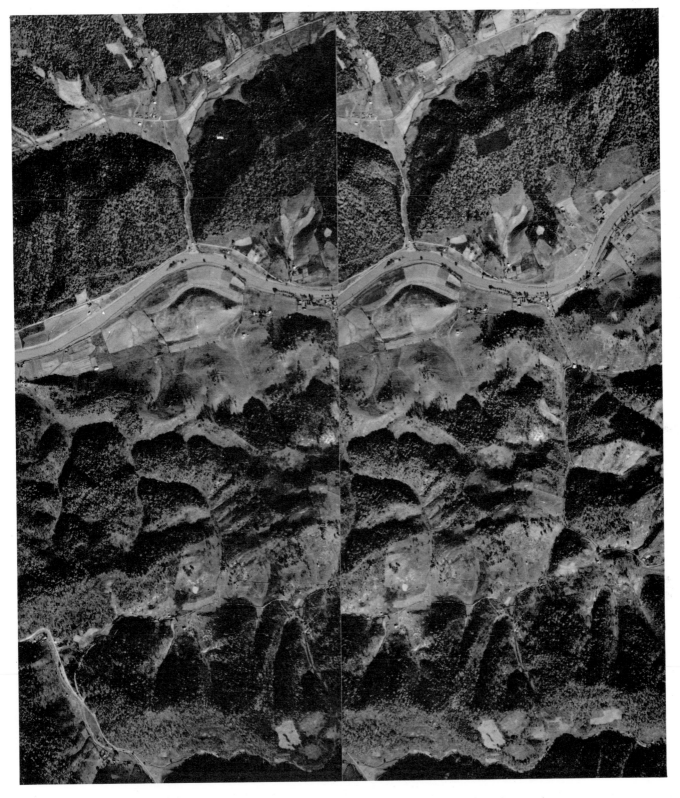

Figure 10-11. Stereogram of a maturely dissected homocline of carbonate and noncarbonate rocks in a humid temperate area. (*Courtesy of Tennessee Valley Authority.*)

3. Draw a topographic profile along line *AB* on the map.

4. Draw a vertically exaggerated topographic profile (as it *appears*) along that part of map line *AB* included in the stereo model.

5. Add a geologic cross section to the exaggerated profile.

6. Transfer the essential geologic relations from the exaggerated cross section and profile to the small-scale, nonexaggerate profile compiled from the map.

7. Contours indicate many streams not shown on the map. Add the complete drainage network to the map.

8. Compare the stereo model with the corresponding area on the map. Do all the streams added to the map appear on the photographs to have the same shape and length? Are they all correctly located on the map?

9. On the map, label all subsequent (*s*), obsequent (*o*), resequent (*r*), and insequent (*i*) streams.

COMPLEX AREA OF SEDIMENTARY AND EXTRUSIVE LAYERED ROCKS

The geologic structure and tectonic history of this area are relatively complex. A complete and detailed interpretation is extremely difficult, if not impossible.

Numerous features, however, are readily identified by their form, position, and photographic tone. The most obvious is the flood plain of the major north-flowing stream A.

Note also the isolated dark outcrop B, lying on a steep valley wall. The upland surface C is composed of similar-appearing rock. The cap rock is a relatively recent lava flow. Outcrop B is a block of lava which has slumped part way down the valley slope. This suggests rapid stream downcutting, with resulting instability of valley wall slopes.

The narrow flood plain of tributary D must, therefore, be of fairly recent origin, since actively degrading streams do not "have time" to form appreciable flood plains.

Another slump block is feature E. Feature F is a smaller, less well-defined slump block, as indicated by the sharp arcuate depression between it and the main spur.

The several steep dark bands which mask parts of the valley slopes (i.e., bands G, H, and I) are detritus derived from the basic lava cap rock. The irregular black marks designated as feature J occur on the right photograph only, and are possibly the result of imperfections on either the original film or the print paper. They may also have been caused by improper handling during processing.

In this general area are Paleozoic marine sediments, Tertiary extrusive rocks, Quaternary gravels and sands, and Quaternary basalts. Many of the outcrops shown can be assigned to these several broad units. Note the following:

1. The smooth, resistant, and in places velvety-appearing dark-gray cap rock (surfaces C, K, L, M, and N). This is the youngest consolidated rock unit in the area, and, as previously stated, is the lava (Quaternary).

2. The well-defined north dip of resistant and nonresistant, conformable strata in area O. These are light to medium toned and can be assumed to represent the Paleozoic sedimentary sequence. The nonresistant intervals are probably shales; the resistant units are probably limestones.

3. The unconformable relation between the dipping Paleozoic strata and the overlying Quaternary basalts (i.e., point P).

4. The excellent dip slope Q, unconformably overlain by Quaternary lava.

5. The pronounced jointing (feature R) in the rocks which form dip slope Q. These and other rocks exposed in the south part of the valley (i.e., outcrops S and T) do not resemble the Paleozoic strata. Their tone, position, structure, and jointing are suggestive of intermediate to acidic extrusive rocks. They may be assigned, tentatively, to the Tertiary extrusive group.

6. The smooth, unbroken slopes (i.e., slopes U and V), which in places underlie the Quaternary basalts, are selected as probably consisting of Quaternary gravels and sands. The criteria for this identification include their (a) relative nonresistance, (b) homogeneity of topographic expression, and (c) stratigraphic position.

Several relations cannot be seen. These include the structural and stratigraphic relations between the Paleozoic strata and the Tertiary extrusive rocks, between the Paleozoic strata and the Quaternary sands and gravels, and between the Tertiary extrusive rocks and the Quaternary sediments.

An easterly-trending fault may be postulated, passing to the south of the Paleozoic strata. The Paleozoic rocks are, in general, relatively resistant (they constrict the flood plain) and would probably not have been removed completely from the central and southern parts of the area by normal erosion.

Probably there was appreciable block faulting, involving the Paleozoic and Tertiary rocks, followed by extensive regional erosion, prior to the infilling by the Quaternary gravels and sands. The Quaternary basalts flowed out over the local Quaternary depositional surfaces and across the truncated Paleozoic and Tertiary strata. In postbasalt extrusion time the entire area has been subjected to dissection, possibly as a result of regional uplift.

EXERCISES

Completely annotate the geology within the area of the stereo model. This should be done one step at a time, as follows:

1. Carefully outline in yellow the Quaternary alluvium along the flood plains of streams A and D. Label these areas Qal.

2. In orange, outline all areas where bedrock (that which is in situ) is mantled and obscured by surficial debris such as slope detritus and slump materials. Label these areas Q or Qu (Quaternary deposits, undivided).

3. Outline in purple the several lava areas. Be careful not to draw these contacts too low (i.e., into areas where the lava detritus has descended the valley wall slopes, as along band I).

4. In purple, try to trace contacts between the possible Tertiary extrusive rocks and the apparently nonresistant possible Quaternary gravels and sands exposures (i.e., between the rocks at outcrop T and slope U).

5. In the area of Paleozoic outcrop, trace key or marker beds in green.

6. Indicate strikes and dips throughout the area, in red.

7. If you believe a fault exists along the south side of the Paleozoic outcrop area, indicate its position by a dashed or dotted questioned line (red).

8. If you don't think a fault is required, complete in this area the drawing of contacts which will provide a nonfault explanation for the observed relations.

9. Draw three parallel north-south topographic profiles and geologic cross sections across the stereo-model area, passing through letters L, C, and P.

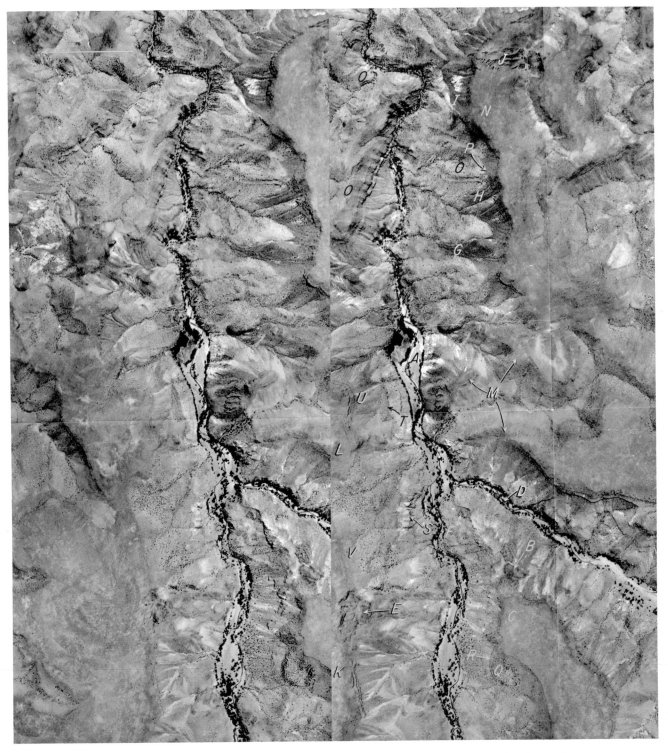

Figure 10-12. Stereogram of flood-plain constriction, dipping strata, an unconformity, and lava-flow remnants in a semiarid area. Four-lens photographs. (*Courtesy of U.S. Dept. of Agriculture, Soil Conservation Service.*)

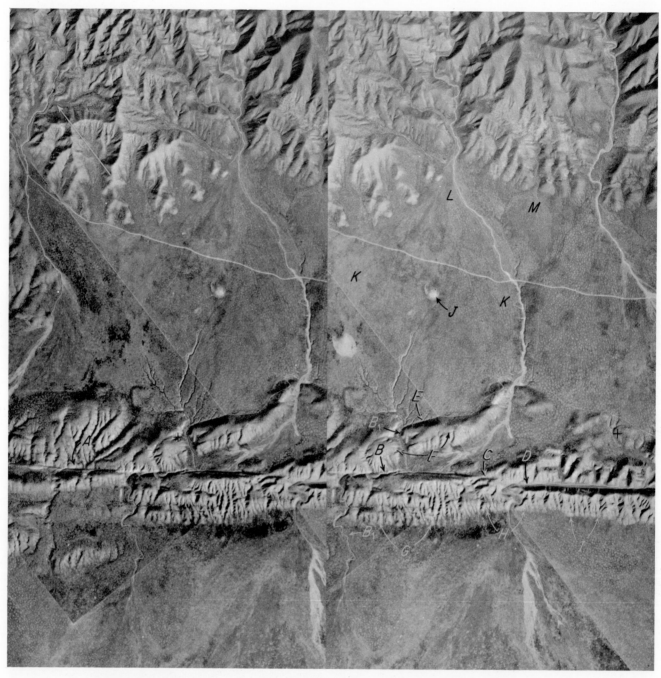

Figure 10-13. Stereogram of a major fault zone in a semiarid area. (*By permission from Fairchild Aerial Surveys, Inc.*)

FAULT ZONE

This is the world-famous San Andreas fault in southern California. The dominant displacement is horizontal rather than vertical.

Several of the many possible topographic expressions of faults are present in this restricted area. Stream segments A, B, C, and D are subsequent stream courses developed and adjusted along a fault trace. Stream BB_1 is deflected to the left, suggesting that the south block has moved to the west with respect to the north block. A similar deflection is suggested by stream D.

At point E a straight stream follows the base of a straight slope. Along line F are small adjusted streams, saddles, and a tonal break. Small spurs end abruptly along lines G, H, and I.

The central lowland K appears to be an area of aggradation. Surfaces L and M are alluvial fans. Isolated outcrop area J is a small outlier.

Might lowland K be a structural depression? In this area of known fault activity, can you find any evidence of block faulting? What structural relations can be observed in the northern hills area?

11

Indirect or Complemental Geomorphology

INTRODUCTION

Direct or supplemental geomorphology, which is the use of geomorphic analysis to ascertain lithologic and structural information and to compile a more complete and reliable photogeologic map, is a relatively straightforward and easily understood branch of photogeology.

Indirect or complemental geomorphology involves the study and understanding of more subtle geomorphic criteria and can only be successful if the photogeologist possesses or can obtain sufficient advanced academic background and experience in applied geomorphic principles.

It is extremely easy to collect many photographs which demonstrate the various facets of supplemental geomorphology. It is quite difficult to compile photographs which illustrate what is implied by and included in complemental geomorphology.

Figures 8-5 and 8-6 are excellent examples of both types of geomorphology. Dip and strike as well as differences in lithology reflected by strike ridges and subsequent valleys and lowlands are determined through the analysis of the mature upland surface (supplemental geomorphology). Extremely active stream entrenchment, the *beginning* of scarp retreat, and a small but well-defined scarplet or knick at the base of the border scarp, combine to suggest relatively *recent* large-scale border fault movement. The order of magnitude of the displacement appears to be more than 1,000 feet. This is an application of complemental geomorphology.

The border scarp and the canyons in the lower courses of the streams expose great thicknesses of strata and provide outcrops from which dip estimates may be made on the photographs. Excellent conditions exist at these places for detailed measurements of the stratigraphic section.

If the photogeologist utilizes the canyons and scarps solely for the purpose of obtaining structural (strike-dip) data to compile on a map, and if the field geologist uses them only as a means of obtaining samples and section measurements, an important structural element could be completely overlooked.

The possibility of recent faulting along the mountain front leads to a consideration of another possibility. Is it not likely that faulting, folding, and epeirogenic warping have occurred in nearby areas only recently? In the study of surrounding areas, special attention should be directed toward those geomorphic features and relations which might disclose crustal movements.

Figures 11-1 through 11-4 are maps and photographs of areas where stream rejuvenation is recorded by (1) the dissection of pediments, and (2) meander entrenchments. Such features *suggest*, but do not prove, structural movement such as epeirogenic uplift. Such nonstructural events as stream capture, climate change, and the lowering of base level by the drainage of a lake or the removal of an obstacle downstream must be considered as possible explanations for such features.

Figure 11-5 shows how a different interpretation can be made when certain features are *absent* from an area. In this area a fault line is suggested by several observable topographic, lithologic, and structural relations. There is no indication of recent structural disturbance, however. Therefore, if a fault exists, it is considerably older than the one shown in Figure 8-5.

In petroleum and minerals exploration, the relative age as well as the existence of a fault may be of critical importance in the appraisal of an area. The offset of a rock unit of known age permits the viewer to date the fault as of post-rock-unit age. The offset of one fault by another permits the assignment of *older* to the first and *younger* to the second. The recognition of the structural significance of topography which has not had time to *adjust* to relatively recent faulting allows a more specific age determination.

See Figure 12-13, which shows an apparently fault-displaced late Tertiary or Quaternary gravel-capped pediment surface.

Faults are not the only structures which can be located and sometimes dated by the study of geomorphic features. When large areas are studied, differential warping may be revealed by subtle as well as obvious contrasts in stream regimen in different parts of the area. The collection of evidence for such an interpretation involves many details appearing on many photographs. It cannot be illustrated satisfactorily or in adequate detail in a few pages of a textbook.

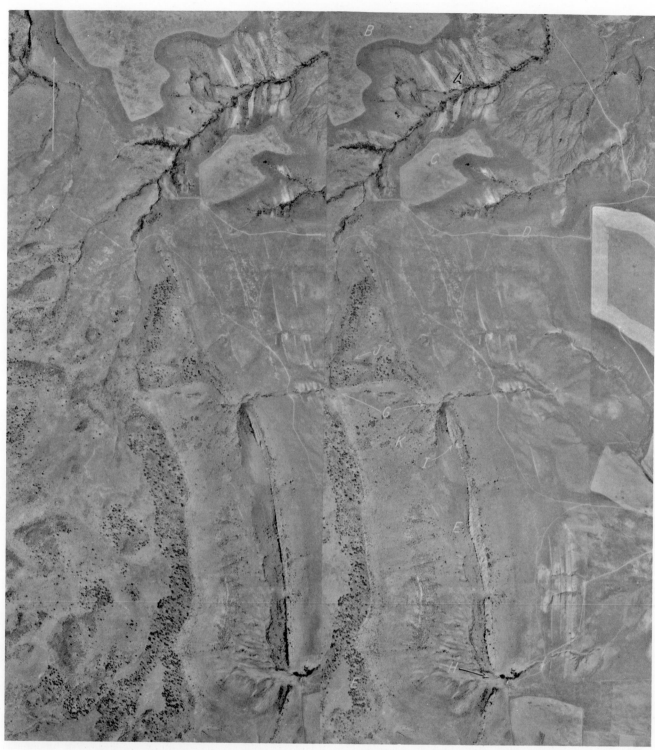

Figure 11-1. Large-scale stereogram of an area of folded sedimentary strata and pediment remnants. See Figure 11-2. (*Courtesy of U.S. Geological Survey.*)

ASYMMETRIC ANTICLINE AND PEDIMENT REMNANTS

The area shown in Figures 11-1 and 11-2 illustrates several aspects and problems of photogeologic mapping and interpretation. They are:

1. Possible epeirogeny as recorded in the erosional history
2. Structural and rock-unit mapping
3. Photograph scale

In this short chapter, primary attention is turned to the problem of noting and interpreting features which might indicate epeirogenic disturbance and crustal warping in areas of outcrop where geomorphology is also used to assist in the mapping of structure and the identification of rock types.

In Figure 11-1, steeply dipping beds are noted in area *A*. These beds have been truncated during a past cycle of erosional planation and covered by a layer of gravels and sands.

152

Figure 11-2. Small-scale stereogram of an area of folded sedimentary strata and pediment remnants. See Figure 11-1. (*Courtesy of U.S. Geological Survey.*)

Remnants of this gravel-sand capping layer are preserved (surfaces *B, C,* and *D*) as isolated topographic benches or terraces. These are gravel-capped *pediment* remnants.

A definite erosional history is recorded here. The area, following folding and an unknown earlier geomorphic history, was extensively eroded to a well-established base level. During this time, areas underlain by relatively nonresistant strata were planed off as an extensive regional pediment, above the surface of which rose isolated hills and ridges, such as the anticlinal hills in area *E* to the south.

The drainage in the area was then rejuvenated. A change from dominantly lateral to dominantly downward cutting occurred. The streams became entrenched through the pediment surfaces into the underlying strata. Stream valley *F* (in Figure 11-2) shows that a lower base level was established and has been maintained to the present time. The flood plain along stream *F* may be considered as the beginning of a new cycle of pedimentation.

The reason for planation, rejuvenation, and later (lower) planation cannot be determined by studying a restricted area. One possible explanation is climatic. A given climate of long duration would permit the establishment of a base level and

the cutting of pediments. An increased humidity, accompanied by greater runoff and greater load capacity, could produce downcutting (rejuvenation) until a lower base level is attained.

Other possibilities are structural; they would include such movements as regional uplift, crustal warping and tilting, and block faulting.

EXERCISES

1. Study and compare the two stereograms, especially noting vertical exaggeration in each, and the details of geologic structure and lithologic differentiation shown on each. Trace several contacts across each stereo model.

2. Note in Figure 11-1 the easterly-trending line *G,* the apparent offset of the beds at its eastern end, the offsets at points *H* and *I,* and the possible fault at point *J*. Also note the numerous large boulders and blocks, derived from the ridge to the west, in area *K*.

3. Can these features be seen on Figure 11-2?

4. What are the probable origin and significance of surface *L* (Figure 11-2)?

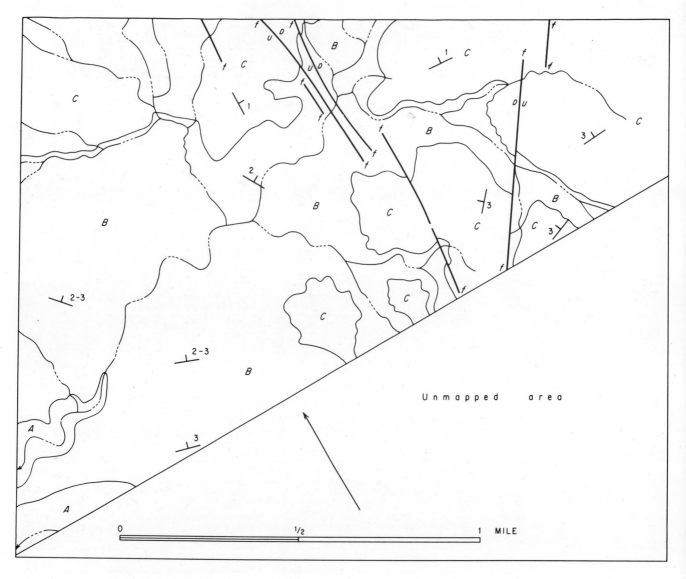

Figure 11-3. Geologic map of low-dipping strata and several small faults. See text for brief descriptions of map units *A*, *B*, and *C*.

ENTRENCHED MEANDERS IN PLATEAU AREA

This is an area of gently dipping marine sedimentary rocks. The boldness of the topography and the virtually complete absence of vegetation attest to arid or semiarid climatic conditions.

The dominant features of the area are the deeply incised abandoned meander in the south and the series of small but easily traced faults in the north.

Throughout the area, dip is extremely low. The only structure apparent in the stereogram is a broad anticlinal warp extending eastward across the central part.

Gentle south dips are noted on surface *a*, a dip slope. Northerly dip can be seen on surface *b*, which is also a dip slope. An impression of extremely gentle south or southeast dip is obtained in area *c*. Careful study of streams *d*, however, suggests tilt. These tributary streams appear to flow slightly *uphill*, to the north.

The strata in this area include marine limestones, shales, and sandstones. Map unit *A* contains appreciable shale, while units *B* and *C* have less shale and more resistant members.

The contact between units *A* and *B*, as shown on the map, lies to the west of the area of the stereo model. Its approximate position on Figure 11-4 is at point *e*. This probably correlates with the white bed (line *f*) in the valley wall of the abandoned meander. The rocks below bed *f* appear to have more shale units than do those above.

The contact between units *B* and *C* is along a pronounced tonal and topographic break. The darker tones of unit *C* may be caused by reddish bedrock colors.

Note the several faults in the northern part of the area. Displacements appear to be extremely small, in places undetectable. The white streaks along the fault traces (i.e., at point *g*) may be white or light-gray carbonate materials deposited by water along the fault planes. Silicified faults (which under certain conditions could also appear as white

154

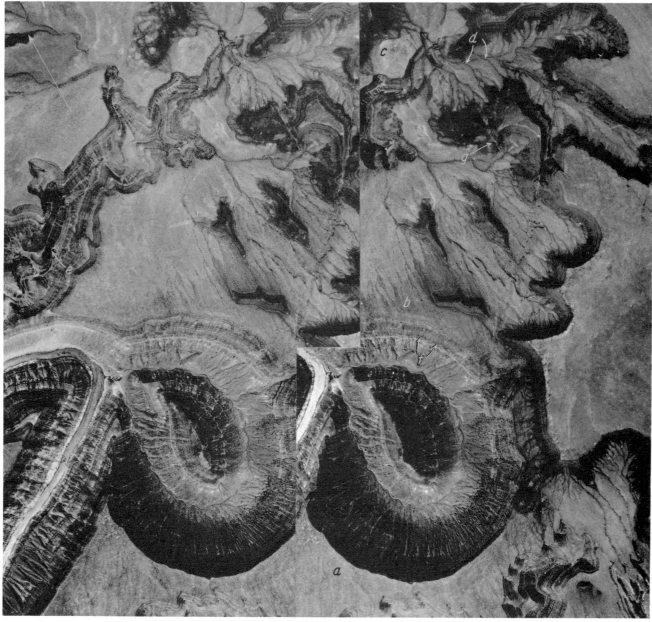

Figure 11-4. Stereogram of an abandoned entrenched meander in an arid plateau area. (*By permission from Fairchild Aerial Surveys, Inc.*)

lines) frequently stand as narrow ridges. In such cases, the resistance of the silicified faults is greater than that of the bedrock in which they occur.

The structural history of the area shown appears to have been simple, consisting of gentle epeirogenic warping of the strata into broad folds, with minor fault displacements in some parts of the area. The relative ages of the folds and faults cannot be determined by the study of such a small area.

The geomorphic history, however, presents an interesting and perhaps an important problem. Entrenched meanders are commonly cut off at their narrow necks, through normal erosional processes (lateral corrasion and rock weathering). Therefore, the existence of the abandoned meander is not especially noteworthy. The *incision* of such a meander, prior to cutoff, is not so easily explained, however, in an area such as this. Details of regional tectonic and geomorphic history would be required, before a definite explanation could be proposed. Two possible explanations may be considered, however.

1. *Superposition.* Prior to entrenchment the master stream could have flowed in a mature course, on an old erosional surface higher than the present upland. Epeirogenic uplift, or a change in climate, could have caused *regional* stream rejuvenation, superposing the meandering course down across resistant strata.

2. *Antecedence.* The meandering course of the river could have developed in an undisturbed, relatively nonresistant sequence of rocks (stratigraphically higher than units *A* and *B*). Relatively *local* epeirogenic warping, folding, and uplift could have produced *local* incision and entrenchment of this part of the master stream.

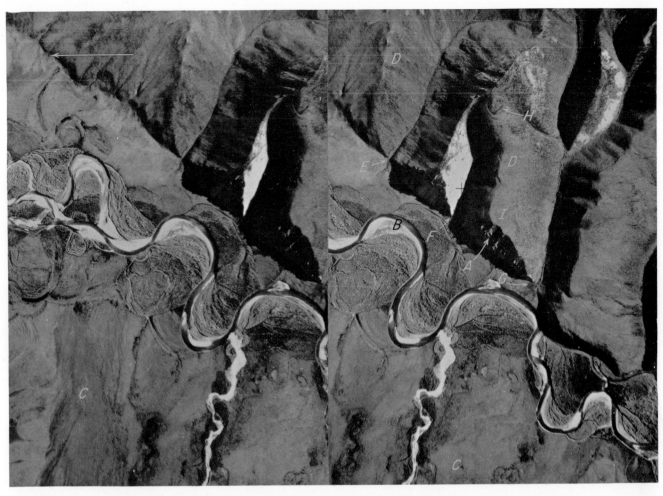

Figure 11-5. Stereogram of a possible fault-line scarp in a subarctic area. (*Courtesy of Royal Canadian Air Force.*)

POSSIBLE FAULT-LINE SCARP

Figure 8-5 shows several features which are interpreted as indicative of possible recent large-scale high-angle fault displacement along a mountain front. Stream rejuvenation, steep scarps, alluvial fans, and small scarplets (which might mark the actual fault trace) are studied and evaluated in that area.

In the area shown above, geomorphic evidence is also used to interpret the presence of a possible fault. In this area, however, the evidence suggests older fault displacement and an absence of recent crustal warping or faulting.

Consider the following features:

1. Abrupt scarp *A* marks the northeast edge of the flood plain of mature stream *B*.

2. A broad south-rising lowland (area *C*) is seen on adjacent photographs to extend uninterrupted many miles to the south. Scarp *A*, therefore, separates two regional topographic levels and is not a valley wall or side slope.

3. Each of the tributaries draining the north upland (area *D*) enters the lowland of stream *B* along a continuous grade (accordant junction). These streams do not descend over rapids or falls where they emerge from the upland valleys. See points *E*, *F*, and *G*.

4. The valley-wall slopes in upland *D*, though relatively steep, do not show evidence of stream rejuvenation.

5. Moderate southeast dip is seen at points *H* and *I*. This rules out the possibility that stream *B* and scarp *A* are in any way controlled by differential erosion of upturned beds.

A possible or questioned fault should be mapped, extending along the base of scarp *A*. Stream *B* may now flow on a considerable thickness of post-fault-displacement lowland or valley fill.

Such an interpretation may be considered reasonable, but it is definitely subject to investigation in the field, as are most geologic interpretations which are largely or completely based on geomorphic criteria.

Note the pronounced apparent eastward *slope* of the lowland, produced by photograph tilt.

12

Independent Geomorphology

INTRODUCTION

The study of areas virtually devoid of bedrock outcrop, in which an attempt is made to ascertain some structural or tectonic information through an interpretation of geomorphic features and relations, constitutes *independent geomorphology*.

Included within this category are: (1) drainage patterns and *anomalies,* (2) tonal contrasts caused by topography, soils, vegetation, and variations in water content (saturation), and (3) topographic features which can be explained by structural or stratigraphic conditions not otherwise expressed.

For many years, geologists have located salt domes in the Gulf Coast by studying drainage patterns. The popular name *creekology* has been applied to such drainage studies. Essentially, this involves the study of drainage maps and noting as *anomalous* those streams or groups of streams which deviate from the regional pattern. Local annular, radial, and occasionally centripetal patterns develop over and call attention to gradually rising salt domes or stationary domes around which settling has occurred.

With the increased use of aerial photography, mosaics eventually have replaced maps in drainage-pattern studies. Mosaics have the added advantage of depicting tonal and vegetative contrasts and cultural activity, as well as drainage lines. The slight elevation of an area that may have permitted the establishment of communities and the practice of agriculture, which would be impossible in the more moist lower areas, may be detected by studying geographic as well as geologic details.

In the following selected photographic illustrations, obvious salt domes are shown (Figures 12-1, 12-2, and 12-3). In addition, less apparent indications of locally *high* areas, suggestive of underlying salt domes, are included on Figure 12-5, a mosaic of part of the Mississippi River Delta.

Independent geomorphology may be extremely productive in glaciated plains areas and in large intermontane basins. In such areas, as in coastal areas, it does not suffice to limit the study to two-dimensional maps or mosaics. Map and mosaic examination is a productive preliminary phase, but stereoscopic analysis is required to obtain a complete impression of the geomorphic history. Too often features which appear anomalous on maps and mosaics can be explained as nonstructural features when studied in the third dimension.

In addition, many streams and areas which *do not appear* anomalous on maps and mosaics can be detected as having had an erosional history suggestive of local structural control when the entire area is examined stereoscopically.

Areas which are covered by alluvium, mantle, moraine, and outwash should be studied in this manner. In some areas the most detailed and painstaking analysis yields little or no information relative to the underlying bedrock. In other areas important tectonic trends, local gentle folds, or epeirogenic warpings may be detected.

It should be stressed that independent geomorphology studies of small coastal, plains, or basin areas are usually unproductive. The main reason for this is that the *comparison* of many features, distributed over large areas, is one of the essential aspects of such a study. A topographic *description* of a small area is quite possible; but a geomorphic analysis can only be carried out in a large area.

Figure 12-8 shows part of an area where drainage *appears* to reflect and to be somehow adjusted to the geologic controls of oil production. Figure 8-9 shows a striking stream diversion around the end of an oil field; it *does not prove* that the stream did not assume that course as a consequent stream forming on an irregular morainal surface.

The two terraces or pediment-capping surfaces shown in Figure 12-13 are not *known* to be fault-displaced parts of the same original surface.

Independent geomorphology demands deductive thinking, extremely thorough photograph study, the use of all other available geologic data, and, finally, a summary of possible alternative explanations for favorable-appearing features.

Such studies must never be assumed to provide conclusive proof of favorable structural conditions. In most cases, immediate leasing and drilling of geomorphic anomalies would be unwise. However, independent geomorphology studies can be used to point out the areas in which seismic and other geophysical programs should be concentrated.

Experience has shown that photogeomorphic analysis of areas for which geophysical work is planned usually produces enough reliable data to effect a considerable saving in both time and costs, by guiding the selection of proper line direction and spacing, and by directing attention to the more anomalous areas. The resulting saving of geophysical costs frequently far exceeds the original cost of the photogeomorphic study.

Areas which appear anomalous to both the photogeomorphologist and the geophysicist should be given first priority in subsequent land acquisition and drilling budgets.

Figure 12-1. Topographic map of a circular topographic high, directly underlain by a salt dome, in a coastal swamp area.

SALT DOMES

This is the type of area where drainage-pattern studies are frequently practiced by professional geologists and laymen alike. The two salt-dome hills are obvious on the topographic maps; one is clearly defined on the mosaic. Both are well outlined by annular drainage.

Many salt domes are expressed topographically by relief differentials which are far less than the one hundred or more feet shown here. In fact, salt domes are occasionally detected by anomalous topographic differentials of one or two feet.

The mosaic shows two other natural features which assist in defining the dome: vegetation contrast and general photographic tonal contrast (due largely to differences in soil and moisture content).

In both areas shown here, the salt is either at or very near the surface of the topographic dome. Note the mine-quarry symbols and the several lake depressions resulting from solution.

Refer to Figures 12-4 and 12-5, a map and mosaic of another area of salt domes. The criteria applicable in that area are different from those used here.

EXERCISES

1. On Figure 12-1 numerous stream valleys are defined by contour configurations. Add all such streams to the map.

2. Can the domal uplift shown in Figure 12-1 be said to have radial as well as annular drainage?

3. Devise a regional drainage map of a hypothetical area showing: (a) regional south-flowing streams, (b) a local area of radial drainage, and (c) well-defined associated annular drainage. In part of the area include an isolated small centripetal drainage pattern.

4. In some Gulf coastal areas a system of northwest- and northeast-trending regional fractures and small faults can be detected by noting linear streams and stream segments. Stream segments A, B, and C, on Figure 12-3, could be adjusted along such a system. Devise a regional drainage map of a hypothetical area (25 miles square) showing: (a) regional gentle south slope, (b) in the north half principally insequent and consequent drainage, (c) in the south half numerous subsequent tributaries and stream segments which define a northwest-northeast fracture-fault system, and (d) drainage anomalies which define a salt dome in each quadrant of the map area.

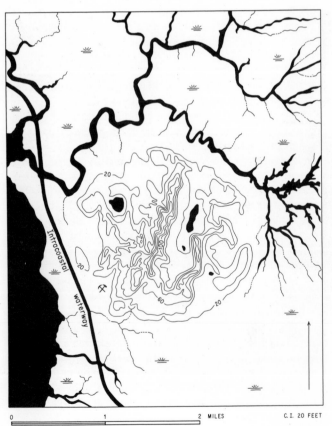

Figure 12-2. Topographic map of a circular topographic high, directly underlain by a salt dome, in a coastal swamp area. This area is shown on the mosaic, Figure 12-3.

Figure 12-3. Mosaic of a circular topographic high, directly underlain by a salt dome. The surrounding area is a lowland coastal swamp. (*By permission from Edgar Tobin Aerial Surveys.*)

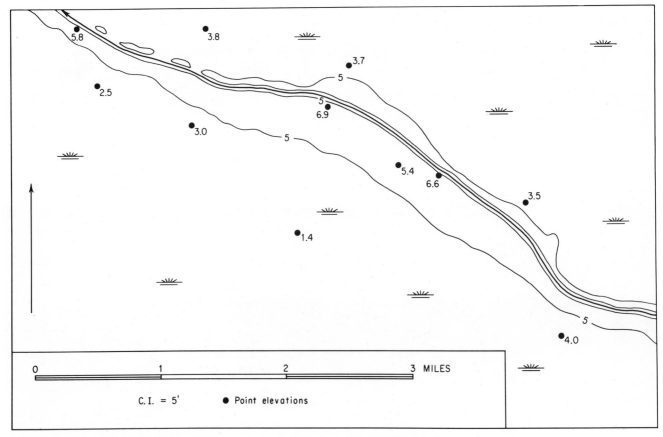

Figure 12-4. Topographic map of part of the lower Mississippi River Delta. This area is included in the north part of the mosaic (Figure 12-5).

SALT DOMES

This is an area of salt domes, many of which have associated oil traps.

There is no bedrock outcrop here. The land surface, that which is not under water or nearly saturated, consists essentially of detritus derived from the waters of the Mississippi River and its distributaries.

The mosaic demonstrates two indications of possible positive structures. They are alike in what they indicate, but different insofar as the features themselves are concerned.

Study feature *ABCD*, the cultivated natural levee of a northwest-flowing distributary or bayou of the Mississippi River system. The narrow dark line passing along the central part of the belt is the present bayou. The light, geometric areas are cultivated plots. The dark areas to the north and south are dense swamp forests. This part of the mosaic area is shown on Figure 12-4.

At point *D* the natural levee is relatively low, and the part above swamp level is quite narrow. At point *C*, downstream from point *D*, the dry cultivated area widens abruptly and, as the map shows, attains a slight increase in elevation toward point *B*.

The bayou has an extremely gentle gradient toward the northwest. Between points *D* and *B*, however, the natural levee rises in that direction. This is a topographic and, in a way, a drainage anomaly. Stream pattern or configuration is of no importance; differential relief is.

A rising salt dome could have lifted part *B* of the levee. A second possibility might be that a salt dome, situated below this part of the levee, locally prevented subsidence of the levee material, while noticeable subsidence did occur upstream to the southeast.

The entire area to the southwest of the levee is what appears to be a former tidal flat. Note the course of the former tidal stream which extends from point *E* through points *F*, *G*, *H*, *I*, and *J*. The several straight lines in this area, such as feature *K*, are artificial canals, used for water transportation and access to oil rigs.

At the time this area was a tidal flat, open water was to the south. Stream *EJ* undoubtedly was a complete channel. At the present time, however, segment *F* is occupied by water, as is segment *H*. Segment *G* is restricted. In fact, most of the connection between segments *F* and *H* is by way of the canals. Segment *G* is near water level, as evidenced by the local concentration of trees along its former channel.

At point *I* the lake segment *H* pinches out. From point *I* through segment *J* to the mosaic border, the former stream channel is completely above water level and is traceable only as a vegetation and tonal band.

Relatively speaking, segments *F* and *H* may be said to be *low*, and segments *G* and *IJ high*. Differential elevations along the entire stream course are probably not more than two or three feet.

In salt-dome exploration, areas *G* and *J* would be designated as anomalous. Note the intricate canal system in area *L*. At the end of each "tributary" canal is a well site. This is an oil-producing salt dome. It lies midway between anomaly *G* and anomaly *B*, suggesting a northeast-trending structural high, centering at area *L*.

Anomaly *J* does not define a specific area. The only impression obtained in this area is that of a structural rise to the southeast from point *H* to point *J*. At the east border of the mosaic, in area *M*, is a concentration of well sites. It may be that anomaly *J* lies on the west flank of a large structure centering at or near area *M*.

Former tidal stream *NO* becomes narrow downstream, from segment *N* toward segment *O*. This could also reflect a

Figure 12-5. Mosaic of an area in the lower Mississippi River Delta. (*By permission from Jack Ammann Photogrammetric Engineers, Inc.*)

marginal rise, on the west flank of a large structural high which includes areas *J* and *M*. It could also result from a local domal structure at or to the south of point *O*.

Once pointed out, such criteria as those discussed above are obvious. In undertaking the study of a plains, basin, or coastal area, however, the photogeomorphologist must not search only for criteria that have "worked" in other areas. He must study *all* features and relations closely, and attempt to discern new and different types of criteria. These must then be thoroughly interpreted.

No two areas are exactly the same. In no two areas should significant criteria be expected to be the same. An anomaly in one area might have a structural cause. In another area, an identical-appearing anomaly might bear no relation whatsoever to bedrock structure.

Photogeomorphology should not only be the mapping of anomalous features, but also the scientific attempt to understand and evaluate them. This cannot be done by the use of *keys!* To a considerable degree, in many areas, identification keys may be helpful. *The only true keys to interpretation are the background, experience, and ability of the photogeologist.*

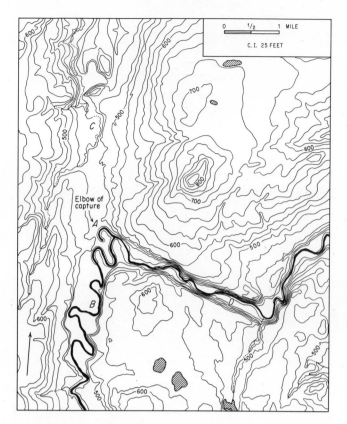

It is a common experience for the photogeologist to encounter unexplainable and unprovable *apparent* relations. This area is one which poses this problem.

It lies within a region of glaciated plains. No outcrop is visible on the aerial photographs. Ground moraine and possibly outwash materials completely cover the nearly horizontal bedrock.

Attention is first called to the area by the recent (late post-Pleistocene) stream capture shown on the two maps and the stereogram. Stream *B* formerly flowed northward, along valley *C*. It was captured at point *A*, and diverted along linear valley *D*. Valley *D* could not have been cut by the captor stream; its walls are too linear and steep; its width too constant and too great. This valley was a glacial runoff channel or coulee, later used by stream *D* as a route of rapid headward (westward) extension.

The recency of the capture is attested by the well-preserved meanders (i.e., features *E* and *F*) and by the sharp cusps (feature *G*) and bluffs (feature *H*) of the abandoned valley *C*.

Figure 12-6. Topographic map of a glaciated plains area. Prominent is an elbow of recent stream capture.

Figure 12-7. Regional map showing oil fields, gas wells, and major drainage of a large glaciated plains area. Outline of area included in Figure 12-6 is shown.

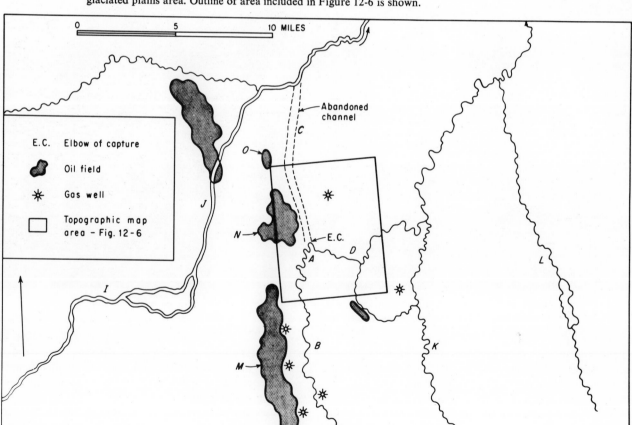

Figure 12-8. Stereogram of a glaciated plains area. Prominent is an elbow of recent stream capture (point *A*). (*Reproduced by courtesy of the Technical Division of the Department of Lands and Forests, Edmonton, Alberta.*)

Note (on Figure 12-7) the regional stream pattern, especially the northward "deflection" of stream *I* to course *J*, and the subparallel arrangement of streams *J*, *B*, *K*, and *L*. These suggest subsequent adjustment along regional strike, although along most, if not all, of their courses, these streams flow in glacial material.

Also note the remarkable alignment of oil field *M*, parallel to stream *B*, and the positions of fields *N* and *O* with respect to abandoned channel *C*.

If there is an *actual* correlation between production and drainage, it may be that the oil is structurally trapped and that the regional drainage flows along linear lowlands developed as subsequent preglacial valleys, incompletely obscured by glacial debris, and reoccupied by postglacial consequent drainage.

EXERCISE

Suppose the oil were reported to be produced from a stratigraphic trap, consisting of up-dip limestone cuestas covered by younger strata. What near-surface *structure* might then explain a production-drainage correlation?

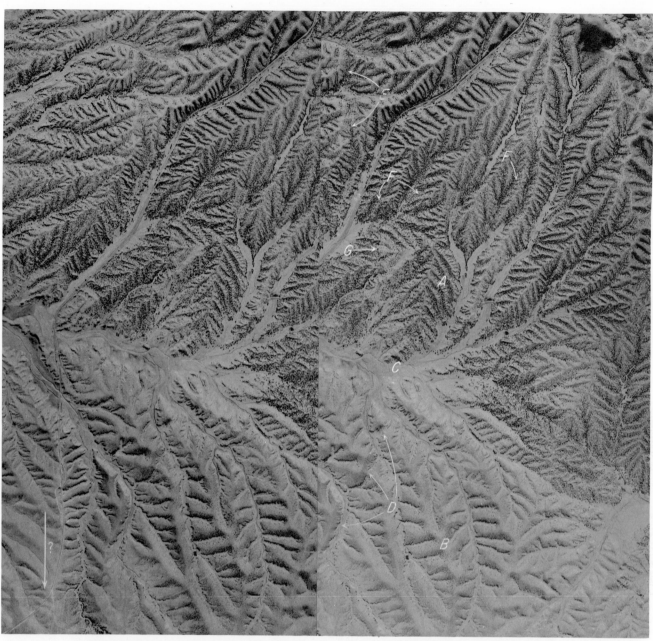

Figure 12-9. Stereogram of possible faults in an area of dissected Quaternary gravels and sands. (*Courtesy of U.S. Geological Survey.*)

POSSIBLE FAULTS IN INTERMONTANE AREA

This is an intermontane area in a semiarid climate zone. The area shown consists of relatively thick unconsolidated and semiconsolidated gravels and sands derived from nearby mountains.

Note the contrast in drainage density and vegetation between the areas to the north (area *A*) and south (area *B*) of stream valley *C*. These characteristics indicate a difference in the materials exposed in the two areas.

One possible explanation is that stream *C* is a subsequent stream, developed along a major fault zone, and that fault displacement has brought different strata to the level of erosion.

An alternate, nonstructural, hypothesis to explain the contrast between areas *A* and *B* is that the source areas of the two areas consist of different types of rock. Detritus derived from different types of rock could well be sufficiently

different in composition, grain size, and cementation to produce contrasting topography and to support different vegetation under identical climatic conditions. However, this possibility does not explain the linearity of the line which separates the two areas.

Probable small faults are noted along lines *D* and *E*. Line *F* is an ill-defined east-trending line which might be a fault trace. At point *G* is a north-trending, west-facing scarp which may be fault-controlled.

EXERCISES

1. Discuss the topography in area *A* and compare it with that in area *B*. What lithologic differences between the materials in the two areas might explain the different topographic details?

2. Trace several other possible faults and list the criteria used in their selection.

Figure 12-10. Stereogram of an annular drainage pattern in an area of faulted and tilted extrusive volcanic rocks. (*Courtesy of U.S. Dept. of Agriculture, Soil Conservation Service.*)

ANNULAR AND RADIAL DRAINAGE PATTERN

This is a drainage anomaly, defined by an annular arrangement of streams *A* and *B*. Radial drainage, centering at the northern part (point *C*) of the outlined oval area, is also present.

In this area the dominant structural grain trends east and west. An impression of regional strike may be obtained from the outcrop area of the highly jointed resistant rocks. These rocks, which extend across the area from point *D* to point *E*, have many of the characteristics (resistance, tone, fractures) of bedded rhyolites.

The rocks in the north half of the stereo model are not identified. The area is too limited, and diagnostic identification characteristics are lacking. Surfaces *F* are probably dip slopes.

Two probable explanations for the anomaly may be advanced, both of which would require field study to substantiate or refute:

1. A local domal structure caused by the intrusion of an oval or circular stock at depth
2. An annular fracture or fault pattern, also resulting from local intrusion and vertical pressure from below

Such a feature as this could lead to the discovery, through drilling, of economically important intrusive and alteration materials which may not be exposed or otherwise indicated on the surface.

EXERCISE

Assign genetic designations to several of the streams within the stereo-model area.

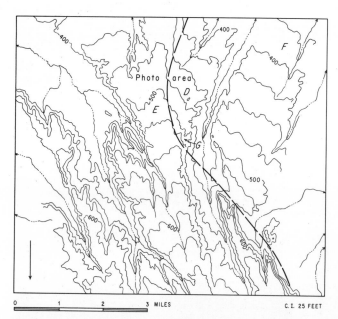

Figure 12-11. Incomplete topographic map of a dissected gravel-capped pediment.

Figure 12-12. Sketch map showing oil fields and lines defined by topographic breaks in slope on gravel-capped pediments.

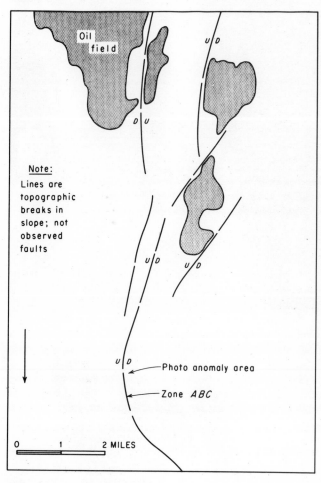

Note:

Lines are topographic breaks in slope; not observed faults

Oil field

Photo anomaly area

Zone *ABC*

0   1   2 MILES

POSSIBLE FAULTED PEDIMENT

This is an area of widespread gravel-capped pediment remnants, frequently referred to as *terraces* or *benches*.

On the photographs, no bedrock is visible, and no impressions of strike and dip can be obtained. Bedrock is completely covered.

In this area are several oil fields (see Figure 12-12). Oil accumulations are reported to be controlled entirely by stratigraphic traps. A regional east-trending structural warp or arch lies several miles to the north.

The break in the upland surface of the pediment-capping materials (zone *ABC*) is shown in the stereo model. Extensive farming has obscured this feature in places. The topographic map shows that the lower surface *D* lies 15 to 20 feet below the upper surface *E*.

It also shows something of great possible importance which cannot be detected in the small area included in the stereo model. The average slope of surface *E* is about 37 feet per mile. Direction of slope is about N 25° W. Slope *D*, which has a direction of about N 35° E, varies from as little as 35 feet per mile at point *F* to over 63 feet per mile at point *G*.

Pediment slopes represent the gradients of the streams which cut them. The slopes of the capping sands and gravels coincide with the gradients and directions of the streams which deposited them.

Zone *ABC* shows no evidence of having been cut by the headward erosion of northeast-flowing streams. North- and northwest-flowing streams cannot easily be imagined cutting slope *D*.

Therefore, the differential in slope elevation, direction, and magnitude may be explained (but not with certainty) by post-gravel-deposition normal faulting.

The possibility of fault movement is strengthened by the remarkable coincidence of the edges of the oil fields with several such topographic lines or zones. This same coincidence would introduce some question into the proposition that the oil fields were entirely stratigraphically controlled.

Features such as zone *ABC* and the analysis of their possible structural importance emphasize two basic problems with which the photogeologist must work.

1. Faults, folds, warps, and regional tilts need not be *old*. In many areas of North America studied by the writer, an impressive number of Quaternary and even Recent faults have been observed on aerial photographs.

2. Photogeology may influence not only an individual's thinking, but even the exploration program and evaluation methods of a department or company. The fact that prior to a photogeologic study some concepts are accepted, and others are not, should not deter the photogeologist from *interpreting* what he *sees* nor limit his thinking to terms of what is *supposed* to be present.

In connection with the original study of this area, the following facts and observations should be pointed out:

1. The location of the arcuate topographic break was made during the stereoscopic study of the area. This is definitely not a feature that could be detected through a two-dimensional mosaic study.

2. Once the feature was observed on the photographs, and no evidence was noted to suggest multiple pedimentation

Figure 12-13. Stereogram of a gravel-capped pediment surface. Note break in slope along zone *ABC*. (*Courtesy of U.S. Dept. of Agriculture, Commodity Stabilization Service.*)

by cyclic stream behavior, the geomorphologist sought an explanation elsewhere. It was at this point that the topographic map was restudied.

3. This feature illustrates the way that photographic, topographic, and subsurface data are integrated in a comprehensive photogeomorphic study.

4. Even if this is a bona fide stratigraphic trap area, it is possible that the observed possible faults are actual Recent faults, that they reflect minor readjustments along older tectonic trends, and that at the time the stratigraphic traps were deposited, fault-produced submarine topography could have caused significant variations in facies and thickness.

13

Routine Photogeology

INTRODUCTION

Photogeologic mapping and interpretation are relatively easy and straightforward in areas where most of the bedrock is clearly expressed and where the various rock units can be delineated.

Actual outcrop is often not required. Distinct soil, vegetation, tonal, and topographic contrasts frequently disclose more information than do barren rock exposures.

In many of the following illustrations considerable bedrock is exposed. In others residual soils mask the bedrock. In some the structure is extremely simple. In others it is complex.

The single element present in all the areas is that the principal geologic relations can be mapped with considerable assurance.

Several of the illustrations selected for this chapter typify areas in which some of the earliest commercial photogeology was carried out. In a way, therefore, the student of photogeology, in progressing through this and the succeeding two chapters, will reenact the history of the application of aerial photographs in geological mapping, exploration, and interpretation over the past two decades. Photogeology began in areas where the geology was clearly expressed and gradually extended out into those areas where an increasing number of difficulties were encountered. At the present time there remains *no* area where *some* geological information, however scant, cannot be expected from a thorough and careful analysis of aerial photographs.

It is rather interesting to note that little more than ten years ago *only* areas such as those here classified as *routine* were considered by most geologists to be areas "where photogeology could be used." It is equally interesting that at that time extremely few photogeologists were on the scene to dispute such statements and to point out the value of aerial photographs in the more difficult areas.

Today most of us take areas of *routine* photogeology for granted. These are the areas that can be mapped with relative success and accuracy by the inexperienced photogeologic trainee. It should not be forgotten, however, that so few years have passed since both the photogeologist and the person who had occasion to use his map were equally pleased if not somewhat amazed by the vast amount of geologic information obtainable from photographs of areas such as these.

At this point it is sincerely hoped that the reader will accept one word of advice. Do not be misled by the fact that the following illustrations have been classified as *routine* or *easy*. In comparison with those selected for inclusion in the last two chapters, especially Chapter 15, such a classification is warranted. But it will be in the present chapter, where you have examples of *routine* photogeology, that you can learn to detect, identify, and *understand* many essential criteria and to appreciate such important factors as the interrelations among structure, lithology, and geomorphic expression. These and other criteria and interrelations, though not so well expressed or revealed in the areas of more difficult photogeology, are the same tools with which you must attack the latter areas. Therefore, you are urged to be especially painstaking in your study of the photo illustrations in this chapter.

Do not permit yourself to be satisfied by the fact that you can *see* certain geologic features and relations. Instead, you should constantly ask yourself *why* you can see them and, if possible, try to imagine how the geology of each area would appear under different conditions of climate, geographic location, and stage of erosional development.

True, these are the *routine* areas, but in many ways from the standpoint of the student of photogeology they are also the *most important*.

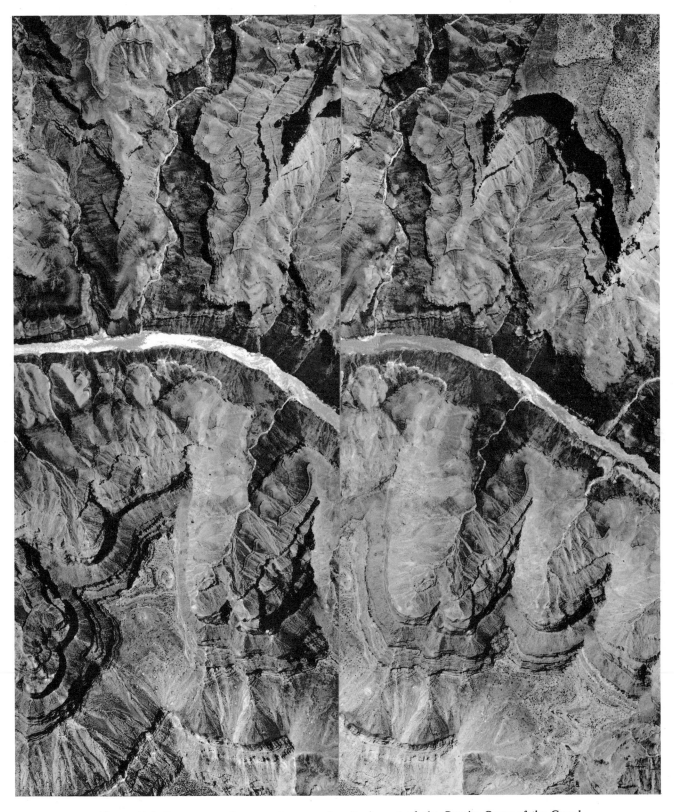

Figure 13-1. Stereogram of an angular unconformity in part of the Granite Gorge of the Grand Canyon of the Colorado River, Arizona. (*Courtesy of U.S. Dept. of Agriculture, Forest Service.*)

THE GRAND CANYON

This illustration is intended primarily as an exercise in tracing and correlating stratigraphic units and in attempting to determine lithology through a study of topographic features and relations.

The area shown is located at latitude 36°20′ N, longitude 112°27′ W. There is some published information pertaining to this area. Much has been written about the general Grand Canyon region.

Note the angular unconformity in the lower canyon walls.

Judging from the shadows, indicate approximate true-north direction.

VOLCANIC NECK AND DIKES

This is an area of contrasts. The dominant feature, topographically, geologically, and from the ground, scenically, is the imposing buttress of the isolated volcanic neck *A*, in the north part of the area.

Surrounding the isolated peak is a lowland underlain by a series of relatively nonresistant strata. At points *B* and *C*, alternate layers of light-gray and medium-gray, nearly horizontal sediments are noted. At those places, and at point *D*, the rocks are intricately dissected, suggesting high shale or clay content. The generally poor resistance of these rocks also indicates shale-clay composition.

Radiating outward from the volcanic neck are several linear, narrow, dark wall-like ridges. These are basic dikes. They are more resistant than the surrounding country rock and owe their positive topographic expression to prolonged differential erosion.

The main volcanic core is surrounded by several small subsidiary vents, each of which stands as an individual low pinnacle. They include features *E*, *F*, *G*, *H*, and *I*.

The numerous white dots, in the southern part of the left photograph, do not appear on the right photograph. There are many similar dots on the right photograph which do not appear on the left photograph. They are imperfections in the prints. Similarly, feature *J*, the long white mark on the right photograph, is an imperfection, probably having been caused in the laboratory.

These photographs are parts of four-lens composite photographs, formerly in wide use in governmental survey projects. As shown here, the "match" lines are commonly marked by abrupt tonal contrasts. If the match isn't perfect, linear apparent topographic offsets result.

There are several man-made features in this area which might cause some confusion. Note lines *K* and *L*. In places, these lines are followed by straight tributary stream segments.

Where line *L* extends northward into the dark alluvial area as line *M*, its light tone and lack of topographic expression combine to suggest a cultural rather than a geological origin. These lines may be old trails. Light-toned line *N* is an apparently usable trail or secondary road.

EXERCISES

1. Trace all dikes and outline all isolated intrusive bodies in purple.

2. Outline in orange all areas covered by stream alluvium and other unconsolidated mantle.

3. South of the large volcanic neck, trace in green the numerous individual beds exposed. Assign numbers or letters to these beds and attempt to correlate them from one outcrop area to another.

4. View the peak from directly above. It should appear to lean to the north. Point *P* is the center of the right photograph. The center of the left photograph lies beyond the left border of the stereogram, along center line *Q*. Move the stereoscope around, maintaining a stereoscopic impression of peak *A*. Find a viewing position from which peak *A* appears to stand vertically. In this viewing position, where is the right lens with respect to point *P*?

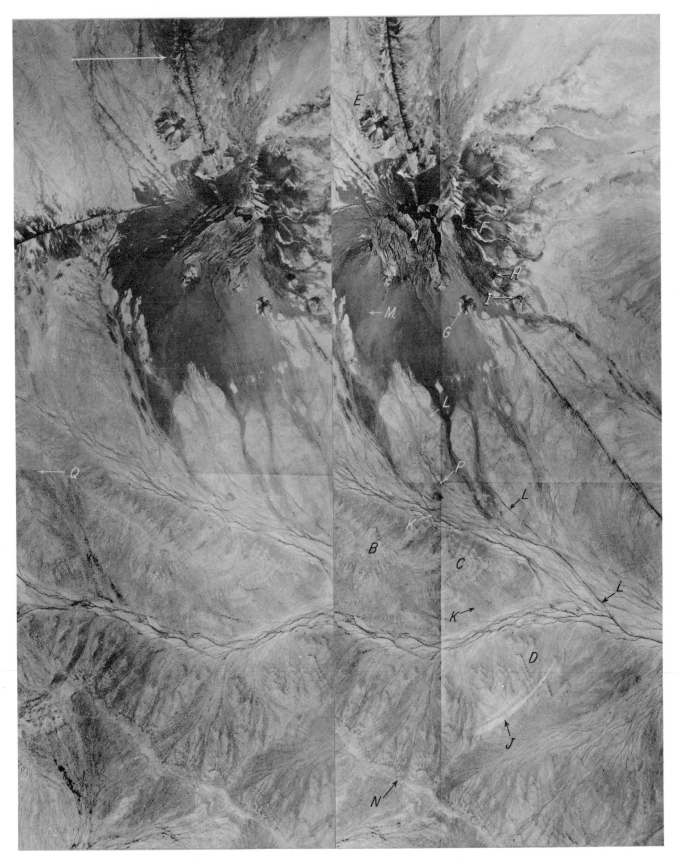

Figure 13-2. Stereogram of an eroded volcanic plug, with radiating resistant dikes. Four-lens photographs. (*Courtesy of U.S. Dept. of Agriculture, Soil Conservation Service.*)

INTRUSIVE ROCKS AND FOLDED STRATA

This is an area of folded sedimentary rocks which have been intruded by a large volcanic neck with accompanying radiating dikes.

A small part of the area (the volcanic neck area) is shown on Figure 13-2, a stereogram. To permit proper stereoscopic viewing, the photographs of the stereogram are oriented differently than is the mosaic shown here. In this figure, true north lies toward the top of the page.

It is a relatively common practice for a photogeologist to examine mosaics prior to or concurrent with the stereoscopic study of contact prints of an area. In addition, a photo index may be studied before the contact prints are either ordered or received.

This is an excellent mosaic to demonstrate some of the types of data to be derived from such a two-dimensional photograph study.

The most obvious feature, of course, is the volcanic neck and radiating dikes. Even without knowing what they are, a correct identification would not be difficult. The considerable apron of dark detritus in area *A,* and in similar dark areas *B* and *C,* indicates erosion of the neck and dikes. The true width of the south-trending dike is obvious at point *D* and can be seen, with careful study, at point *E.* Similarly, the width of the western dike is clearly defined at point *F.*

The neck and, more important, the dikes, are a source of erosional material. It can therefore be deduced that these features stand higher than the adjacent terrain. Erosion has had considerable time to bring this about.

Belts *G* and *H* are sedimentary outcrops. The linearity at point *G* indicates steep dip. The more irregular trend at point *H* at first suggests lower, but still appreciable dip. Lower topographic relief, and consequently steeper dip, are suggested by the narrower shadow bands along belt *H.* Here variations in outcrop trend may be the result of changes in strike. Outcrop patterns at points *I* and *J* suggest relatively low dip in these areas.

With the exception of the radiating basic dikes, the dark lines and irregular patches are shadows. The rocks casting those shadows must be quite resistant. The smooth, shadow-less bands probably represent shale lowlands.

An excellent impression of structure can be obtained at point *K* and at several points nearby to the northwest, along the prominent hogback outcrop. At point *K* the hogback is crossed by a northeast-flowing tributary to stream *L.* The ridge-crest outcrop makes a sharp swing to the east, down to stream level. The west-facing outcrop bands, to the north and south of this point, are gently curved and arcuate. Dip here is to the east. This fact can be extrapolated, to permit the assumption of east dip from this point northward to the edge of the mosaic, and southward to point *J.*

Similar criteria applied at point *M* provide indications of north dip. When these beds are followed southward, to belt *G,* east dip is again established.

With these factors determined, it is possible to indicate, passing between points *J* and *M,* a northeast-plunging syncline, and immediately southeast of point *M,* a northeast-plunging anticlinal nose.

The area to the east of outcrop belts *G* and *H* appears to be devoid of obvious outcrops. However, as seen on Figure 13-2, flat-lying shaly or clayey beds occur at point *N,* and it may be assumed that similar rocks are present at several places throughout the remainder of the central and eastern lowland areas.

In these areas are good examples of features which might be confused or misidentified. In addition to the linear dikes, other somewhat similar-appearing linear features may be noted, including feature *O,* which is a road, and feature *P,* which is a stream. Other vegetation, drainage, and tonal lineations require caution before identification is attempted. In some instances it would be advisable to withhold identification until the specific features could be examined stereoscopically on the larger-scale contact prints.

SUGGESTED PROJECT

This is an excellent area to study as part of a practical or academic training program. Geographic coordinates are: latitudes 36°30′ to 36°45′ N; longitudes 108°45′ to 109° W.

The mosaic reproduced here is one of a series of 15-minute quadrangle photo maps, scale 1 inch to 1 mile, available from Fairchild Aerial Surveys, Inc. (Address inquiries regarding availability and prices to the Los Angeles office.)

A 15-minute quadrangle mosaic of the area may be obtained from the U.S. Department of Agriculture, Soil Conservation Service. This government agency can also supply stereoscopic coverage of the entire area. These photographs have a scale of 1:31,680 and were taken in 1935 by a four-lens camera having a focal length of 6 inches. Figure 13-2 is a stereogram of two photographs of this coverage.

Government photography can be purchased only on a prepayment basis. Orders *by area* are not filled. It is necessary to obtain photo-index sheets first, and from them prepare a list of specific photographs by *reference number.* This list must then be submitted, accompanied by a check or money order.

There is a U.S. Geological Survey topographic map of this area. Several geologic maps and references to the area are also available. Appropriate topographic and geologic index maps should be consulted for further information.

If a mosaic or photo map, stereoscopic photo coverage, topographic map, and geologic data are obtained, the student can carry out a complete photogeologic study of the area, including photograph annotation, compilation to mosaic or mosaic overlay, transfer to base map, map coloring, and the writing of a report.

If this is a class laboratory or special assignment, it is suggested that two students be assigned to each single project. Each can make his own interpretation and map; however each should have the opportunity to check his colleague's work and the advantage of having his own work checked.

Figure 13-3. Mosaic of an area of folded sedimentary strata and igneous intrusive rocks, in an arid area. See Figure 13-2. (*By permission from Fairchild Aerial Surveys, Inc.*)

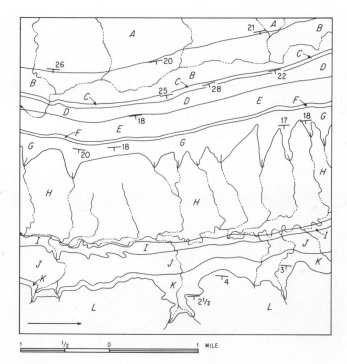

Figure 13-4. Geologic map of a sequence of south-dipping sedimentary strata. *A,* clays and friable sandstones? *B,* nonresistant mudstones and sandstones; *C,* sandstone; *D,* siltstones and sandstones; *E,* variegated shales and clays; *F,* cross-bedded sandstones; *G,* sandstones, siltstones, and limestones; *H,* cross-bedded sandstones; *I,* mudstones and sandstones; *J,* sandstones; *K,* sandstones, sandy siltstones and shales; *L,* sandstones.

HOMOCLINE IN SEMIARID AREA

This area offers the student an excellent opportunity to study the influence of lithology on topography, under semi-arid climatic conditions. Much of the bedrock is exposed, and very little vegetation is present.

Many of the relations and principles shown here can be used in areas of widespread mantle and soil cover, extensive vegetation, or appreciable agriculture. The primary factors are: relative rock resistance, color, and composition.

Briefly refer to each mapped stratigraphic unit, designated by corresponding letters on the stereogram.

A. The clay members permit the development of the intricate drainage system. The apparently thin sandstone members are resistant enough to maintain small dip slopes (i.e., slope *a*).

B. The mudstones and sandstones of this unit must be extremely nonresistant, to permit planation (as of surface *b*) and the selective course of subsequent (strike) stream *c*. Were the geologic map not available, this unit would probably be assumed to be a shale formation.

C. Unit *C* is expressed as a well-defined low bluff. The pronounced linearity of the south side (feature *d*) of the flood plain indicates locally high resistance to lateral corrasion.

D and *E.* These units are truncated by linear pediment surface *e,* which is in most places capped by gravel and sand. In area *f* unit *D* is exposed. Unit *E* outcrops in area *g.* Note here the extremes of photographic tones (white and black bands), typical expressions of variegated beds. The upper part of unit *E* occurs in the steep obsequent slope of the main ridge. It is partly mantled by debris descending from the ridge crest. Some of this debris consists of large sandstone blocks. Pedestal rocks may have developed at the base of the scarp (see point *h*).

F. This unit must crop out as a narrow band, along the upper steep part of the obsequent ridge slope. Its contact

with overlying unit *G* can only be approximated. Its composition can only be supposed by the fact that it maintains such a steep slope.

G. Several rock types are included in this map unit. Note the strike joints *i* and *j* (accentuated by vegetation), the nonresistant (siltstone?) unit *k* near the top, the dip slope *l,* and the north-south joints or erosional lines *m* (festoon cross-bedding?).

H. The canyons (feature *n*), the cross-bedding (feature *o*), and the over-all resistance of this unit combine to facilitate its mapping, identification, and, were it to occur elsewhere in a project area, its correlation. The uppermost part of this unit must be shaly or silty, as indicated by its mapped upper contact with unit *I* (see Figure 13-4), lying in part south of the large subsequent stream *p.*

EXERCISES

1. Describe the photographic characteristics of units *I, J, K,* and *L.* Explain the features noted.
2. Note the contrast between the flood plain of stream *c* and the entrenchment of stream *p.* This cannot be explained by conditions observed within the area shown. List as many *possible* explanations as possible.
3. Draw an exaggerated north-south topographic profile across the stereo model, passing through letter *G* (on the photograph).
4. Determine the approximate vertical exaggeration of the stereo model, by comparing the apparent dip of unit *G* and the 17° and 18° dips shown on the map.
5. Using the computed approximate vertical exaggeration factor, make a *true* topographic profile along the line used in Exercise 3.
6. To the reduced profile, add a geologic cross section. Indicate those parts of the stratigraphic section which outcrop and those parts which are covered by slope mantle, pediment capping, and flood-plain alluvium (entrenched as well as along present stream level).

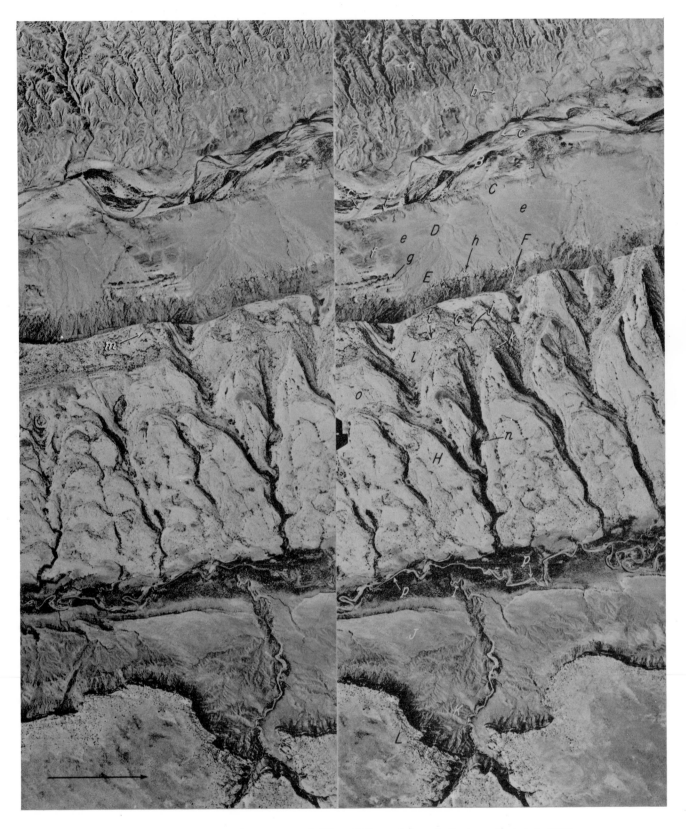

Figure 13-5. Stereogram of a sequence of differentially eroded south-dipping sedimentary strata in a semiarid area. (*By permission from Fairchild Aerial Surveys, Inc.*)

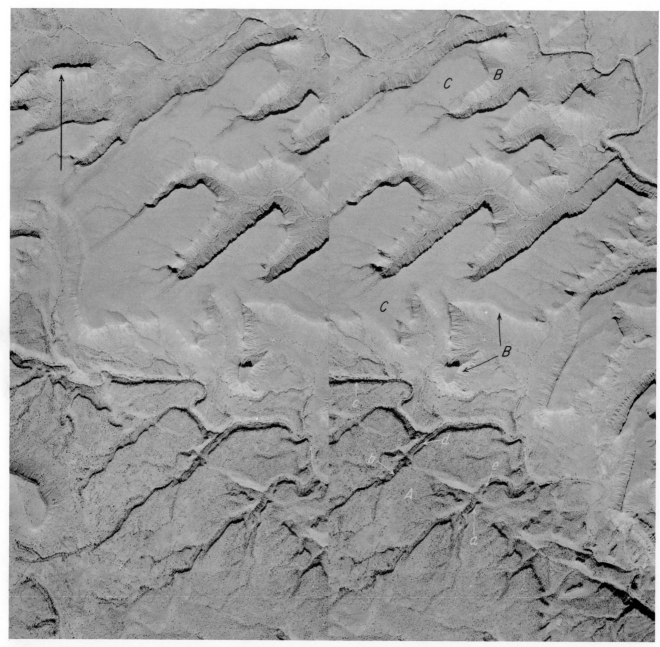

Figure 13-6. Stereogram of joint-controlled drainage in an area of gently dipping sedimentary strata. Arid to semiarid climate.

(Courtesy of U.S. Dept. of Agriculture, Soil Conservation Service.)

JOINTED STRATA

Stream adjustment to parallel northeast-trending joints and small faults is outstanding in this area.

Dip is eastward in the south half and southeastward in the north half of the area.

The following arbitrary stratigraphic map units may be delineated and traced across the entire stereo model:

Unit *A*, the oldest unit, consists of interbedded resistant and nonresistant strata. Note the cliffs formed by the highly jointed upper member (i.e., at points *a, b,* and *c*) and the widespread vegetation this member supports. Note the smooth gentler slopes formed on the underlying nonresistant (shale?) member (i.e., at points *d* and *e*).

Unit *B* is a light-toned sequence of nonresistant beds, possibly shales or clays. Note the closely spaced gullies which drain the slopes underlain by these beds.

Unit *C* is a medium-toned, relatively thin unit, including at least two thin resistant members (at the top and bottom). It is stripped, to form excellent dip slopes.

EXERCISES

1. The approximate location of this area is latitude 39°00′ N and longitude 110°36′ W, Emery County, Utah. Search the geologic literature of this area to obtain data which will permit a tentative identification of the strata and a better understanding of the lithologies exposed.

2. Trace all faults in red and, where possible, indicate relative displacement for each. Trace all joints in pink. Trace stratigraphic contacts in purple, and several key or marker beds in green. Be consistent in showing offsets produced by fault displacements. Throughout the stereo-model area indicate strikes and dips.

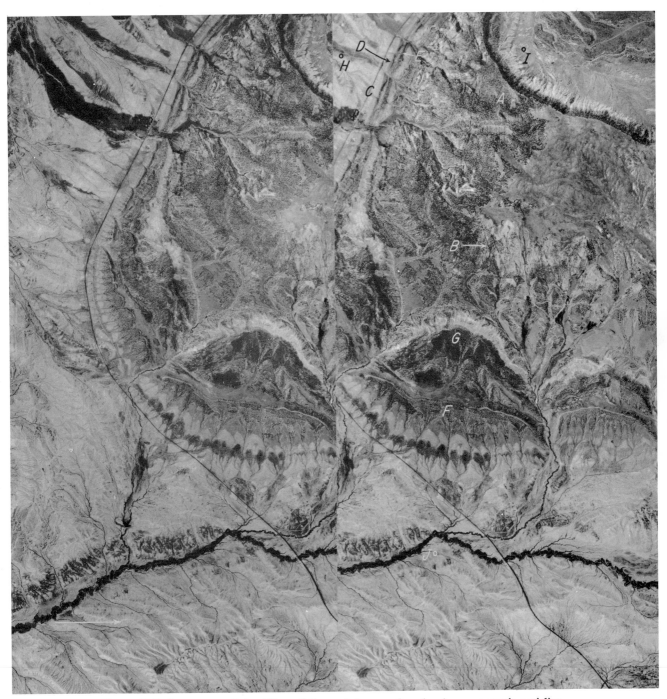

Figure 13-7. Stereogram of the differentially eroded nose of a plunging asymmetric anticline. (*By permission from Fairchild Aerial Surveys, Inc.*)

ANTICLINAL NOSE

The many dip slopes and outcrops in this area permit the rapid mapping of the essential structural relations.

Most of the bedrock consists of sandstones and shales. In the preliminary study of this area, it would be acceptable to consider the resistant units to be sandstones and the non-resistant units to be shales.

The oldest resistant unit (area *A*) is considerably jointed. Intersecting joints are clearly expressed in dip slope *B*.

This area offers an excellent opportunity to study the inverse dip-ridge height and dip-outcrop width relations which occasionally permit the detection of dip change in areas of covered or obscured strata. Note the steep dip and low straight ridges in area *C*. Here outcrop width is extremely narrow. Beds *D* and *E* can be traced southward to form secondary ridge *F* and high peak *G*, respectively. Here outcrop width is much greater, as is ridge height.

EXERCISES

1. Draw vertically exaggerated topographic profiles and geologic cross sections along lines *HI* and *JI*.

2. Draw a second set of profiles and cross sections along these lines, reduced to "true" vertical scale (assume a vertical exaggeration factor of 3.0).

177

Figure 13-8. Stereogram of a homocline in a sequence of shales and sandstones. Climate is semiarid. (*Courtesy of U.S. Air Force.*)

SMALL-SCALE PHOTOGRAPHY

The photographs of Figures 13-8 and 13-9 are so-called *high-altitude* photographs. Photograph scale is approximately 1 mile to the inch, which is considerably smaller than the scales of most other available government and commercial photography.

The strata in these areas consist essentially of shales and sandstones. Bentonite is present in some of the formations.

In Figure 13-8 most of the area is underlain by shales. The intricate dissection of these rocks is typical of shale areas. Two southwest-dipping sandstone beds (beds *A* and *B*) interrupt the shale topography. Bed *B* is the more resistant, as indicated by its slightly higher ridge crest, its more sharply defined outcrop, and its dip slopes. The abrupt north end of bed *C* is suggestive of fault truncation. Insufficient area is shown to permit an assured interpretation at this point.

In Figure 13-9, at least four mappable sandstone beds are exposed, at points *H, I, J,* and *K*. White bed *L* (bentonite?)

is an excellent marker or key bed. Note the close association of trees with a single stratigraphic interval. There are numerous excellent dip slopes in this area.

EXERCISES

1. Locate on Figure 13-8 one or more places where stream capture will shortly occur.

2. Study the northwest-trending divide *DE* (Figure 13-8). Can you explain the difference in erosional characteristics on opposite sides of the divide?

3. Unit *B* (Figure 13-8) can be traced southeastward to point *F*. Unit *A* appears to extend to point *G*. The separation between these two stratigraphic units is greater across interval *FG* than in the *AB* area. What are three possible reasons for such a change in outcrop separation?

4. Completely annotate the geology included in the stereo model of Figure 13-9. Use several easily traced stratigraphic breaks as arbitrary contacts. Make a colored geologic map of the area.

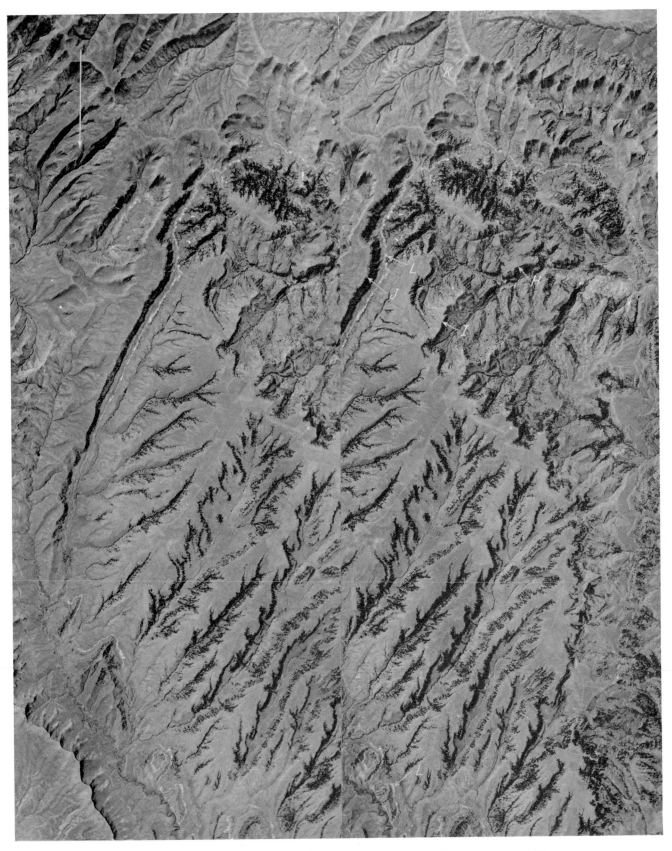

Figure 13-9. Stereogram of a broad anticline in a sequence of shales and sandstones. Climate is semiarid. (*Courtesy of U.S. Air Force.*)

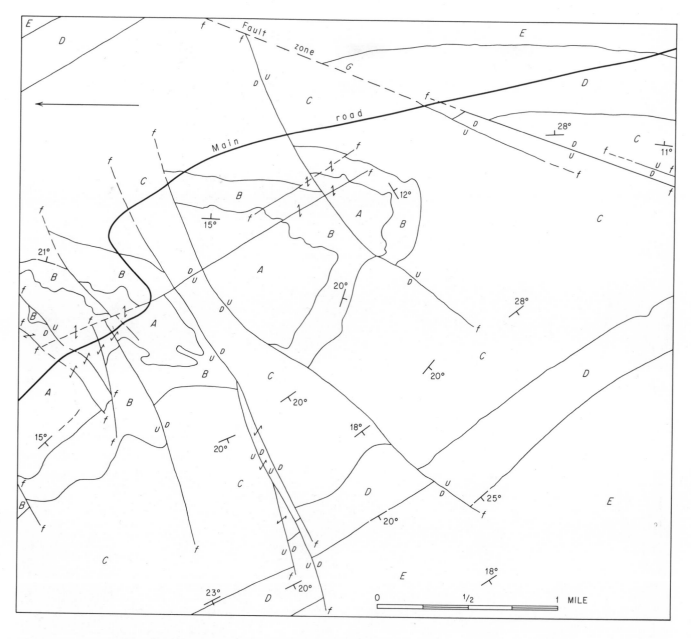

Figure 13-10. Geologic map of a faulted plunging anticline. *A*, shales; *B*, sandstones; *C*, shales and sandstones; *D*, sandstones and shales; *E*, sandstones and shales.

FAULTED PLUNGING ANTICLINE

The general structure of the northeast-plunging anticline *A* (Figure 13-11) is easily determined by a brief study of the stereo model.

To the north of the main road (see Figure 13-10) stands an old, subdued erosional surface. This appears to be a remnant of a formerly extensive regional undulating plain which has been destroyed to the south by stream rejuvenation. Numerous strike lines (i.e., features *B* and *C*, Figure 13-11) are visible in the northern upland, but reliable structural mapping is considerably hindered by a lack of differential relief.

Several faults cross the dipping beds in this area. By comparing the geologic map with the stereo model, some faults can be located and traced on the photographs with considerable assurance. Note the abrupt ending of several strike ridges, as at points *D*, *E*, and *F* (Figure 13-11). Also study the fault offsets which are evidenced by displacements of vegetation, tones, topography, and recognizable sequences of beds.

The trace of fault zone *G*, which is shown on the geologic map, can be detected on the upland surface as a sharp tonal break (feature *G*). Note the pronounced intersection of white bed *H* with the arcuate white outcrop of bed *I*, suggesting a fault at or near point *J*.

Note also the configurations of the strike lines north of fault zone *G*. At points *K* and *L* the dip appears to be to the north. At point *M* light and dark bands indicate strike to the northeast. At point *N*, strike sharply bends to the northwest and west. This fact, as well as poorly defined low ridge asymmetry, suggests south dip at points *O*, *P*, and *B*.

A small syncline, trending through points *N* and *Q*, may thus be mapped in this area. It may end at fault zone *G*.

180

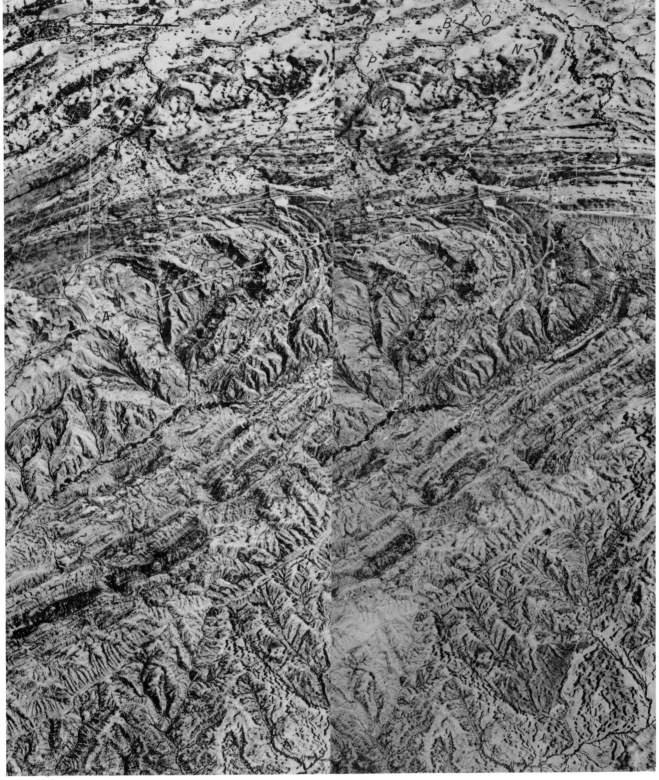

Figure 13-11. Stereogram of a maturely dissected faulted plunging anticline. (*By permission from Fairchild Aerial Surveys, Inc.*)

EXERCISES

1. Trace all apparent faults within the stereo-model area. Indicate, where possible, relative vertical displacements.

2. Trace at least fifteen marker or key beds on the stereo model. Some of these may coincide approximately with the contacts shown on the geologic map.

3. Assume that all strata in this area are either shales or sandstones. Describe the lithology, erosional characteristics, vegetation associations, photographic tones, and bedding characteristics

(i.e., massive, thin-bedded, or variable) of each stratigraphic interval defined by the artificial "contacts" previously traced as Exercise 2.

4. What is the probable significance of the intricate road system and bulbous road ends such as features *R* and *S?*

5. Trace the drainage network on one of the photographs.

6. Label several subsequent, obsequent, and resequent streams. Are there any consequent streams in this area? Any insequent streams?

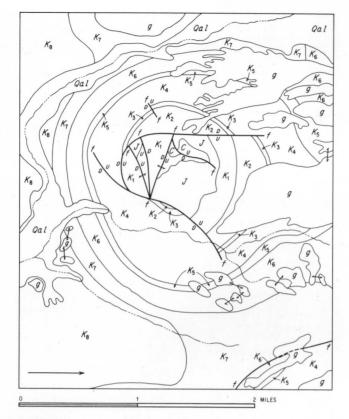

Figure 13-12. Geologic map of a faulted dome in Paleozoic and Mesozoic strata. The fault pattern and displacements produce a "trap-door block" structure. *C*, limestones; *J*, limestones and shales; K_1, sandstones with a middle shale; K_2, shales with a middle sandstone; K_3, shales; K_4, shales with a middle sandstone; K_5, sandstones; K_6, shales; K_7, shales and sandstones; K_8, shales; *g*, pediment gravels; *Qal*, alluvium.

FAULTED DOME

Part of the dome shown on the map is included in the stereo model. The general circular form is shown on the photographs, but many of the structural details are masked; others lie beyond the stereo-model area.

Many of the dips around the dome are extremely steep. Note the narrow, regularly curved outcrop bands at points *A*, *B*, *C*, *D*, and *E*. Smaller, higher outcrop hills define steep southwesterly dip at point *F* and steep northeasterly dip at point *G*.

Some of the faults can be located on the stereo model. The entire dome would have to be studied stereoscopically, and the details of stratigraphy carefully traced, to permit the mapping of the faults without the aid of the map.

The trace of the southern fault is expressed by the low topographic saddles at points *H* and *I*. The linear valley at point *J*, to the left of the stereo model, is an obvious feature. It probably follows a fault.

Along line *K* a stratigraphic unit is clearly defined by selective tree growth. The eastern end of the west-plunging asymmetric syncline *L* is partially defined by trees. Dip slopes and outcrop patterns also contribute to the structural understanding of this part of the area.

The tight syncline *M* lies along the north side of the dome. It plunges easterly and westerly from point *M*. The east plunge can be seen in the stereo model; the west plunge is apparent from outcrop pattern alone. The curvature of outcrop belt *N* suggests the presence of another dome to the north.

The erosional history of this area can be partially determined from a study of the stereo model. Note the following:

1. The central core *O* rises above the surrounding area.

2. Surface *P* truncates and mantles the underlying upturned strata.

3. Surfaces *Q* and *R*, lower than surface *P*, also cover and truncate the underlying dipping beds.

4. Low surface *S* has recently been entrenched by the mature stream *T* and its tributaries.

Surfaces *P*, *Q*, and *R* are gravel surfaces which blanket pediment remnants. The two pediment levels represent two former times of erosional adjustment to local base levels. The upper pediment was cut during the first recognized period of stability and was partially destroyed by stream rejuvenation, following which a second base level was established and pediments *Q* and *R* were cut and concurrently capped by stream gravels.

A second rejuvenation caused stream downcutting and the partial destruction of this intermediate capped pediment surface.

Eventually, stream equilibrium and stability were reestablished with the cutting and masking of surface *S*. The recent entrenchment of this surface may have resulted from a temporary change in the climate of the area, a regional rejuvenation due to uplift, or the recent lowering of base level. It may reflect a minor, normal downcutting cycle in the life of a graded stream.

The two earlier stages of stream rejuvenation may or may not have had a structural origin.

During repeated pedimentation and stream rejuvenation, core area *O* has stood as an island of nontruncated resistant strata (limestones).

EXERCISES

1. Draw several vertically exaggerated topographic profiles and geologic cross sections across the stereo model to show the essential relations among domal structure, faults, relative rock resistance, and the several pediment levels.

2. Annotate all observable geologic relations on one of the photographs. Be especially meticulous in the outlining of the various map units. Compare the details of the annotated photograph with the corresponding part of the map.

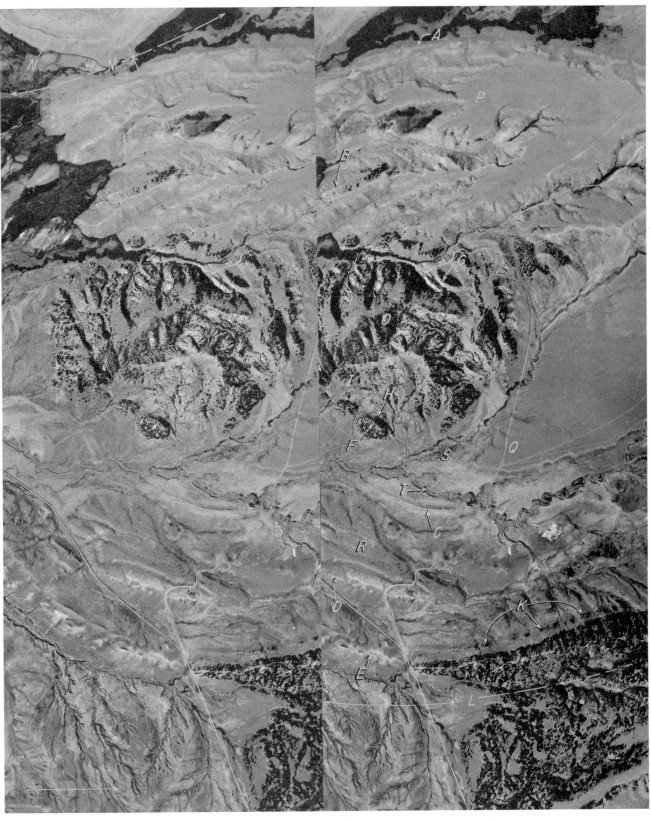

Figure 13-13. Stereogram of an eroded, partially obscured faulted dome in sedimentary strata. (*By permission from Jack Ammann Photogrammetric Engineers, Inc.*)

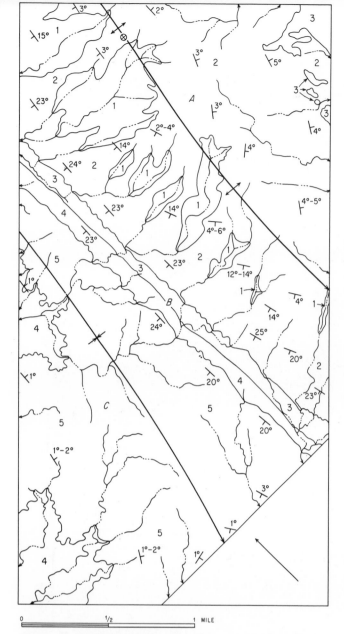

Figure 13-14. Photogeologic map of an asymmetric anticline and syncline in sedimentary strata.

ASYMMETRIC FOLDS

Shown here are a deeply dissected asymmetric anticline and syncline. The rocks present include sandstones, limestones, mudstones, and clays.

The climate of the area is semiarid, as evidenced by the almost complete lack of vegetation, the absence of rounded slopes, and the presence of primarily intermittent streams.

Figure 13-14 is a part of a published photogeologic map of the area showing the essential structure and the stratigraphic differentiation. As indicated on Figures 13-14 and 13-15, the area may be divided into three natural stratigraphic, structural, and topographic zones:

Zone A. A southeasterly plunging asymmetric anticline developed in a thick series of resistant marine limestones and sandstones, with considerable interbedded shales and some mudstone

Zone B. A homoclinally southwesterly dipping sequence of less resistant marine sediments consisting of dominantly red-colored sandstones, mudstones, and limestones overlain by similar-appearing brownish-red sandstones and siltstones

Zone C. An asymmetric syncline involving dark- and light-toned generally nonresistant friable sandstones, clays, and gypsum beds

The differential erosion of the sedimentary units in zone *A* has produced numerous cliffs, escarpments, waterfalls, and abrupt variations in slope. In several places, nonresistant units have been completely stripped from underlying resistant beds. Note that certain members produce waterfalls where crossed by drainage lines (i.e., at point *a*). Both photographic tone and topographic expression can be used to trace individual stratigraphic units in this area.

The steepest dips within this area lie along and adjacent to zone *B*. Here the relatively less resistant sedimentary rocks have been eroded to form low topographic relief and have been slightly more intricately dissected than the rocks in zone *A*. The red color of many of the units in zone *B* is well expressed on the aerial photographs by dark photographic tones. The relatively greater drainage density in zone *B* can be attributed to a generally higher shale or mudstone content.

In zone *C* the relatively nonresistant impervious nature of the sediments is expressed by generally low-lying badland topography. Along its northeastern edge, zone *C* has steep southwesterly dipping beds (note the white basal unit *f*), while to the southwest the dip rapidly decreases, finally becoming almost flat along the synclinal axis.

Were the stratigraphic section not known in this area, certain deductions could be made which would be of assistance to both the photogeologist and the field geologist who may later study the area. The relative resistance of the rocks has already been mentioned. Especially noteworthy is the intricate dissection of the strata in zone *C*. This is typical badland-like topography developed in an area in which there is high shale and clay content. The limitations of stratigraphic identification are pointed out by the fact that in zone *A* both sandstone and limestone members are present. However, it is impossible through a study of the photographs alone to distinguish those units which are sandstones and those which are limestones.

In the northeastern part of the stereoscopic area, beds *b* and *c* are indicated. Bed *b* can be traced southward and southwestward to the steep dip belt adjacent to zone *B* (i.e., to point *d*). Bed *c* correlates with one of the units at or near point *e*. The stratigraphic interval *bc* appears at first to be much thicker than the section exposed between points *d* and *e*, in the central part of the area. Nevertheless, section *bc* does not include any dark-toned strata resembling those which are mapped in zone *B*. The geologic map substantiates this observation.

It must not be concluded that in such a short distance the stratigraphic sequence *bc* undergoes a pronounced thinning from northeast to southwest. This stereoscopic model has a vertical exaggeration of at least 3.0. Therefore, the section *bc,* as seen in the north, is in reality perhaps only one-third as thick as it appears to be on the photographs. Where the dip of this same stratigraphic section is relatively steep, the vertical exaggeration cannot produce such a noticeable "thickening" of section.

EXERCISES

1. The structural and stratigraphic information shown on Figure 13-14 was annotated on aerial photographs and transferred to a base map by the use of a Kail Radial Planimetric Plotter. The dips shown on Figure 13-14 are visually estimated dips adjusted from an exaggeration factor of 3.0. Check those dips included within the stereo-model area by estimating their apparent magnitudes on the photographs and converting the

184

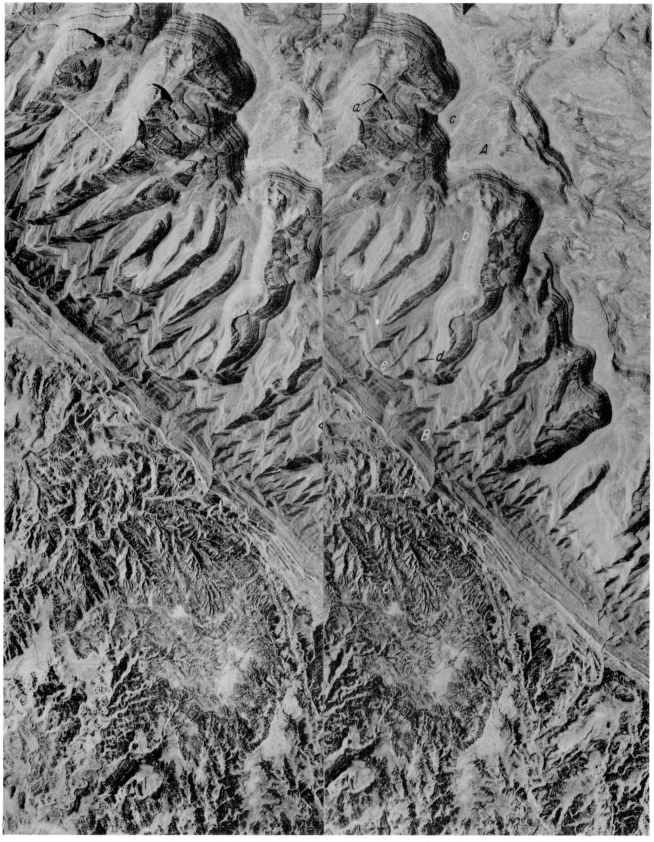

Figure 13-15. Stereogram of a dissected asymmetric anticline and syncline in sedimentary strata in a semiarid area. (*By permission from Fairchild Aerial Surveys, Inc.*)

estimated values to true values. The graph of Figure 2-11 should be used for the conversion.

2. Using Figure 13-14 as a guide, trace the major drainage lines on one of the photographs.

3. Using Figure 13-14 as a guide, trace the several stratigraphic contacts on one of the aerial photographs. It should be noted that the map does not possess the planimetric displacements and distortions which are present on the photographs. Therefore, some of the contact lines seen on the photographs will not have identical forms and positions when compared to the map. This is especially true of the mapped contact between formations 2 and 3 along the steep dip belt between zones *A* and *B*.

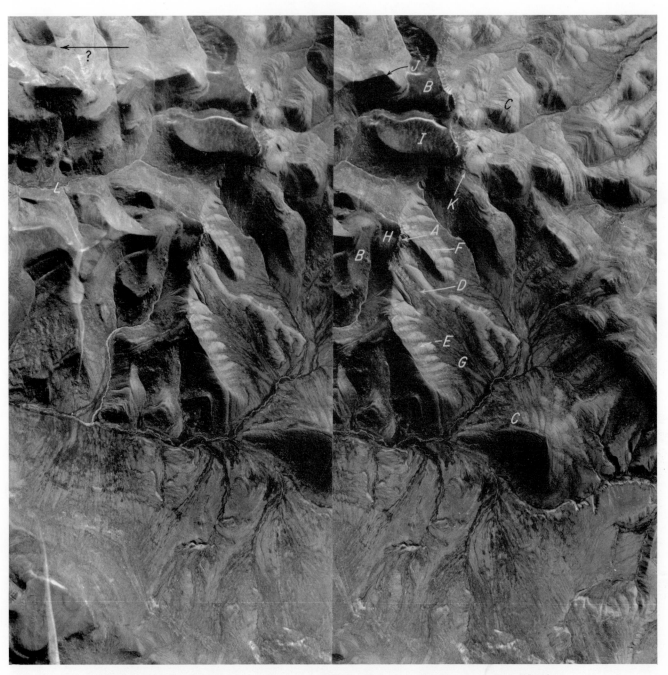

Figure 13-16. Stereogram of an angular unconformity. This is a subarctic area; note solifluction in the southern part. (*Courtesy of Royal Canadian Air Force.*)

ANGULAR UNCONFORMITY

At several places the trace of an unconformity is exposed, as at point *A*. The dark tone, topographic expression, and gentle dips of the younger strata *B* contrast sharply with the lighter tones, thinner bedding, more intricate dissection, and steep dips of the older strata *C*.

Drainage in the area is well integrated. However, it appears that considerable downslope movement of surface slope debris is accomplished by creep and widespread solifluction. Note, for example, the shinglelike surface at point *D*.

Compare the spacing of the dark thin beds in the obsequent slope *E* and that in slope *F*. These could represent two similar stratigraphic units, sequence *E* lying above sequence *F*. They could be the same, in which case pre-unconformity faulting would have to be proposed, the trace of the fault, upthrown to the southwest, passing northwestward along lowland *G* and obscured by surficial debris.

The dips and relative elevations of beds *H* and *I* prevent the projection of one across the valley to the other. Bed *H*, for example, projects above bed *I* to a place near point *J*. This discordance may be due to folding, evidence of which has been removed by erosion. It may also have been caused by minor faulting. The small scarplet *K* could mark the surface trace of an east-trending fault, most of which is hidden by slope mantle. Stream *L* could be a subsequent stream, developed along such a fault zone.

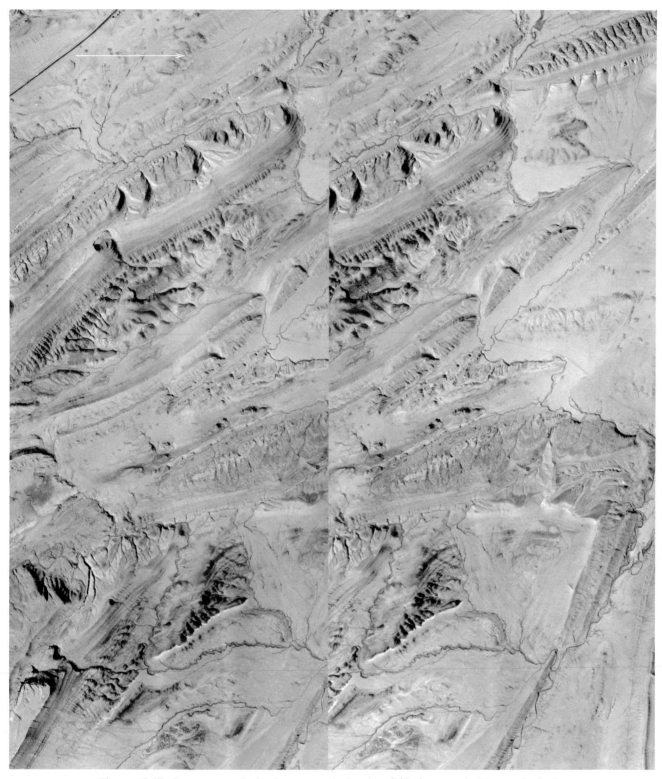

Figure 13-17. Stereogram of clearly expressed plunging folds in a semiarid area. Latitude 44°40′ N, longitude 108°15′ W. (*By permission from Jack Ammann Photogrammetric Engineers, Inc.*)

PLUNGING FOLDS

The general structure of this area is obvious. Numerous stratigraphic units can be traced and correlated within the limits of the stereo model.

The geographic coordinates are given to permit the student to locate geologic maps and other data pertaining to the geology of the area.

Each stratigraphic unit should be described, including photographic tone, relative resistance, and erosional and lithologic characteristics. Using available published data, assign formational names to the mapped strata.

Careful study will disclose numerous small transverse and oblique faults.

It should not prove difficult to extend the mapping into the nonstereoscopic marginal areas.

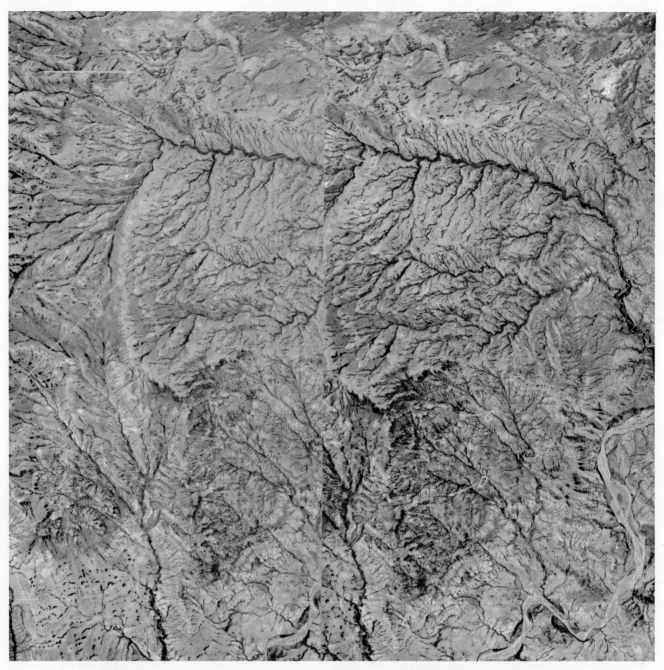

Figure 13-18. Stereogram of faults in gently dipping thin-bedded marlstones, shales, sandstones, and limestones. (*By permission from Fairchild Aerial Surveys, Inc.*)

FAULTS

Faults may be defined on aerial photographs in many ways. For example, in Figure 13-18, fault traces are shown by vegetation lines or breaks (feature *A*), minor tributary deflections (feature *B*), tonal contrasts (feature *C*), local linear scarps (feature *D*), and bedding offsets (area *E*). Frequently two or more such features will exist along a single segment of a fault.

In Figure 13-19, the major fault clearly offsets strata (i.e., bed *A*), has associated drag folding (anticline at point *B*), is followed by subsequent streams (streams *C* and *D*), and has brought barren strata into contact with tree-covered beds (feature *E*).

EXERCISES

1. Describe the criteria used in mapping a northeast-trending fault at point *F* (Figure 13-19).

2. Consult published maps or reports to obtain stratigraphic and regional structural data for the area shown in Figure 13-19. What relation exists between rock type and relative resistance to erosion in this area? What is the climate here?

3. Completely annotate, on an acetate overlay, the geology, drainage, and culture included in the central photo of Figure 13-19.

4. Map all faults which can be detected in Figure 13-18. Number each and list criteria used for mapping each. Where possible, indicate relative displacements.

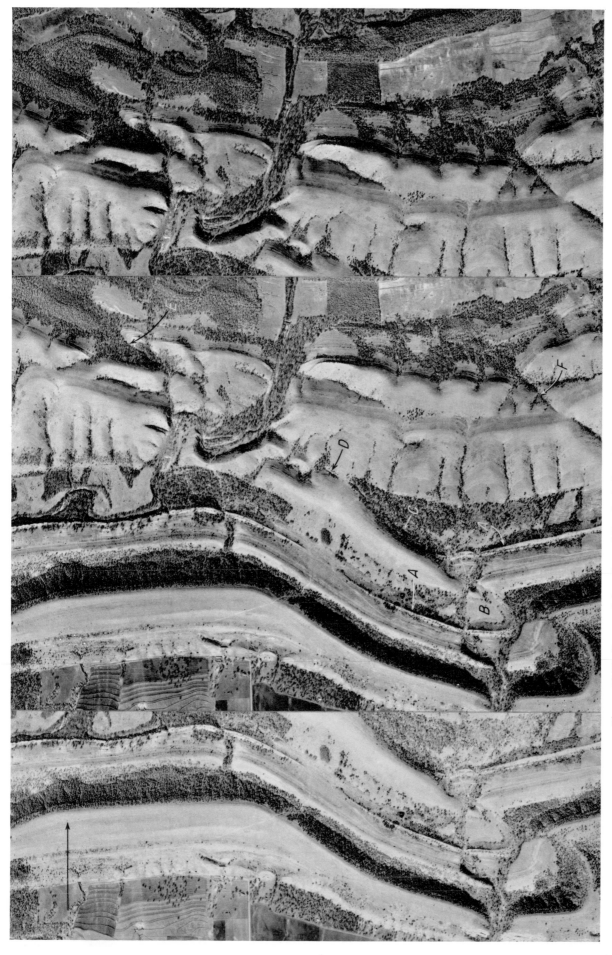

Figure 13-19. Stereo triplet of an obliquely faulted homocline. Latitude 34°21' N, longitude 97°12' W. (*Courtesy of U.S. Dept. of Agriculture, Commodity Stabilization Service.*)

189

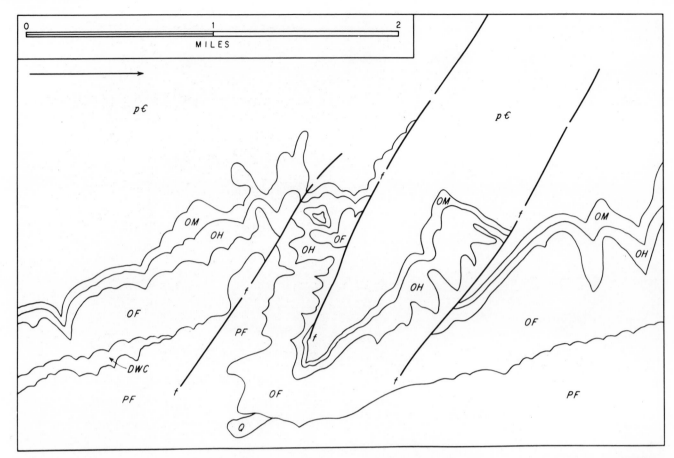

Figure 13-20. Geologic map of an obliquely faulted mountain front. *p€*, pre-Cambrian red or gray Pikes Peak granite; *OM*, Ordovician Manitou formation (limestones); *OH*, Ordovician Harding formation (sandstones, interbedded with shales); *OF*, Ordovician Frement formation (magnesian limestones); *DWC*, Devonian Williams Canyon formation (limestones with calcare- ous shale partings and a few thin sandstone beds); *PF*, Pennsylvanian Fountain formation (red arkosic sandstones and conglomerates); *Q*, Quaternary sediments, undivided. (*By permision from C. Maynard Boos, Margaret Fuller Boos, and the Carter Oil Company.*)

FAULTS

The map and stereo model show the faulted contact between the pre-Cambrian "basement" and overlying Paleozoic sedimentary strata.

The dark-toned basement rocks contrast sharply with the light-gray, in places almost white, strata. As seen stereoscopically, the higher ridges and peaks are underlain by the granite, attesting to its relatively high resistance to erosion. The least resistant rocks in the area are those of the Fountain formation, which underlie the southern part of the area.

Numerous criteria for fault recognition may be noted in the stereo-model area.

1. *Tonal Contrast.* Line *A* separates the light sediments from the dark granites. The linearity of the contact virtually precludes a normal stratigraphic relation, since the area has been extensively eroded and the contact plane must be nearly vertical. Dips immediately to the west are gentle to moderate.

2. *Truncation of Beds.* Beds *B* and *C,* which are separated by an appreciable stratigraphic section, abruptly end at line *A,* as do the exposed beds beneath bed *C.* Alone, such evidence does not prove the existence of the fault. Combined with the factor of tonal contrast, it strengthens the fault interpretation.

3. *Absence of Features Observed along Nearby Normal Contact.* Study the slopes to the south of point *D.* Note the tonal contrast at point *E,* the plane surfaces *F, G,* and *H,* the thin nonresistant unit immediately above these surfaces (indicated by small subsequent valleys *I* and *J*), and the over-all accordance of dip from point *E* to the base of the ridge (line *K*), where the uppermost resistant light beds are overlain by the erosion-truncated, nonresistant darker beds of the Fountain formation. These several relations do not exist along line *A.*

4. *Abnormal or Anomalous Stream Linearity.* Small southwest-flowing tributary stream *L* flows entirely within the granite outcrop area. It is extremely linear and lies parallel to fault *A.* This stream probably follows a relatively nonresistant plane or narrow zone along a fault trace.

5. *General Topographic Discordance.* Tree-covered ridge *M* stands above lowland *N,* though the geologic map indicates that both areas are underlain by granite. A relatively linear scarp or steep (though dissected) slope separates the two surfaces. When compiling a photogeologic map of this area, it would be advisable to draw a line along the base of this slope (i.e., through point *O*). This line may be designated as a questionable fault or as a topographic feature "of unknown origin."

EXERCISES

1. Trace fault *A* to the northeast. It should extend at least to point *P.*

Figure 13-21. Stereogram of oblique faults along a mountain front. (*Courtesy of U.S. Dept. of Agriculture, Forest Service.*)

2. How can tonally defined line *Q* be explained?

3. Trace the complete drainage network of the stereo model. Label several resequent, insequent, and subsequent streams by appropriate letters.

4. On what slopes might one find small obsequent rills or gullies (too small to see on the photographs)? Label such slopes accordingly.

5. Surfaces *F*, *G*, and *H* resemble dip slopes. What other explanation could be advanced for these surfaces, were it learned that they did not consist of sedimentary strata?

6. Note stream *R* in the south lowland. Could this be a structurally controlled stream? Note apparent truncation of beds *S* along line *T*, an eastern extension of the line defined by stream *R*.

7. What is the nature and probable composition of the materials which constitute surface *U*?

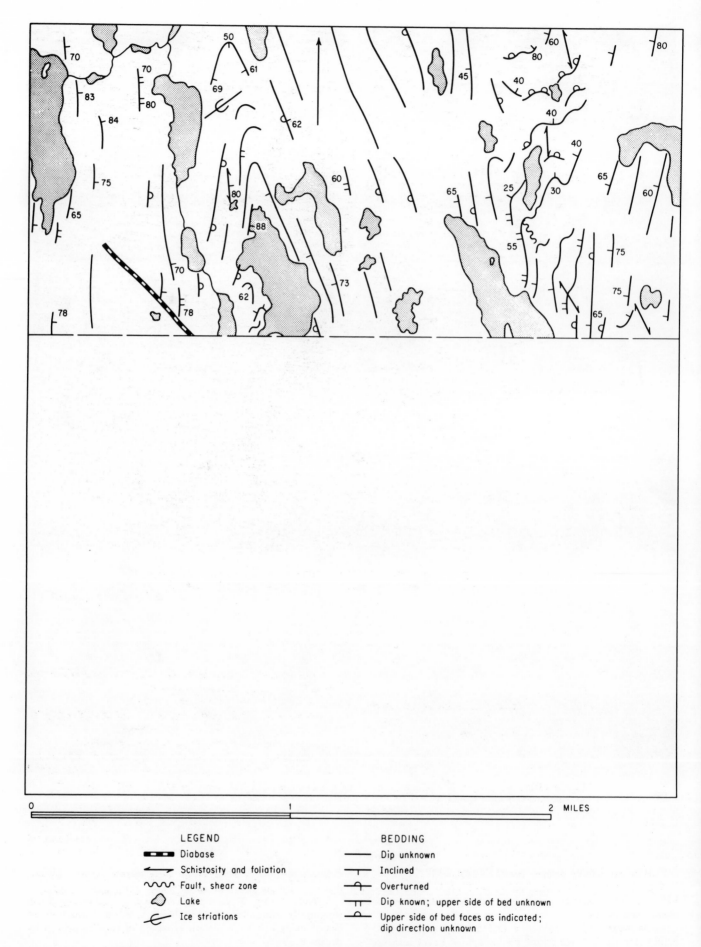

Figure 13-22. Geologic map showing part of the area included in Figure 13-23. White areas consist of argillite, greywacke, minor arkose, quartzite, grit, and amphibolite beds (tuffs?).

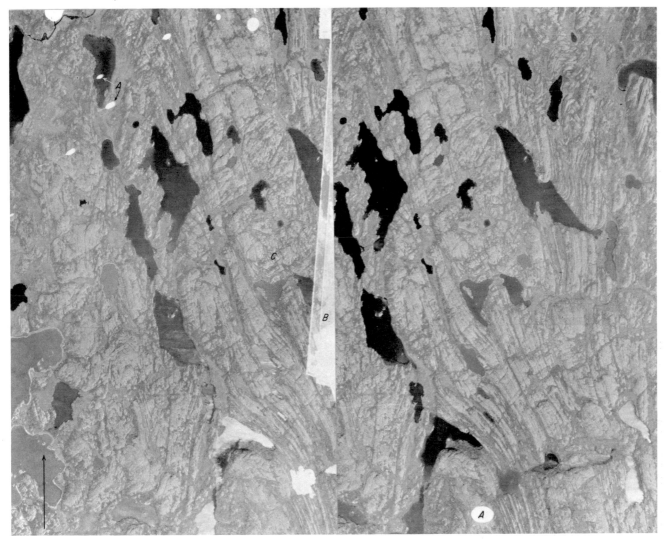

Figure 13-23. Stereogram of highly deformed pre-Cambrian metamorphosed sediments. This area has been overridden by continental ice sheets. (*Courtesy of Royal Canadian Air Force.*)

SHIELD AREA

The bedrock here consists of metamorphosed sediments.

This area has been scoured by continental ice sheets. It has considerable differential relief. Many of the rocks here appear to be quite resistant to erosion.

The photographs illustrate several kinds of imperfections and distracting markings. Several white ovals (features *A*) appear on the photographs. These are presumably the result of damage to negative or print by chemical droplets during processing. The large white wedge *B* on the left photograph is produced by the printing of a negative patched by a semi-transparent material, probably acetate tape. The well-defined palm print, centered at point *C* on the left photograph, was probably made by the person who taped the negative.

EXERCISES

1. Trace the many excellently exposed and expressed key or marker beds included in the stereo model.

2. Determine dip direction at as many places as possible and plot strikes and dips on the photographs.

3. Draw fold axes on the photographs.

4. Outline all areas obscured by muskeg or swamp materials.

5. Trace all possible faults or shear zones.

6. Is there evidence of strike or near-strike faulting?

7. The northern part of the area is shown on the map. In the blank part of the map, sketch in the streams and lakes, strike lines, muskeg areas, and faults or shear zones. Add strike and dip symbols in this part of the map area.

8. What is the scale of the photographs in Figure 13-23?

9. Figure 13-23 is a reduced reproduction of the original photographs. The stereo model has been reduced in width from 10.8 inches to fit this page. What is the scale of the original photographs?

10. Assume that the photographs were taken with a camera having a 6-inch lens and that the average ground elevation is 350 feet above mean sea level. From what elevation were the photographs taken?

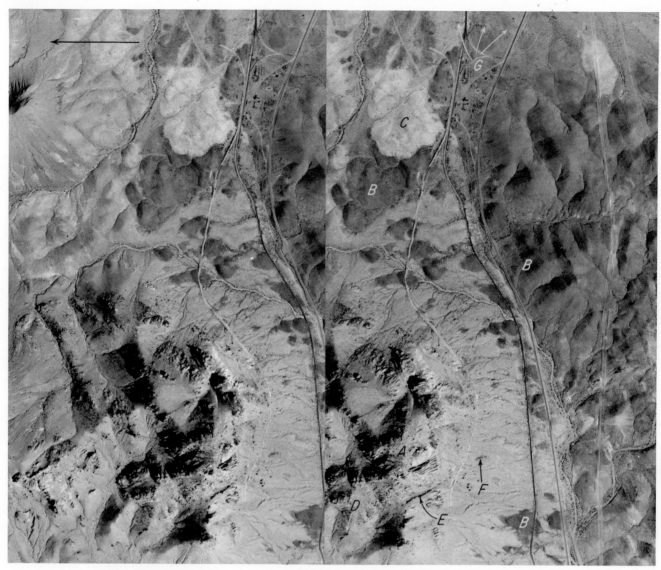

Figure 13-24. Stereogram of well-exposed and clearly defined pyroclastic and intrusive rocks in a semiarid area. (*Courtesy of U.S. Dept. of Agriculture, Soil Conservation Service.*)

PYROCLASTIC AND INTRUSIVE ROCKS

One of the fundamental concepts of photogeology is that rarely can the study of aerial photographs alone result in a *complete* and accurate geologic map and interpretation. This is demonstrated in this area.

Several rock types can be outlined and their apparent relations noted. Their *approximate* nature and composition can be proposed. Their precise structures and exact compositions must be determined by a thorough field study, however.

There is no obvious evidence of a fault contact between the resistant, jointed, light- to medium-toned rocks of area *A* and the less resistant, darker rocks of area *B*. It may be assumed that unit *A* overlies unit *B*, the contact being near the base of the major east-facing scarp.

Several characteristics of unit *A* suggest acidic composition, possibly rhyolitic or dacitic. A gross bedding or layering is noted in these rocks.

Unit *B* is more basic. It may include rock ranging from andesite to basalt. This would be in accordance with its lower resistance, gentler slopes, and relatively fine-textured drainage.

Unit *C*, which is surrounded by unit *B*, is irregular in outline and is almost certainly an acidic intrusion. Rhyolite intrusives frequently have this appearance.

A medium to basic dike extends across the south part of the area. It is exposed at points *D*, *E*, and *F*.

Note the possible dike or fault expressed by tone and vegetation along line *G*.

EXERCISES

1. Outline all areas within the stereo model where the bedrock is covered by unconsolidated Quaternary materials.

2. Draw contacts between the different rock units, where the contacts are not masked by surface detritus.

3. Suppose you were given one day in which to check this area in the field. Make a list of the general and specific questions for which you would attempt to find the answers.

4. Where would you go to obtain the required data, and in what sequence would the selected ground check points be visited?

194

14

Moderately Difficult Photogeology

INTRODUCTION

There are many dependent and independent variable factors which can affect the relative ease or difficulty with which a given area can be mapped on aerial photographs.

Frequently, the degree to which an area is covered by alluvium, colluvium, outwash, or moraine determines the completeness and accuracy of the compilation.

Vegetation and cultivation obscure some areas. Photograph scale may be too small or too large for the solution of certain problems. Some geologic features and structures resemble others having a different origin. For example, angular unconformities occasionally appear to be thrust faults. The reverse may also be true (compare Figures 13-16 and 14-8).

The relative complexity of geologic structure may have little bearing on the ease or difficulty with which photogeologic mapping and interpretation can be accomplished. In some of the areas classified as *routine* (Chapter 13), the structure is much more complicated than is the structure in many of the illustrations included in this chapter. Compare, for example, the several folds shown in Figure 13-17 with the plunging simple anticline in Figure 14-5 or the faulted homocline of Figure 14-7.

A serious pitfall awaits the inexperienced (and occasionally the experienced) photogeologist who, in studying an area generally characterized by *routine* geology, encounters local areas of more difficult photogeology. That pitfall may best be described by the simple and homely expression "jumping to conclusions."

There are many areas (i.e., exposed fold areas in Wyoming) where most of the structure and stratigraphy are exposed and sharply expressed. The photogeologist, in map-

ping such areas, may unwittingly become complacent or careless. If isolated centers of obscured or *moderately difficult* geology occur within a large *routine* area, he may pass over them rapidly and either miss some critical features or relations or misinterpret them.

For example, if a given structural trend can be traced many miles to an area where it is completely or partially covered by mantle, the photogeologist should not automatically assume that the structure continues uninterrupted across the obscured area. In many instances it will so continue, and can be "picked up" on the other side of the mantled area. However, it is a sound practice in mapping such areas to dash the structure across the hidden interval and to insert question marks at selected points along the dashed lines. This will inform the person who may later study the map that in the covered area the structure is inferred but was not actually observed.

There may be other instances where, though not obscured, local structural complexities occur in an area of otherwise simple structure. It is not uncommon for such complexities to be completely overlooked by the photogeologist who has the preconceived idea, based on his study of the photographs up to that point, that the entire area is simple and can be mapped rapidly and with little or no attention to detail.

The photogeologist must establish and firmly maintain the attitude that, regardless of how simple or *routine* an area may *appear* to be, there may be unexpected and unsuspected complexities or problems on the photo he is about to study. The exercising of restraint and caution, though increasing the time to complete a project, is well worthwhile.

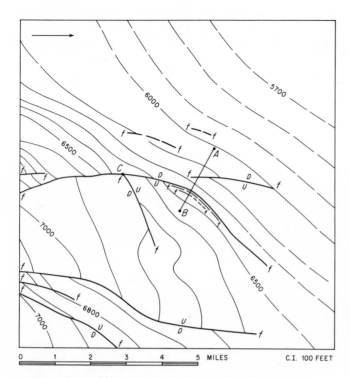

southern upland. At point *C* this fault branches toward the east, where it is principally represented by faults *E* and *F*. Though largely beyond the stereoscopic area, fault *F* can easily be traced.

These faults can be mapped on the basis of (1) gross topographic break, (2) abrupt discontinuation of bedding, (3) linearity of tonal break, and (4) apparent displacement of a recognizable stratigraphic interval (study section to the north and south of fault *F*).

Note the details of topography, tone, stratigraphic sequence, and bed thickness at point *G*. The stratigraphic sequence exposed here can be identified at several places to the west (i.e., points *H*, *I*, *J*, and *K*). At point *K* this sequence is appreciably lower than it is at point *G*. This discordance of elevation cannot be explained by observable dips. In fact, at point *K* dip is *toward* point *G*.

A fault can be detected at several places along the trend of the major north-flowing stream *S*. Note scarps *L*, *M*, and *N*, formed by the thick resistant bed which underlies sequence *G*. This unit can be seen at points *O*, *P*, and *Q*. The zone separating the two levels marks the approximate trace of the fault. Careful study will reveal its actual position in some places (i.e., point *R*).

Figure 14-1. Structure contour map of faulted gently dipping sedimentary strata. Line *AB* indicates the position of the geologic cross section shown in Figure 14-2. Point *C* corresponds with point *C* on the photographs (Figure 14-3). The photographs cover a small part of the area included in this map. (*After A. N. Strahler, 1948.*)

EXERCISES

1. Trace all detectable faults within the stereo-model area. Indicate relative movement, where possible.

2. List for each the evidence for location and the criteria for interpretation of relative displacement.

3. Indicate details of dip and strike within the entire stereo-model area.

4. Outline on Figure 14-1 the approximate area included in Figure 14-3.

5. Draw a north-south vertically exaggerated topographic profile and geologic cross section across the stereo-model area, passing through the letter *H*.

6. Draw an exaggerated north-south profile and cross section through ground point *L*.

7. Draw an exaggerated west-east profile and cross section through ground point *R*.

8. Though it follows a meandering course, the major north-flowing stream *S* is a young stream; it has no appreciable flood plain. In a general way, it follows the trend of the fault which passes through point *R*. Is this a subsequent stream?

9. If this is not a true subsequent stream, could it have been one at a previous time?

10. Propose a logical past history for this stream. Assume that the younger strata, now stripped from the area, were largely nonresistant sedimentary beds.

FAULTS

Dip in this area is relatively gentle. Numerous dip slopes and scarp and valley-wall outcrops permit the determination of dip and strike directions, and the estimate or measurement of approximate dip magnitudes throughout most of the area.

The low regional dip of the area is interrupted by numerous steeply inclined faults. Fault traces are either straight or extremely gently curved. Some faults are obvious; others are more difficult to detect. The location, tracing, and interpretation of the faults require that close attention be given to several factors, including photographic tones, topographic relations, and stratigraphic sequences.

The major fault in the photograph area is the east-trending fault *D*, which follows the base of the scarp bordering the

Figure 14-2. Geologic cross section of a faulted homocline in sedimentary strata. Line of section (*AB*) is indicated on Figure 14-1. The section shown here lies to the right of the area shown in Figure 14-3. (*After A. N. Strahler, 1948.*)

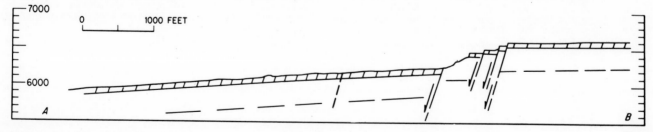

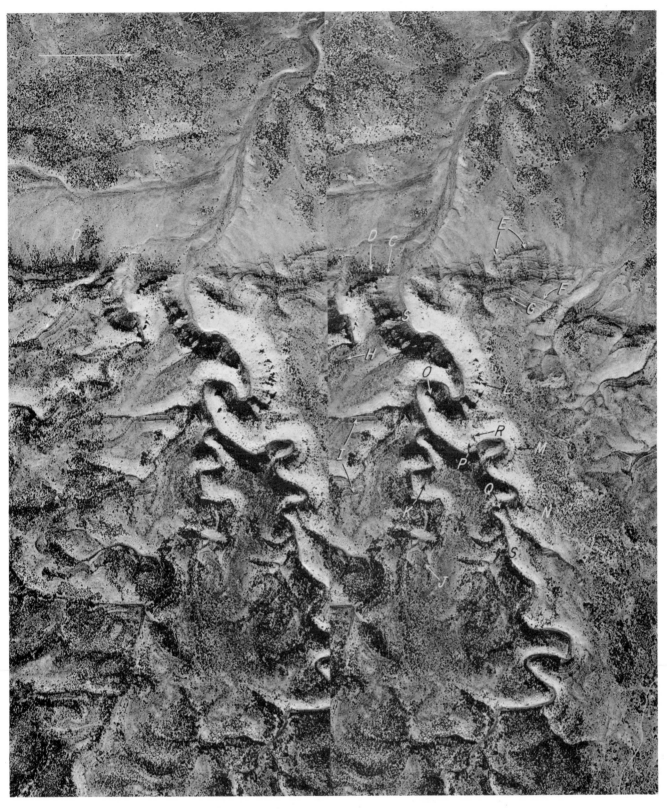

Figure 14-3. Stereogram of faulted gently dipping sedimentary strata, in a semiarid area. The exposed beds consist of limestones and shales. Photograph scale is approximately 1:20,000. Point C corresponds with point C on the structure contour map (Figure 14-1). (*Courtesy of U.S. Dept. of Agriculture, Forest Service.*)

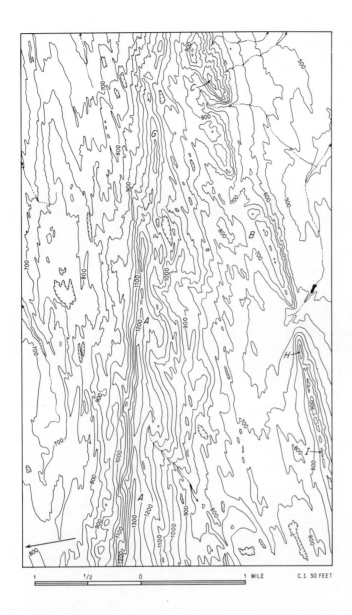

Figure 14-4. Topographic map of a maturely eroded, plunging, faulted anticline partially obscured by sand dunes.

ANTICLINE AND SAND DUNES

Two converging northerly trending strike ridges (ridges *A* and *B*) dominate the topography of this area. A northwest-trending series of longitudinal sand dunes stands out on the photographs, and can be detected on the topographic map.

The structure along ridge *B* can be determined on the photographs with relative ease. Steep east dip can be seen in blocks *C* and *D*, where the differential dissection of the resequent east slopes has formed many steep flatiron-like features and where the obsequent west slopes, probably underlain by shales, are smooth and uniform. To the east of the stereo model, the same elements along ridge *B* and segment *E* indicate east dip.

Stream segment *F* is subsequent along an east-trending fault. The displacement along the fault between blocks *C* and *D* is seen to be down on the south and up on the north. The continuity of ridge segment *G* indicates that the fault does not extend this far to the west. It may, however, trend more northwesterly and cross ridge *A* beyond the north edge of the stereo model.

On Figure 14-4, the east dip of block *C* is suggested by

the contours in this area. Along ridge *HI*, Figure 14-4, steep east dips are also indicated; at point *H* by ridge asymmetry and at point *I* by the proximity of the small closed crest contours to the western flank of the ridge.

On Figure 14-4, pronounced ridge asymmetry along ridge *A* (south of point *J*) strongly suggests *east* dip. Slight opposite asymmetry along segment *G*, however, attests to west dip. Along the entire length of ridge *A* dip is westward.

EXERCISES

1. Within the central anticlinal lowland are secondary strike ridges, as well as sand dunes. On Figure 14-5, trace sand dunes in orange pencil, and strike ridges in green. Outline areas of exposed bedrock, areas where bedrock-produced topography is revealed despite sand cover, and areas where the sand is thicker and hides the bedrock.

2. Transfer all outlines, sand-dune trends, and strike-ridge trends to the map.

3. Ridge *A* is displaced at one point by a transverse fault. On the photographs, trace the detectable part of the fault in red, and indicate relative fault movement. Plot this fault on the map.

198

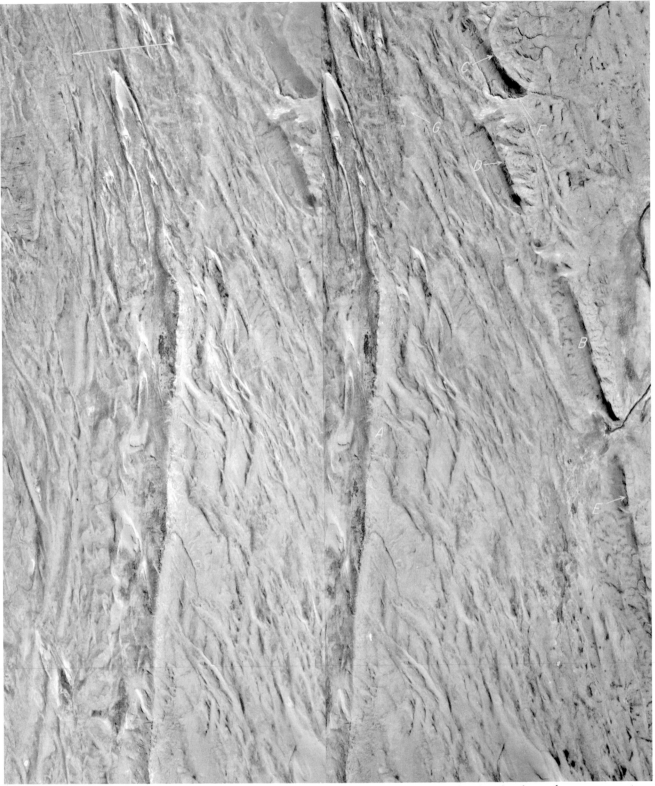

Figure 14-5. Stereogram of a maturely eroded, plunging, faulted anticline largely obscured by sand dunes. (*Courtesy of U.S. Geological Survey.*)

4. Can the contours and nonstereoscopic study of ridge *B* be used to detect another fault across this flank of the anticline? If so, trace the fault and show displacement, on both the photographs and the map.

5. Assume that the ridge-forming stratigraphic unit is a known

formation. Trace the "contacts" at the base and top of this formation and transfer these lines to the map.

6. Estimate dip throughout the stereo-model area and transfer these data to the map.

7. Color the now fully annotated geologic map.

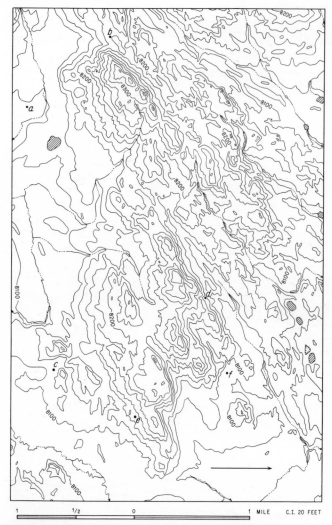

Figure 14-6. Topographic map of an area of faulted, moderately dipping strata. Some northeast-trending faults can be detected by topographic offsets and by local contour configurations.

FAULTS

This area illustrates a phenomenon frequently encountered in the study of aerial photographs. It may be called *progressive disclosure*. By this is meant that the longer the photographs are studied, the more information is disclosed.

In many areas, photogeologic mapping is essentially a matter of tracing, adding structural details, and thus assembling a reasonably complete map.

In this area, some features are observed first, since they are the most obvious. With continued study, additional features will suddenly be noted and understood, though they had been *seen* earlier.

The apparent regional structure here is moderate southwest dip, which can be observed in many places. Study the outcrops, slopes, and other indications of dip at points *A*, *B*, and *C*, for example.

The next element to which attention is directed is a series of lines. The most obvious are, of course, man-made, such as roads *D* and *E* and a small road and parallel fence (line *F*).

There are many other lines which are not artificial, however. Study these carefully. The easiest to detect are lettered *G* through *K*. Lines *K* are parallel to strike, and are probably subsequent valleys developed along nonresistant beds.

Lines *G*, *H*, *I*, and *J*, however, extend across the strike. At some places they are defined by tonal breaks (points *L* and *M*), and at other places they consist of lines of small shrubs or dark soil (lines *N* and *O*). Elsewhere, they mark the abrupt termination of strike ridges (points *L* and *P*). Locally streams have adjusted along them (stream *Q*).

These and numerous other such lines in this area are faults. Along some, relative displacements can be determined. The stereo model is too limited to permit reliable estimates of the displacement along others.

The faults designated thus far are parts of a set of parallel faults. This set is the best defined and easiest to map in this area. Other faults, with different trends, can also be mapped. An outstanding one is fault *R*, which has a more northerly trending trace. Offset is suggested at point *S*.

A north-trending zone of possible faulting is designated as line *T*. Line *U* may mark a curved southward extension of fault *T*.

Note the dark linear depression which obliquely crosses a short ridge, at point *V*. A similar line is at point *W*, and other suggestions of faulting can be seen northward, as at points *X*.

The topographic results of block faulting can be seen on Figure 14-6. The regional strike is clearly defined, and ridge offsets are obvious at several places. Note that northeast-trending lines can be drawn through points *a* and *b*, *c* and *d*, and *e* and *f*.

One noteworthy fact, apparent on both the map and the stereo model, is the relative dearth of fault-controlled subsequent streams. In general, this suggests that in this area fault lines and fault zones are not appreciably less resistant to erosion than the unfaulted bedrock. *Healed* faults or zones cemented with materials having a resistance comparable to that of the bedrock could exist here. Another possibility is that the strata are relatively nonresistant, perhaps poorly cemented, and that fault zones in such materials do not offer greater erosion opportunities to running water.

EXERCISES

1. Trace all observed fault and fracture lines (some may have no displacements). Where possible, indicate relative displacements.

2. List each fault or fracture by letter or number, and tabulate criteria for detection and interpretation of each.

3. Trace several key beds or stratigraphic units in the stereo-model area.

4. Attempt to correlate beds across faults. This will require intense study in many cases.

5. The location of this area is latitude 40°42' N, longitude 106°19' W. What formation is exposed at the surface here? What is the age of the strata? What lithologies are present? Reconcile these data with the topography and the stratigraphic and erosional details noted on the photographs.

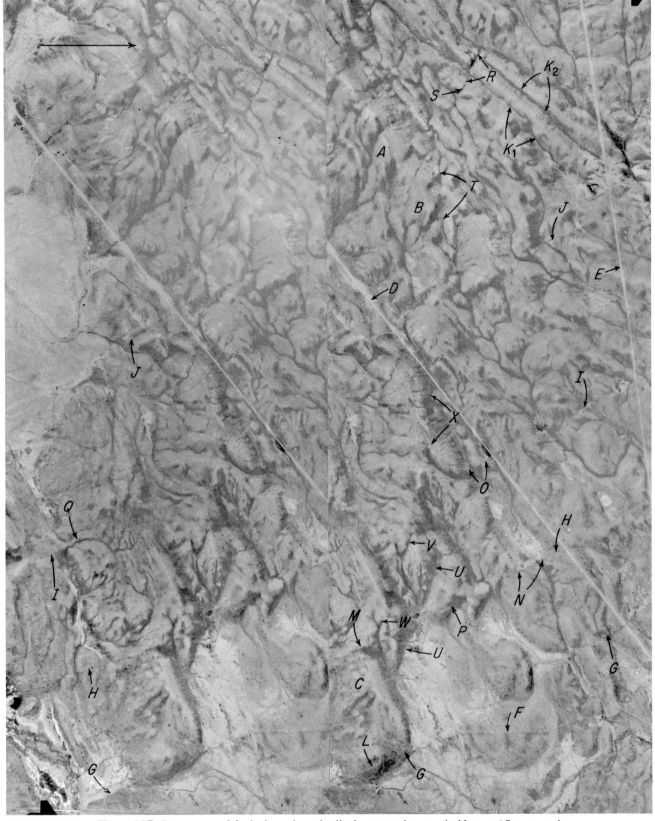

Figure 14-7. Stereogram of faulted, moderately dipping strata in a semiarid area. (*Courtesy of U.S. Geological Survey.*)

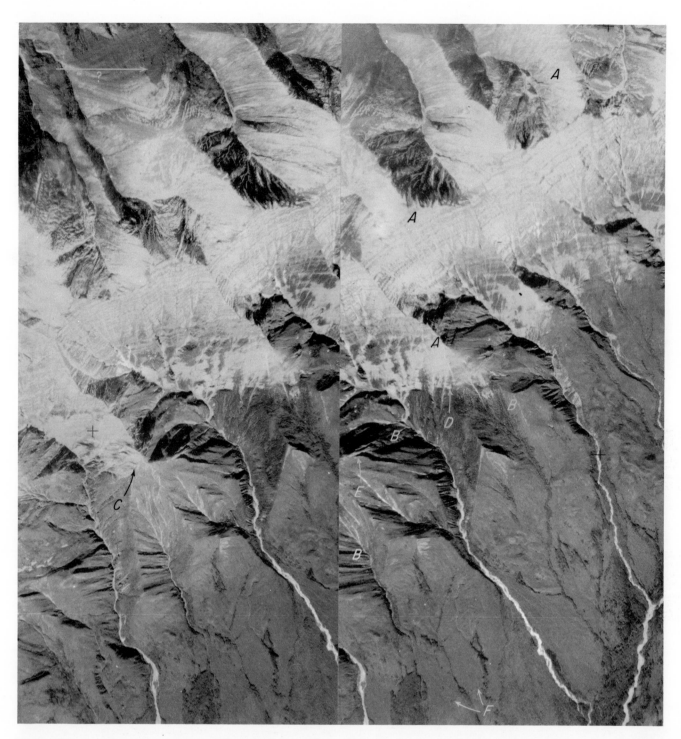

Figure 14-8. Stereogram of a reverse or thrust fault in a snow-obscured mountainous area. North-dipping resistant beds are thrust southward over less resistant south-dipping younger beds. This area is in a semihumid subarctic climate zone. (*Courtesy of Royal Canadian Air Force.*)

REVERSE OR THRUST FAULT

This area shows a relatively clearly exposed and well-expressed reverse or thrust fault. It resembles a pronounced angular unconformity. The resistant mountain-forming strata (area *A*), however, are known to be Carboniferous in age, and the underlying beds (area *B*) are Cretaceous in age.

To the west of the stereo model, the fault contact is believed to be at point *C*. Within the stereo model, it appears to be at point *D*. At point *E* the Cretaceous beds seem to be nearly vertical, or overturned, probably due to drag.

Note the linear scarplet along line *F*. This suggests minor strike faulting in truncated younger, nonresistant strata which are mantled by Quaternary debris.

EXERCISE

Indicate strikes and dips, the fault trace, key beds, and alluvium distribution within the stereo model. Attempt to extend the mapping into left and right marginal areas.

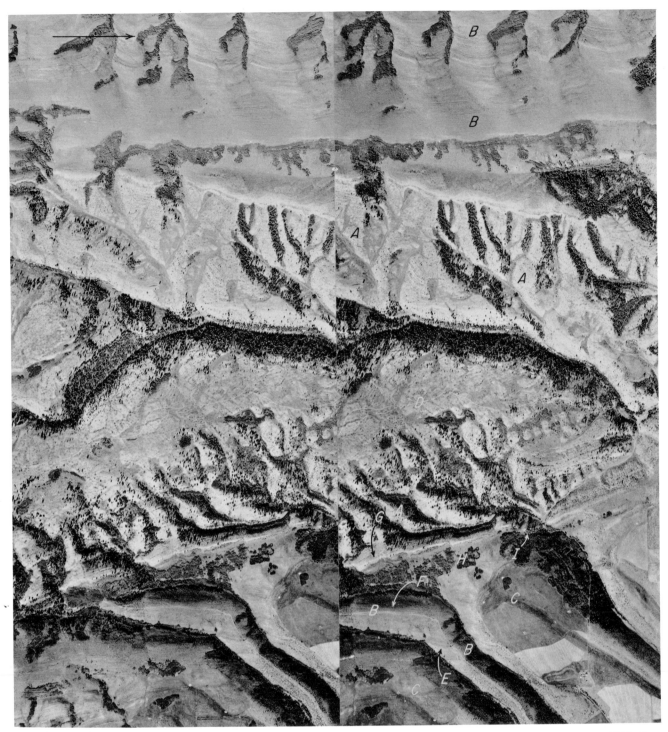

Figure 14-9. Stereogram of a dissected asymmetric anticline, an angular unconformity, and a possible reverse or thrust fault.

Latitude 42°37′ N, longitude 111°00′ W. (*Courtesy of U.S. Dept. of Agriculture, Forest Service.*)

ANTICLINE, UNCONFORMITY, AND POSSIBLE REVERSE OR THRUST FAULT

Three principal stratigraphic units can be mapped in this area: light-toned resistant unit *A*, the oldest; medium-toned thin-bedded unit *B*, somewhat less resistant; and gently dipping, thin, obscuring unit *C*, which lies unconformably upon the truncated beds of unit *B*.

North dips are moderate. An apparently stripped resistant bed in the lower part of unit *A* occupies the axial belt *D*. South dips are steep.

Note that at point *E* the beds of unit *B* dip steeply to the *north*. Strike ridge *F* converges westward toward strike ridge *G*. These relations suggest, but do not prove, the existence of a strike reverse or thrust fault along subsequent lowland *H* and subsequent valley *I*.

EXERCISE

Obtain all available geologic reference maps and other source data for this area, and make a complete geologic map of the stereo-model area.

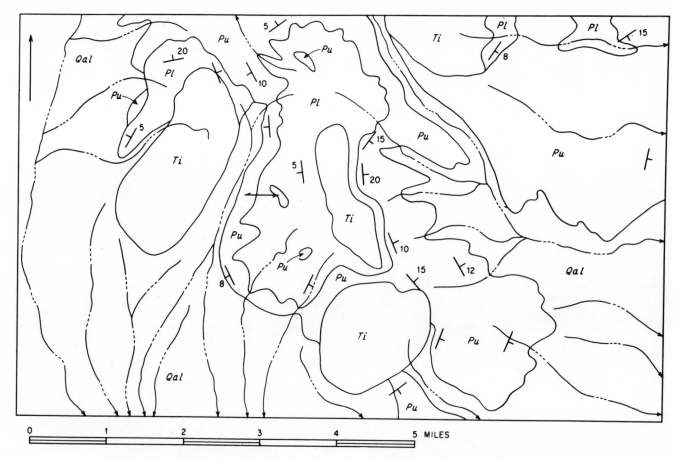

Figure 14-10. Geologic map of folded Paleozoic limestones intruded by Tertiary igneous bodies. *Pl,* Lower Paleozoic limestones; *Pu,* Upper Paleozoic limestones; *Ti,* Tertiary intrusive rocks; *Qal,* Quaternary alluvium.

LACCOLITHS

Elsewhere in this book are a number of illustrations of igneous dikes, irregular intrusive bodies, and circular domes produced by the upward movement of intrusive masses. One of the characteristics which those features have in common is their *discordant* relation with surrounding country rock.

Parts of three igneous bodies are shown in Figure 14-11. In places, their contact with the country rock is remarkably *accordant.*

Intrusive *A* is well exposed. Careful study will reveal a semicircle of steep outward dips around the south and east margins of this mass (points *B, C,* and *D*). Where the beds are nearly vertical (points *B* and *C*), they have been almost entirely reduced to the plane of the surrounding lowland. Where dip is less steep, as at point *E,* they lap up on the igneous rock and form local hills.

The northwest border of intrusive *A* is different from the south border. Around the margin (points *F, G,* and *H*) the sedimentary rocks appear to *underlie* the intrusive rock. At point *G* the two are unconformable, since the igneous material cuts across the bedding. The intrusive rock is in contact with lower beds at point *H* than at point *G.*

Intrusive *A,* therefore, appears to be a laccolith, rather than a stock or small batholith. The several tabular surfaces, such as surfaces *I, J,* and *K,* appear to be remnants of the top of the intrusive body from which the overlying strata have been stripped.

Intrusive *L* occupies the eroded core of an asymmetric anticline (defined by gentle west dips at points *M* and *N* and by steeper east dips at points *O* and *P*). Igneous rocks are exposed at point *L.*

Most of the southern lowland *Q* is obscured by accumulations of sand and gravel. Small dark outcrops, as at points *R* and *S,* resemble the larger outcrops of intrusives *L* and *A.*

A small northwest-trending fault may extend through points *T* and *U.* Note, at point *T,* the abrupt southwest termination of the southeast-dipping strata. Dip increases sharply from point *O* to point *U.*

EXERCISES

1. Outline in orange all areas covered by alluvium and other accumulations of unconsolidated debris.
2. Trace in purple the contacts between the igneous and the sedimentary rocks.
3. In red, add a *complete* system of dips and strikes. Trace fold axes and possible faults.
4. In green, trace several key or marker beds, taking special pains to show the accordant or discordant igneous-sedimentary contact relations.
5. Draw vertically exaggerated profiles and geologic cross sections along line *VW,* along line *VX,* and along line *YX.*

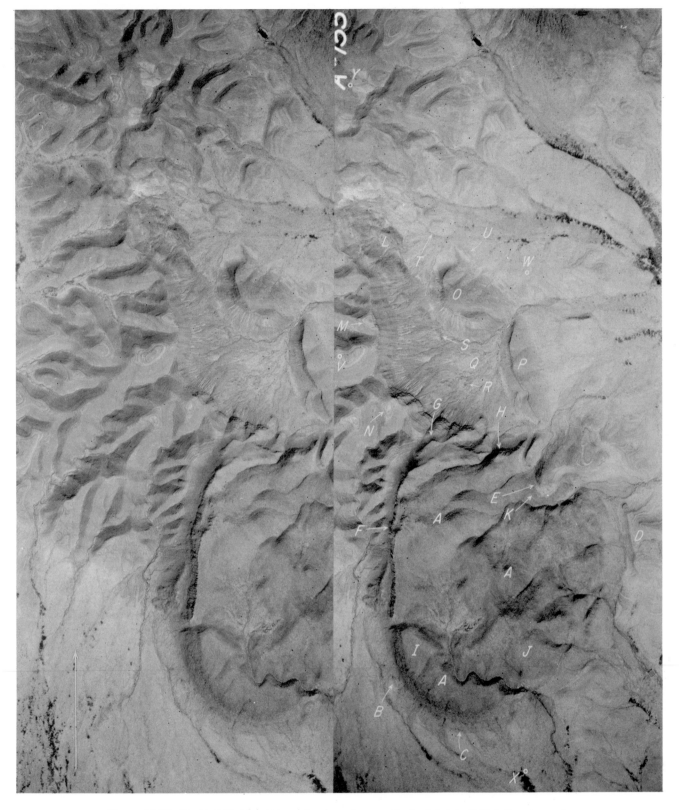

Figure 14-11. Stereogram of igneous intrusions (apparently basic) into folded limestones, in an arid area. (*By permission from Muldrow Aerial Surveys Corporation.*)

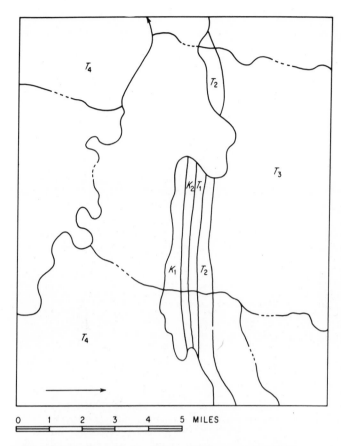

Figure 14-12. Geologic map of an angular unconformity in rocks of Cretaceous and Tertiary age. This figure is an enlargement of part of a state geologic map, published at a scale of 1:500,000. K_1, sandstones and sandy shales; K_2, more or less sandy shales and clays; T_1, sandstones and shales; T_2, shale, clay, sandstone, and a basal conglomerate; T_3, variegated sands, clays, and shales; T_4, soft, whitish, thin-bedded, highly calcareous siliceous silts.

ANGULAR UNCONFORMITY

When an area has been selected for photogeologic mapping and interpretation, all available maps, reports, and other pertinent geologic data are consulted. Some areas have never been mapped, and no source information can be obtained. In some cases, only incomplete and generalized data exist. This area may be considered as representative of the latter group.

Figure 14-12 is an enlarged part of a state geologic map. The map provides approximate rock-unit distribution and formation names. Thicknesses and lithologic and stratigraphic details were obtained from publications dealing with other areas in the region.

The general structural relations shown on Figure 14-12 can be noted on the photographs without great difficulty. The steeply dipping beds which crop out in the south part of the area are the Cretaceous (K_1 and K_2) and Tertiary (T_1 and T_2) units shown on the map. The tree-covered upland in the north consists of nearly horizontal Tertiary unit T_4. The unconformity can be traced, though in some places its position must be approximated.

Some correlation and stratigraphic identification can be attempted, despite the limited coverage of the stereo model.

The parallel, in places knifelike, ridges A, B, and C are composed of steeply dipping resistant sandstones. The more easily eroded materials underlying strike valleys D and E, and those underlying smooth slope F are probably shales or clays.

Belt GH is seen to contrast with belt IJ, despite the fact that these areas lie outside the limit of stereo cover. Streams I_1 and J_1 are subsequent streams which flow along the wide lowland belt IJ. Belt GH consists of strike hills and ridges. The resistant rocks in belt GH may, therefore, be assumed to be the sandstones and sandy shales of unit K_1, and the nonresistant beds of belt IJ to be the sandy shales and clays of unit K_2.

The sandstones and shales of unit T_1 probably include the strata designated as features A through F and may extend upward in section to about point L.

The whitish, badland-like outcrop area M could be an exposure of the clays and shales included in unit T_2. Note similar outcrops at points N and O.

Outcrops at point P may be the basal part of the variegated beds of unit T_3.

The low-dipping silts of unit T_4 are scored by many small, closely spaced gullies, as at points Q, R, and S. Similar erosional features are noted at points T, U, and V, to the south. In these areas, strike ridges and valleys, typical of the areas of exposed steeply dipping older rock units, are not present. The higher parts of the south-central hills thus appear to be capped by isolated remnants of unit T_4.

The northwest-trending lowland of streams W and X may be a significant topographic feature. Note the wind gap at point Y and the extremely linear course of stream W. This lowland belt may have developed along a fault zone.

The sandstone-shale belt of features A through F can be traced north-northwesterly to about point Z. If the beds of outcrop M are conformable on the older units, and if dip magnitude doesn't change appreciably northward, these beds would probably extend beneath unit T_4 to about point M_1.

Beds believed to correlate with those at outcrop M have been noted at points N and O. At point N, strike seems to be slightly west of north. At point O, the strike appears to be a few degrees east of north. A southward projection of these beds, along the strike observed at point O, would bring them to about point S, apparently displaced westward from trend MM_1. Note the detectable, but poorly defined, north-north-easterly–trending *grain* in the general QR area. This probably reflects the strike of the underlying beds.

The above relations support an interpretation of a fault along belt WX. If this is a normal fault, it must be preunit T_4 in age, since the outcrops of unit T_4 in areas T, U, and V are at about the same elevation as those to the north. A postunit T_4 strike-slip fault is an alternate possibility.

EXERCISES

1. Outline areas of alluvium, mantle, and similar surficial deposits in yellow.

2. Outline unit T_4 in orange.

3. Trace mappable key beds in green.

4. Trace possible contacts in purple.

5. Indicate, in red, a probable fault along lowland belt WX, and show apparent relative displacement.

6. Make a colored geologic map of the stereo-model area and, if possible, the marginal photo areas.

Figure 14-13. Stereogram of an angular unconformity between nearly vertical Cretaceous and Tertiary strata and overlying low-dipping Tertiary beds. (*Courtesy of U.S. Dept. of Agriculture, Soil Conservation Service.*)

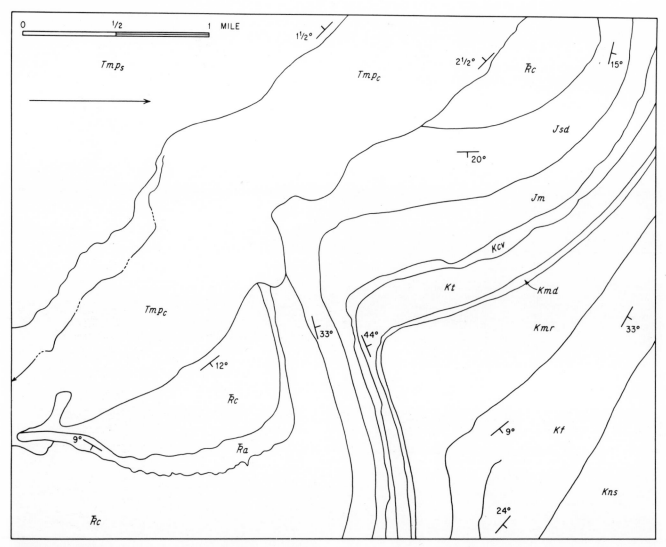

Figure 14-14. Geologic map of folded Mesozoic strata unconformably overlain by undisturbed Tertiary formations. Ɍc, Triassic Chugwater formation; Ɍa, Alcova member of the Chugwater; Jsd, Jurassic Sundance formation; Jm, Jurassic Morrison formation; Kcv, Cretaceous Cloverly formation; Kt, Cretaceous Thermopolis formation; Kmd, Cretaceous Muddy formation; Kmr, Cretaceous Mowry formation; Kf, Cretaceous Frontier formation; Kns, Cretaceous Steele and Niobrara formations undivided; Tmpc, Tertiary Miocene and Pliocene strata, mostly conglomerate; Tmps, Tertiary Miocene and Pliocene strata, mostly sands. (*After James A. Barlow, Jr., 1952.*)

ANGULAR UNCONFORMITY

The structure of the folded Mesozoic formations is clearly defined by outcrop pattern, differential erosion, dip slopes, tonal banding, and minor erosional characteristics. Students familiar with the stratigraphic section in this area should experience no difficulty in transferring formational contacts from the geologic map to the photographs.

Students who do not know the lithologies of the mapped formations should use the photographs as an exercise in identification and interpretation.

It is suggested that the student approach the problem in the following manner:

1. Trace the unconformity in purple. It is easy to locate in the nonstereoscopic marginal parts of the photographs as well as within the area of the stereo model.

2. Using a sharp green pencil, trace about ten persistent key or marker beds.

3. Assume that each contact shown in Figure 14-14 follows a break in lithology and does not follow a subtle facies change or a paleontologic break. Transfer the contacts from Figure 14-14 to the photographs, in purple.

4. Determine strike and dip (including apparent magnitude) and fully annotate these data on the photographs.

5. Sketch in fold axes, including plunge arrows.

6. If any minor faults can be located, they should be traced on the photographs in red. Indicate relative displacements.

7. Explain variations in formation outcrop width.

8. Do the photographs show enough area to permit the location of the source of the sand dunes in the northern part of the area?

9. If reference materials are available, research this area, and determine the lithologies of the mapped units. Do the contacts previously transferred to the photographs agree with this new information? If not, one or more contacts may have to be moved up or down in the section.

10. How can the direction of dip of the beds shown in the extreme lower right corner of the right photograph be determined without stereo coverage?

208

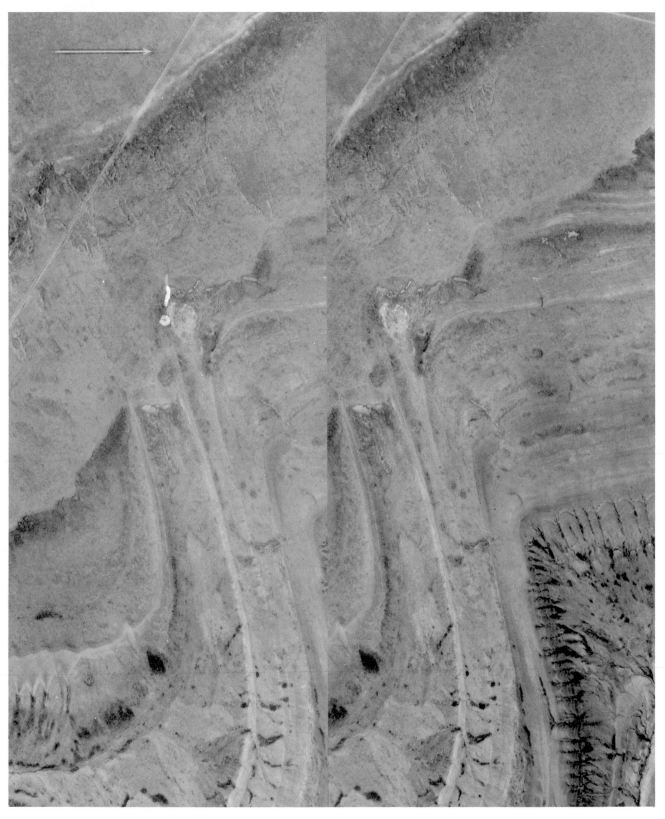

Figure 14-15. Stereogram of an angular unconformity in a semiarid area. The location of the area is latitude 41°50′ N, longitude 107°10′ W. (*By permission from Jack Ammann Photogrammetric Engineers, Inc.*)

ANGULAR UNCONFORMITIES

In areas such as this, where most of the bedrock is exposed or at least clearly defined, it is possible to compile a reasonably detailed and accurate geologic map from the study of aerial photographs. Stratigraphic unit ages may not be determined, of course, and lithologic identifications must be generalized.

From north to south, note the following features and their relations to surrounding features (letters correspond to photo annotations).

A. Gentle west dips in white and light-gray beds. Numerous gullies suggest high clay or shale content.

B. West dip in overlying beds, which include thin resistant members, possibly sandstones.

C. Steep south dips in resistant dark strata.

D. A possible oblique fault line. White beds in small outcrop area *E* could correlate with those of area *A*. They may be preserved in the down-dropped eastern block.

F. A well-defined but mantle-covered angular unconformity or fault. Relations to the south indicate that it is an unconformity.

G. Incised stream which crosses the strike of a thick section of steeply dipping beds. Variations in bedrock resistance are reflected by differences in the stream valley, such as flood plains in segments *H, I,* and *J* (nonresistant rock areas) and canyons in segments *K, L,* and *M* (resistant rock areas).

N and *O.* Excellent dip slopes. The light-toned beds which overlie bed *O* are intricately dissected and were planed off at a high level during an earlier erosional cycle, as shown by preserved erosional surface *P*. These beds are probably shales or clays and thin interbedded sandstones.

Q and *R.* A relatively smooth *dip-slope-appearing* north-sloping surface which truncates nonresistant white beds (beneath surface *Q*) and extremely resistant strata (beneath surface *R*). This surface is overlain by intricately dissected sediments *S*. Beds *S* are unconformable on the older, steeply dipping beds; surface *QR* is the uncovered or exhumed unconformity (erosional) surface. Numerous truncated beds (strike lines) may be seen in section *R* of this surface.

T. A restricted ridge composed of steeply southeast-dipping resistant strata. Its south flank is a dip slope. It is unconformably overlain by shaly beds of areas *U* and *V*. The rocks of ridge *T* resemble those of ridge *W* more than those of area *C*. Minor fault *D*, if extended, might pass just southeast of ridge *T*. Surface *X* is a local gravel-capped pediment remnant. Its presence indicates considerable erosion of the younger beds (beds *A, S, U,* and *V*). If a fault does pass southeast of ridge *T*, is must be prepediment in age. However, it could be either preunconformity or postunconformity in age. The study of a larger area might clarify this questionable relation.

Y. A thick sequence of thin-bedded variegated sediments which dip gently southward and southwestward. To the east (area *Z*) their strike suggests southwest dip. Small dip slope *AA* exhibits moderate southwest dip. These beds converge toward linear outcrops *BB* and directly overlie them at point *CC*. The entire stratigraphic interval lying between point *Z* and beds *BB* is absent at point *CC*. This indicates the possibility of a second, less pronounced angular unconformity.

DD. This tree-covered area, though beyond the limits of the stereo model, resembles area *EE* to the north, which area consists of beds *S*. The more intricately dissected strata of area *Y* may pass unconformably beneath the beds of area *DD*.

EXERCISES

1. The geographic location of this area has been indicated. The general geologic relations are known and the several stratigraphic units have been mapped and identified. Obtain all available maps and reports which pertain to this area.

2. Indicate strikes and dips throughout the stereo-model area.

3. Trace *apparent* contacts, including unconformities, in purple. If reference material is available, attempt to locate and trace the actual contacts.

4. Draw a north-south vertically exaggerated topographic profile and geologic cross section across the stereo-model area, passing through the annotated letter *F*.

5. Write a *complete* geologic history of this area. If strata ages and lithologies are known, include the periods of deposition in the history.

6. Give two possible explanations for the course of stream *G*. This problem would make an excellent classroom or group discussion subject.

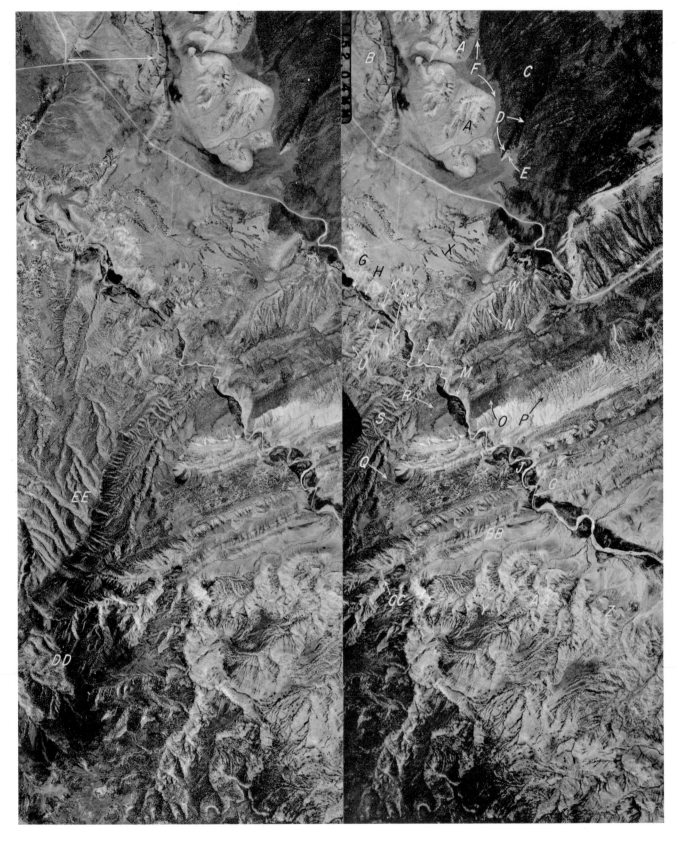

Figure 14-16. Stereogram of differentially eroded steeply dipping strata, angular unconformities, and an exhumed erosional surface in a semiarid area. This area is at latitude 40°47′ N, longitude 108°40′ W. The area shown in Figure 14-17 lies about five miles to the right of this area. Much of the stratigraphic section exposed here also occurs in that area. (*By permission from Fairchild Aerial Surveys, Inc.*)

ANGULAR UNCONFORMITY

The areas shown here and in Figure 14-16 have apparently undergone regional planation or peneplanation at least twice. In Figure 14-16, two angular unconformities can be detected and traced.

In this area, the younger unconformity is preserved locally. The strata immediately above and below the older unconformity are in fault contact in this area. From a study of this stereo model, therefore, the presence of the older unconformity cannot be determined. This illustrates the contribution which the understanding of one area can bring to the mapping and study of a nearby area.

Beginning at the north, note the following features and relations (letters correspond with figure annotations).

A. The dark, in places tree-covered, strata in the northwest corner of the area. The linear strike of these beds indicates steep dip, the direction of which cannot be determined. (These rocks are equivalent to those indicated on Figure 14-16 as area *C*.)

B. Steeply south-dipping resistant strata. (These correlate with rocks in ridge *W* in Figure 14-16.)

C. Nearly perfect south dip slope. (The resistant bed on which this slope is formed is the same as the one which forms dip slope *O* in Figure 14-16.)

D. Nearly horizontal thin layer of materials which overlie a surface of erosion. The erosional surface truncates bed *C* and beds stratigraphically above and below it. This angular unconformity (point *E*) can be identified to the east and south (i.e., at points *F*, *G*, *H*, and *I*). The *dip-slope-appearing* surface *J*, between points *H* and *I*, is virtually an exhumed erosional surface or peneplane remnant, since it is capped by, at most, an insignificant veneer of the younger materials.

The postunconformity beds in this area (areas *D*, *K*, *L*, and *M*) correlate with those indicated in Figure 14-16 as units *A*, *S*, *U*, and *V*.

One interesting and probably important factor to consider is that in Figure 14-16 the plane of the unconformity dips northward (surface *QR*) and westward (along line *F*), while in this area, it is nearly horizontal at point *D*, dips southward at point *G*, and dips southeastward at point *J*.

If it is assumed that these surfaces were originally almost horizontal immediately following their formation by erosional truncation, the several attitudes of the observed remnants may be interpreted as evidence of postunconformity folding and warping.

The younger beds *D* (beds *A* in Figure 14-16) are mapped on the state geologic map as late Tertiary in age. The folding and warping of them and the surface on which they rest must then be assumed to have occurred in late Tertiary (Pliocene?) time, at the earliest.

Reference maps of this area indicate that the strata south of stream *N* are of Eocene age. They stratigraphically *underlie* the unconformity. Note the steep to vertical beds at points *O* and *P*. Along a northeast-trending line passing through point *Q*, a convergence of strike is seen. Beds *R* approach this line from the east; beds *O* strike parallel to the line. Line *Q* should be indicated as a possible fault trace. It may be traced, slightly curved, to points *S* and along tonal break *T*.

The steep dips at point *U* suggest drag along a fault near this point. A relatively wide fault zone, rather than one or two identifiable faults, should be considered as a possible explanation for the above relations.

One question which must be considered is that of relative movement or displacement along the fault lines or zone. The beds at point *O* and in area *V* are reported to be Cretaceous in age. Those south of stream *N* are Eocene in age. A fault zone through the steep-dip belt would therefore automatically be assumed to have involved down-dropping of the beds in the southern block.

But surface *J* does not fit such an interpretation. How could this surface have been *formed* at a level even lower than its present position (with respect to the Eocene rocks to the south)?

Surface *J* would logically be assumed to have been formed at a higher level, and then fault-dropped (and tilted) to its present position.

There is, therefore, evidence for both up and down movement of the north block. Major up-faulting of the north block, followed by local or regional planation, followed by down-faulting of less magnitude, may be the correct explanation.

Note wind gap *W*. This was cut by a major stream, probably of a size comparable to present stream *N*. This former stream was apparently captured when local base level was at the level of the wind-gap floor.

EXERCISES

1. Draw a vertically exaggerated topographic profile and geologic cross section along line *XY*.

2. Locate reference maps and reports of this area. Make a completely annotated photogeologic map of the stereo-model area, using published data for control.

3. Write a *complete* geologic history of this area.

4. Note the linear east-facing scarp at point *Z*. Could this be a fault scarp? A fault-line scarp? Could it be the result of something other than faulting?

5. Examine the areas immediately north and south of point *Z*. What criteria can be cited to substantiate your answers to Exercise 4?

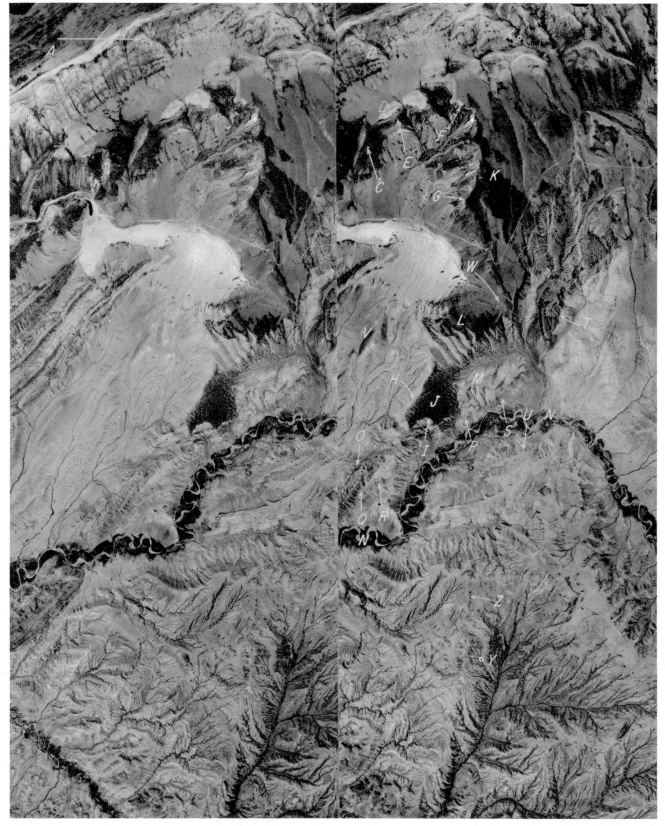

Figure 14-17. Stereogram of an area of differentially eroded strata, a major fault, an unconformity, and a wind gap. Climate in this area is semiarid. The area shown in Figure 14-16 lies about five miles to the left of this area. Many of the strata here are also shown in that stereogram. The location of this area is latitude 40°51′ N, longitude 108°41′ W. (*By permission from Fairchild Aerial Surveys, Inc.*)

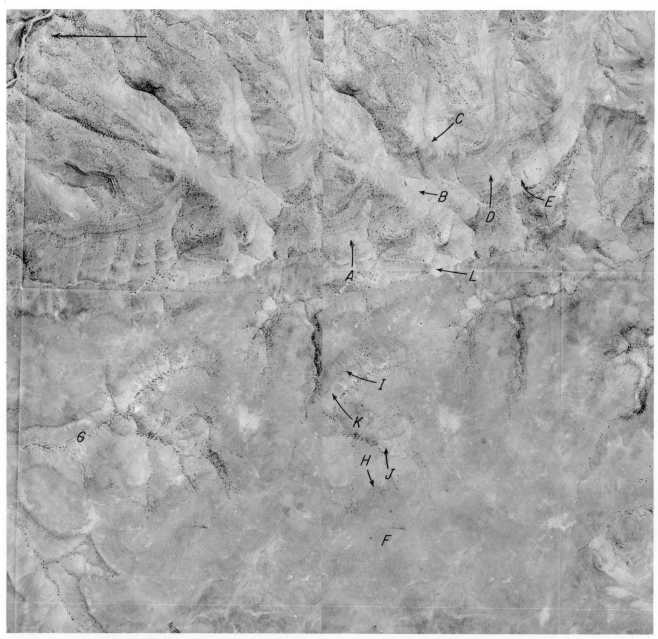

Figure 14-18. Stereogram of a dissected basalt plateau, faults, and dipping sedimentary beds in a semiarid area. Four-lens photographs. (*Courtesy of U.S. Dept. of Agriculture, Soil Conservation Service.*)

BASALT PLATEAU, UNCONFORMITY, AND FAULTS

In the north part of this area is a series of north- and northwest-dipping strata, probably shales and limestones. Careful study of this outcrop area discloses the presence of several faults which are not at first apparent.

The relatively smooth, light-toned slopes at point *A* are probably formed on nonresistant shales. These can be traced eastward to point *B*. They are underlain and overlain by darker, more resistant beds. There is a dip component to the west, from point *B* to point *A*.

The shale unit should be expected to continue to point *C*, but it does not. It does appear, however, at point *D* and, though largely beyond the stereoscopic area, is apparently exposed at point *E*. A logical explanation of these relations is block or normal faulting.

In the south, observe the irregular dissected dark plateau. This is a typical basalt surface. The locally high feature *F* is probably a vent or source area. Prebasalt materials are noted in stream valley *G*. The unconformity is clearly defined at points *H* and *I*.

Some of the older rock *J* resembles that which forms the mountains in the north. Generally nonresistant rock at point *K* may be poorly consolidated "fill" material, possibly late Tertiary or early Quaternary, prebasalt intermontane debris.

The pronounced topographic border between the sedimentary hills and the basalt plateau (i.e., point *L*) may be a prebasalt fault or fault-line scarp zone, up to the base of which the basalts extended during extrusive activity. An alternate possible explanation is that border zone *L* is a postbasalt fault which has either dropped the basalts down to their present position or has lifted the dipping strata to their higher position.

15

Difficult Photogeology

INTRODUCTION

The following illustrations include a representative few of the many ways in which topography, structure, climate, and other factors render photogeologic mapping and interpretation extremely difficult.

In many of the areas shown in previous chapters, deposited materials, such as alluvium and glacial debris, cover and hide underlying bedrock geologic relations. This same problem is present in some of the areas shown in this chapter.

In addition, there are many regions where prolonged weathering under humid climatic conditions has produced thick residual soils and a modified topography. In such areas, the terrain largely fails to reflect structure or differences in rock type (see Figure 15-15).

The more difficult and numerous the problems encountered in the photogeologic study of an area, the more will be the mapped features which are questionable. For example, in some areas, faults can be traced and relative displacements indicated and measured. In others, a fault may only be inferred or deduced. Such a fault should be indicated as a possible or probable fault.

The field check of a *routine* area usually consists of several rapid traverses, directed toward a review of the general geology or the investigation of selected critical and important features and relations.

When *difficult* areas are checked, much more time is required. The field study almost always supplies data which change or correct the photogeologic maps. It also substantiates or refutes doubtful photogeologic interpretations and identifications, and supplies many details in incompletely mapped areas.

In many areas, the study of black and white photographs can provide such detailed and accurate maps that the additional cost of color photography is not warranted. In other areas, where differences in soil color *might* be recorded on color photographs, but do not appear as different *tones* on black and white photographs, the added expense of procuring color photography could be more than offset by the amount of additional information it would provide.

Several of the areas shown here could undoubtedly be more completely mapped and interpreted through the use of color photography.

Although aerial photographs are being used in an increasing number of academic studies, most photogeologic work is still in the fields of commercial exploration and governmental surveys. Photogeology in either of the latter two fields entails the participation of at least two individuals: the photogeologist and the recipient of the map which the photogeologist prepares. The proper and most productive application of photogeology in *difficult* areas demands certain attitudes and understanding on the part of both individuals.

On the one hand, the photogeologist is predestined to failure if he approaches his study area with a defeatist attitude. Though faced with many problems (some insoluble), he must patiently and persistently devote considerable time and effort to a task from which he can only hope to derive incomplete if not partly incorrect results. He has no way of knowing in advance how important his findings may prove to be. In some cases they may be essential to the solution of critical problems.

On the other hand, the recipient of the map, whether he is a client or the photogeologist's immediate superior, should appreciate the *advantages* as well as the obvious limitations of photogeology in *difficult* areas. This is especially true in petroleum exploration. In the United States, for example, at least most of if not all the *routine* areas have been mapped; many have been remapped several times. Most of the obvious "structures" have been delineated and investigated.

We have now reached the point where a large percentage of the areas left for photo study are *difficult* areas. But this is not a valid reason to rule out photogeology as an exploration tool. Instead, the photogeologic study of *difficult* areas by competent photogeologists should be used by petroleum companies as an integral *part* of their exploration and evaluation programs.

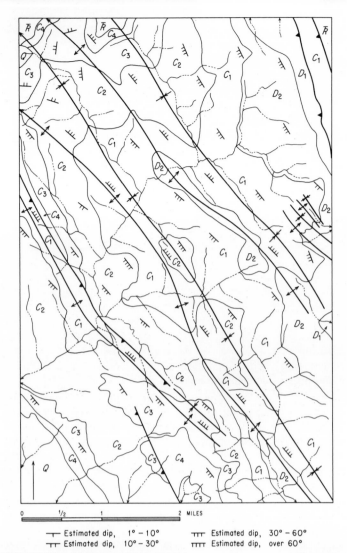

Figure 15-1. Photogeologic map of an area of tight folds and thrust faults. This is part of a map compiled from aerial photographs; it was not checked in the field. D, Devonian strata; D_1 dolomite, with some shale; D_2, dolomitic limestone; C, Carboniferous strata; C_1, black calcareous shale and argillaceous cherty limestone; C_2, limestone and dolomitic limestone; C_3, limestone, dolomite and black, red, and green shale; C_4, quartzite, sandstone and shale; Ŧ, Triassic siltstone and shale; Q, Quaternary materials, undivided. (*After map prepared by V. C. Miller & Associates Photogeologists Ltd., Calgary, Alberta, Canada.*)

0   ½   1   2 MILES

—┬— Estimated dip,   1° – 10°   ┬┬┬ Estimated dip,   30° – 60°
—┬┬— Estimated dip, 10° – 30°   ┬┬┬┬ Estimated dip, over 60°

TIGHT FOLDS IN MOUNTAIN AREA

The area shown here lies a few miles east of the famous Banff resort area, in southwestern Alberta, Canada. The geology and the problems of mapping and interpretation in this area are representative of tens of thousands of square miles in the Canadian Rocky Mountain Front Ranges.

The structure is relatively complex. Dips can be seen in most of the area, however, and fold axes can be drawn. Several resistant and nonresistant stratigraphic units can be traced across most of the stereo-model area.

Map unit C_1 may be considered one of the *keys* to the mapping of the area. This unit may be divided into three members: a lower nonresistant shale member (outcrop *A*, Figure 15-2); a middle resistant member, probably limestones (outcrop *B*); and an upper nonresistant shale member (outcrop *C*).

The lower shale member is exposed at points *D, E,* and *F,* within the stereo model. It can also be seen at points *G, H, I,* and *J,* to the east.

The upper shale member is exposed at points *K, L, M, N,* and *O.*

Mapped unit D_1 does not crop out within the stereo-model area. The resistant limestone unit D_2 forms the core of the anticline which crosses stream *P* at point *Q.* It forms the low ridge *R* and the pronounced bench *S.*

Shadows usually hinder, rather than assist, photogeologic studies. In this area are examples of both.

The geology in dense shadow areas *T* and *U* is completely obscured, though it may be imagined from exposed and visible areas along strike.

The structure and lithologic characteristics in shadow areas *V, W,* and *X,* however, are clearly shown, perhaps *because* of the shadows.

The beds at point *V* can be correlated with those at point *W.* They resemble those at point *W* far more than those at point V_1, though they can actually be traced across the divide to the latter area.

In some barren bedrock areas, exposed to direct sunlight, the glare or hallation effect is so strong that geologic and topographic details are almost completely obscured. Note areas *Y* and *Z,* for example.

EXERCISES

1. Using the geologic map as a guide, trace the several contacts within the stereo-model area.

2. Attempt to extend the photograph annotations to the east and west marginal areas.

3. Draw vertically exaggerated west-east topographic profiles and geologic cross sections across the area, one passing through annotated letter *T,* and another through letter *V.*

4. Assume that the vertical exaggeration factor of the stereo model is 3.0. Construct corrected or reduced profiles and cross sections along the lines designated in Exercise 3.

5. The geologic map shows what are known as *group* dip symbols. The number of "teeth" on each dip symbol indicates the approximate magnitude range within which that dip falls. Carefully estimate apparent dips throughout the entire stereo-model area. Note the small cross which marks the center of the left photograph. Using the assumed vertical exaggeration factor of 3.0, reduce the apparent values to *true* values and completely annotate the structure on the stereogram.

Figure 15-2. Stereogram of a mountainous area of tightly folded strata. In this general area, high-angle thrust or reverse faults constitute an important element of the structure (see Figure 15-1). Note the white areas, caused by glare, and the large dark areas of shadow. Vegetation is restricted to the lower slopes and valley floors. (*Reproduced by courtesy of the Technical Division of the Department of Lands and Forests, Edmonton, Alberta.*)

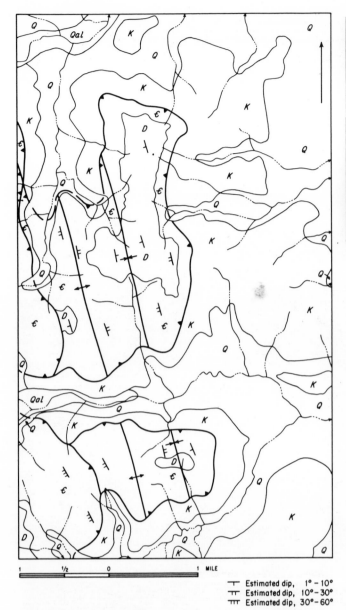

Figure 15-4. Ground photograph (looking north) of the area shown in the center of the photogeologic map and the stereogram (Figures 15-3 and 15-5). Note the unconformity between the light-toned strata (Ghost River) and the underlying Cambrian beds (€). (*Photograph courtesy of L. M. Clark.*)

Figure 15-3. Photogeologic map of an overthrust, which has carried lower Paleozoic strata over Cretaceous beds. This is part of a map compiled from aerial photographs; it was not checked in the field. €, Cambrian strata, dark dolomitic limestone. The top of this map unit consists of Devonian (?) black, gray, and pink dolomite and green and red dolomitic shale. This top unit could not be mapped as a separate formation throughout the map area; D, Devonian strata, principally massive black dolomite; K, Cretaceous sandstones and shales; Q, Quaternary deposits undivided; Qal, Quaternary stream alluvium. (*After map prepared by V. C. Miller & Associates Photogeologists Ltd., Calgary, Alberta, Canada.*)

LOW-ANGLE THRUST FAULT AND ANGULAR UNCONFORMITY

Two examples of dip discordance may be noted in the stereo model. They are the critical structural relations.

In the north lowland, relatively steep southwest dip can be detected. The lowland has been glaciated, and the bedrock is masked by glacial debris of various thicknesses. However,

slopes *A* and *B* are well-defined dip slopes. The strike of the beds is readily established here. Strike is also shown by the trend of the small ridges *C* and *D*.

The topographic irregularities at points *E* and *F* can be ascribed to the traces of steeply dipping, thin, resistant and nonresistant beds. Slope *G* may be a modified dip slope. South of slope *G* the structure of the rocks underlying the lowland cannot be mapped, though at one or two places an impression of dip is afforded.

Dip in the mountains is extremely gentle. Westward dip of a few degrees is noted at point *H*, for example, and at points *I* and *J*. A gross impression of west dip is provided along scarp *K*.

All dips in the resistant mountain-forming strata are moderate to low; all in the lowland are steep. This discordance could be explained in two ways: an angular unconformity or a thrust fault. In this case, it is a thrust fault. The plane of the fault cannot be seen. It can be mapped with reasonable accuracy near the top of the gentler slopes, as at points *L, M, N,* and *O*.

Note the syncline which is defined, in the south mountain spur, by dip reversals in beds *P, Q,* and *R*.

The second discordance in dip is more difficult to detect. It is more restricted in areal extent. Transfer to the photographs the contact at the base of map unit *D*. This contact is marked by a distinct tonal break. It is most apparent at points *S, T,* and *U*, though it can be traced to and around the north end of the northerly ridge. Immediately beneath the tonal break is a thin nonresistant unit (see points *V* and *W*), which appears accordant with the darker overlying strata.

At points *S* and *T* the beds dip a few degrees to the west, into the major syncline. Older beds, exposed at point *X*, have a much steeper west dip. The base of the thin nonresistant unit marks a plane of discordance. In this case, it is an angular unconformity. This relation is shown in Figure 15-4.

Note the obscuring effect of both glare and shadow at several places in the stereogram.

Figure 15-5. Stereogram of a low-angle thrust fault. The mountains are composed of resistant Paleozoic strata which have overridden less resistant Cretaceous beds. Cretaceous rocks occupy the surrounding lowlands. (*Reproduced by courtesy of the Technical Division of the Department of Lands and Forests, Edmonton, Alberta.*)

FAULT ZONE

Though several beds can be traced across this area, such factors as slope, tone, rock weathering and erosional characteristics, vegetation, and drainage patterns must be considered in mapping and interpreting the geology.

Some regional relations can be learned from publications which include nearby areas, but do not cover the area shown here.

1. A large area to the east consists of gently folded and block-faulted lower Paleozoic strata, chiefly limestones and shales. Many of the limestones are reported to contain chert layers.

2. A large intermontane lowland lies to the north and northwest.

3. About fifteen miles to the northeast, Quaternary gravels and sands have been mapped in unconformable contact with underlying bedded rhyolites and older limestones.

4. The rhyolites mapped are shown in a ground photograph to be extremely resistant, intricately jointed, and to form light-toned, in places almost white-appearing cliffs and scarps.

5. The limestones of the rhyolite area, as shown in a ground photograph, appear as generally dark, rounded slopes, with occasional poorly defined ledges or breaks in slope produced by more resistant layers or beds.

It is possible that all or some of the units described and mapped in the areas to the northeast and east also occur in this area. The first step, therefore, is to study and describe the units shown on the photographs. The rocks in this area may be divided into six mappable units, as follows (numbers correspond with photo annotations):

1. Quaternary alluvium and mantle. These materials should be outlined and designated *Q*.

2. Maturely dissected, homogeneous, relatively nonresistant rocks which are virtually devoid of traceable bedding. Small, nearly horizontal ledges at points *A* and *B* indicate at least local resistant lenses and suggest, but do not prove, an undisturbed structural attitude in the entire area occupied by these rocks. These materials would be tentatively identified as the Quaternary gravels and sands.

3. This resistant, gently dipping unit has been stripped to form a dissected bench or topographic shelf. It may be assumed to be composed of resistant strata which produce a variable photographic tone. In most places it appears gray, but in valley slope *C* it is relatively light-toned. In an arid or semiarid area, such as this, it could be carbonate rock.

4. Though a thin resistant member forms a low bench at point *D*, this rock unit is chiefly nonresistant, light-toned in the upper part, and somewhat darker in most of the lower part. It is probably a thick shale unit.

5. The basal member of this unit forms the most pronounced scarp (feature *E*) in the area. This member is assumed to be a moderately thick limestone bed. It is overlain by relatively nonresistant beds, perhaps interbedded shales and thin limestones.

6. The youngest unit in the upland area consists of resistant but well-rounded medium-dark gray rocks. Note that very few tributary streams have developed in this area, compared with the dense drainage in area 2.

Stratigraphic contacts can be drawn along precise horizons. The contact between units 3 and 4 is at points *F*, *G*, and *H*. The contact between units 4 and 5 is at points *I*, *J*, and *K*. The contact between units 5 and 6, which is at points *L*, *M*, and *N*, is a tonal, a topographic, and a vegetation break.

Note the difference in the stratigraphic and topographic interval between points *G* and *E*, and between points *F* and *I*. This difference may be explained by the presence of a northwest-trending fault which passes through points *O* and *P*. The western block appears to have been down-dropped. This fault continues through point *R* (with less displacement), and probably extends southward, with decreasing displacement, along stream valley *S*, perhaps to point *T*.

Stream valleys *U* and *V* combine to suggest the trace of a minor fault.

Note streams *W* and *X*, scarps *Y* and *Z*, and the sharply defined tonal break *AA*. These combine to suggest a fault zone along the northwest side of the upland.

The north block was apparently down-dropped, bringing the Quaternary sands and gravels into contact with the lower limestone unit.

The displacement along this fault must have a total magnitude of hundreds of feet. The fact that in this area the Quaternary sediments appear to be displaced does not necessarily mean that total fault movement occurred after the deposition of these sediments. This could be a much older fault which has undergone repeated small displacement.

In such a case, the Quaternary sands and gravels could have been deposited in a lowland area produced by the down-faulting of the north block. Relatively small fault rejuvenation could then have occurred, to produce the relations observed in this area.

The rhyolite of the area to the northeast apparently does not occur in this area. The limestones on which the rhyolite rests in the area to the northeast may be those designated here as unit 6. The major border fault must decrease in displacement to the northeast, and units 3, 4, and 5 must descend northeastward along the fault, until the unfaulted Quaternary sands and gravels directly overlie the younger units (unit 6 of this area).

EXERCISES

1. Draw a vertically exaggerated topographic profile and geologic cross section across the area, from point *BB* to point *CC*.

2. Assume that *all* displacement along the border fault occurred *after* the deposition of the Quaternary gravels and sands. Draw a series of diagrammatic northwest-southeast cross sections to depict the structural and erosional history of the area.

3. Assume that *most* of the displacement along the border fault occurred *prior* to the deposition of the Quaternary gravels and sands. Draw a series of diagrammatic cross sections to depict the structural, depositional, and erosional history of the area.

Note: "Publications" on the geology of nearby areas, referred to in the text which accompanies Figure 15-6, are fictitious.

Figure 15-6. Stereogram of a major fault zone in a semiarid climate. (*Courtesy of U.S. Dept. of Agriculture, Soil Conservation Service.*)

OBSCURED FAULT

When these photographs are examined for the first time, it would be natural for the student to obtain the impression that bedrock outcrops throughout almost the entire area.

Such is not the case, however. A closer estimate would be that about 30 to 35 per cent of the bedrock is completely covered and obscured.

It is suggested that this area be mapped, in the following manner, rather than studied at the offset as an integrated whole.

1. The large stream has undergone minor changes in regimen in relatively recent times. Its valley floor is wide, but its *present* flood plain is somewhat restricted. Note the low but distinct bluffs at points A and B. In the west, the flood plain is restricted to the belt extending from point A to point C. The flood plain should be outlined and labeled *Qal* (Quaternary alluvium). Note tilt in this area.

2. There is a transition from alluvial surface D to the small fan E. Numerous such transitions can be seen in the area. Such composite alluvial and mantle areas should be grouped, outlined, and indicated as Q (Quaternary undivided). Valley floors F, G, and H should be outlined and included in this map unit.

3. Note upland surfaces I, J, K, and L. These are gravel and sand cappings of erosional surfaces (pediment remnants) and are not bedrock conformable on older strata. The angular unconformity can be seen in many places. Thin, dark-toned resistant bed M, for example, rises to the northwest and passes beneath the horizontal-appearing dark capping layer. At point N the beds dip to the southeast, though the upland surface slopes gently to the west. Outline all gravel-capped surfaces and designate each as *Qpg* (Quaternary pediment gravel). The steep slopes in the northeast (i.e., at point O) are similar pediment features developed along the flank of the upland P.

4. The areas which have not been outlined are bedrock areas. Structural and stratigraphic mapping and interpretation will be limited to these areas. Attention is next directed to the general stratigraphic sequence.

South of the major stream, the gently northeast-dipping strata consist of thin, light- to medium-toned nonresistant and resistant interbeds. The nonresistant members are probably shales, and the resistant units may be sandstones or marlstones.

North of the stream is a marked tonal and topographic break, which for mapping purposes may be used as a contact. It is clearly exposed at points R and S, and may be assumed at point T. It does not extend westward into area U.

The dark crenulate erosional surface of the beds (beds V, W, and X) immediately above the contact appears in several places (i.e., points Y and Z) to the north, at a considerably higher elevation.

A northeast-trending fault can be seen at point AA. The beds immediately southeast of this line dip steeply to the southeast, apparently due to drag along the fault. The south side was down-dropped. The fault can be located at point BB and, to the west of the stereo model, can be traced from point CC through point DD. Note the displacement of scarp-forming unit EE to point FF.

One remarkable feature of the fault is that it has no appreciable topographic expression. It usually does not produce scarps by the offsetting of beds, it is not followed by subsequent streams (unless at point GG), and does not form dikelike ridges.

EXERCISES

1. Indicate strike and dip throughout the stereo-model area. The photographs possess tilt, and the dips indicated should be considered *assumed* or *apparent*, for exercise purposes only.

2. Trace the fault discussed above. Can it be detected northeast of point AA?

3. Trace several key beds.

4. Trace the contact located at points R and S.

5. Draw a vertically exaggerated north-south topographic profile and geologic cross section through point T.

6. Draw a vertically exaggerated west-east profile and cross section through joint J.

7. This area is located at latitude 40°51′ N, longitude 108°35′ W. Obtain all available maps and references which will provide details of stratigraphy, regional tectonics, and erosional history of the area.

8. Prepare a *complete* description and report on the area shown on the photographs. Identify the outcropping formations, describe their photographic characteristics, and give a detailed summary of the geomorphic and structural history of the area. Supplement the report with regional sketch maps, stratigraphic tables, cross sections, and block diagrams.

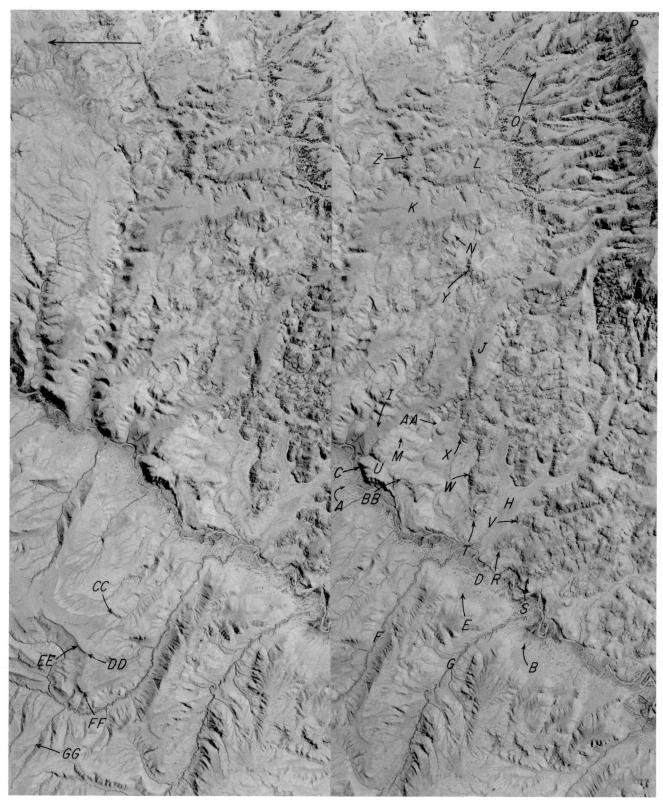

Figure 15-7. Stereogram of a fault in a sequence of thin-bedded mudstones, shales, marl-stones, and sandstones. Gravel-capped pediment remnants obscure some of the geologic relations. This is a semiarid area. (*Courtesy of U.S. Dept. of Agriculture, Soil Conservation Service.*)

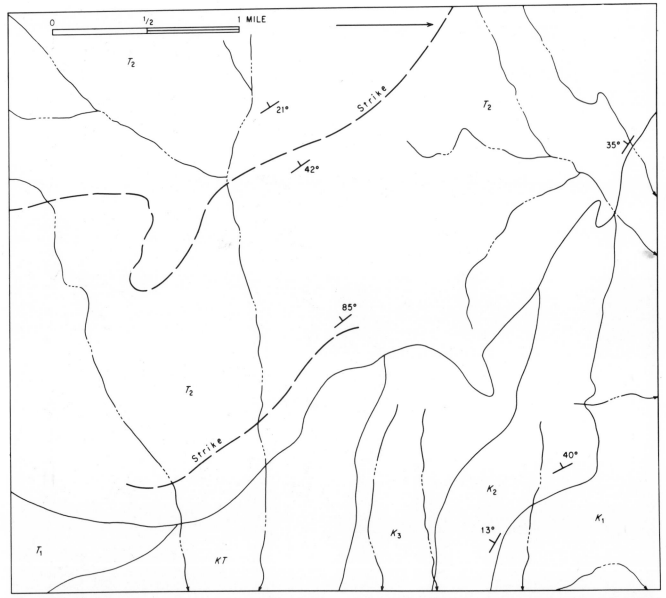

Figure 15-8. Geologic map of a steeply inclined folded angular unconformity. *K*, Cretaceous strata; *T*, Tertiary strata; *K₁*, dark-gray shale with intercalated beds of sandstone and shaly sandstone; *K₂*, a lower member of gray to white sandstone and gray shale, a middle member of brown to gray sandstone and thin irregular coal beds, and an upper member of whitish sandstone and gray shale; *K₃*, chiefly dark-gray shale, with thin intercalated beds of shaly sandstone and some beds of light-colored massive to heavy-bedded sandstone; *KT*, Cretaceous-Tertiary light-colored to gray carbonaceous shale, gray to brown sandstone, and thin irregular beds of coal; *T₁*, light-colored to dark-gray carbonaceous shale, buff to brown sandstone, pockets, lenses, and thin beds of conglomerate in lower part, and numerous coal beds; *T₂*, alternating beds of dark-gray, yellowish, and brown shale and sandstone, conglomerate, and numerous beds of coal.

FOLDED ANGULAR UNCONFORMITY

Though much of the structure in this area is clearly depicted on the aerial photographs, some problems require considerable study and interpretive ability for solution.

In much of the area, an old, mantle-covered topography precludes *detailed* strike and dip mapping. Strike ridges and subsequent (shale) valleys define the essential structure.

Streams *A*, *B*, and *C* are tributaries of a drainage system which has been rejuvenated. Note the intricate topography produced by the differential erosion of upturned resistant and nonresistant strata in this part of the area. Probably streams *D* and *E* formerly drained some of the area to the east, now drained by the smaller tributaries of streams *B* and *C*.

The primary geologic feature in this area is the angular unconformity. It shows in Figure 15-8 as the base of unit *T₂*.

Beds *F* (on the photographs) converge northward toward beds *G*. The unconformity is about at point *H* and extends southwestward, parallel to beds *G*, to point *I*.

The geologic map indicates that the unconformity is exposed approximately at point *J*. A discordance in strike (between beds *K* and *L*) can be seen along line *MN*, however. This may be a fault or an unconformity.

On the geologic map it is not possible to determine whether the contact between map units *KT* and *T₁* is conformable or not. Line *MN* could be an unmapped northeastward extension of an unconformable contact between these units. It could be the major unconformity (beds *K* somewhat resemble beds *G*), duplicated or displaced by faulting. It could also be a fault trace.

Note the discordance between beds *K* and *F*.

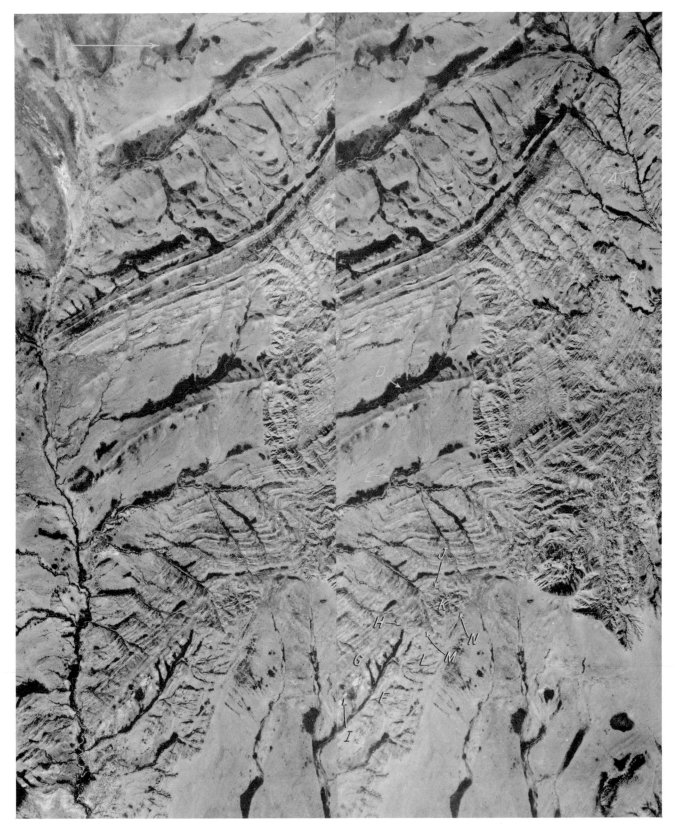

Figure 15-9. Stereogram of a folded angular unconformity, an old erosional surface, differential erosion in an area of drainage rejuvenation, and probable multiple stream capture. This is a semiarid area. (*By permission from Jack Ammann Photogrammetric Engineers, Inc.*)

EXERCISES

1. Trace numerous key beds and (where possible) the unconformity, indicate dips and strikes, faults, and fold axes, and transfer formational contacts from Figure 15-8 to the stereo model.

2. As stated above, there are several possible explanations for the geologic relations in and near area *K*. Make three sketches of this area, showing line *MN* as: (*a*) a second unconformity, (*b*) a fault, and (*c*) the major unconformity duplicated by faulting. Which solution appears to be correct?

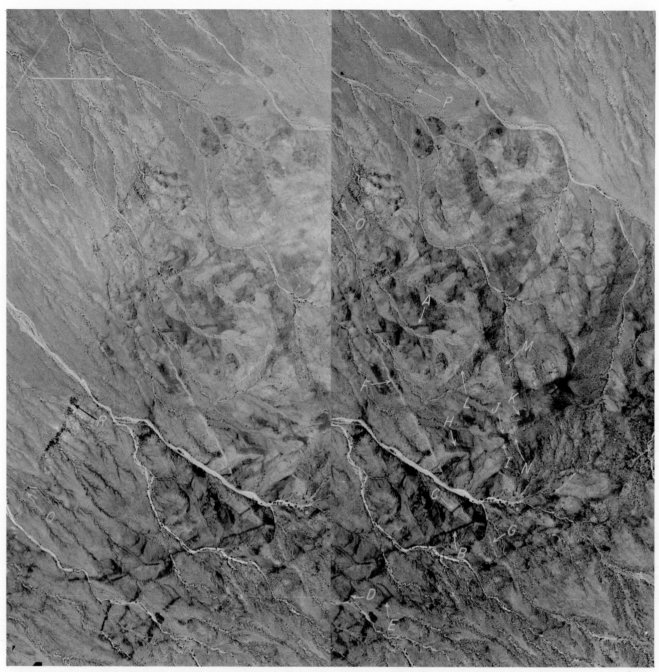

Figure 15-10. Stereogram of intersecting acidic and basic dikes, joints, and faults in a semi-arid area. (*Courtesy of U.S. Dept. of Agriculture, Soil Conservation Service.*)

INTERSECTING DIKES IN COMPLEX AREA

In this area, numerous individual rock units can be outlined and some general relations established. A much larger area would have to be studied, all available maps and reports consulted, and intensive field work carried out, to obtain the detailed information required for complete mapping and interpretation of this area.

The obvious features here are the well-defined light and dark lines.

Many of them, such as lines *A, B, C, D,* and *E,* are apparently basic dikes. Some, such as lines *F* and *G,* are probably acidic dikes.

Steep west dip is suggested by the outcrop pattern at points *H* and *I.* These may be bedded volcanic materials, possibly extrusive flows or pyroclastics. Dark beds *J* and *K* could be parts of a basic sill.

Note the affinity of the dark shrubs or trees for the lighter-toned rocks, such as at points *L, M,* and *N.* May slope orientation be a factor in selective vegetative development here?

A line of low trees or shrubs (line *OP*) extends across the northwestern lowland. Much of this line occurs in the gravel and sand alluvial apron, though part of it is in exposed bedrock. Line *OP* should be shown on a map of this area, indicated as a possible fault line. It should be thoroughly investigated in the field.

A similar trend is line *QR,* also defined by vegetation. It does not resemble nearby basic dike outcrops.

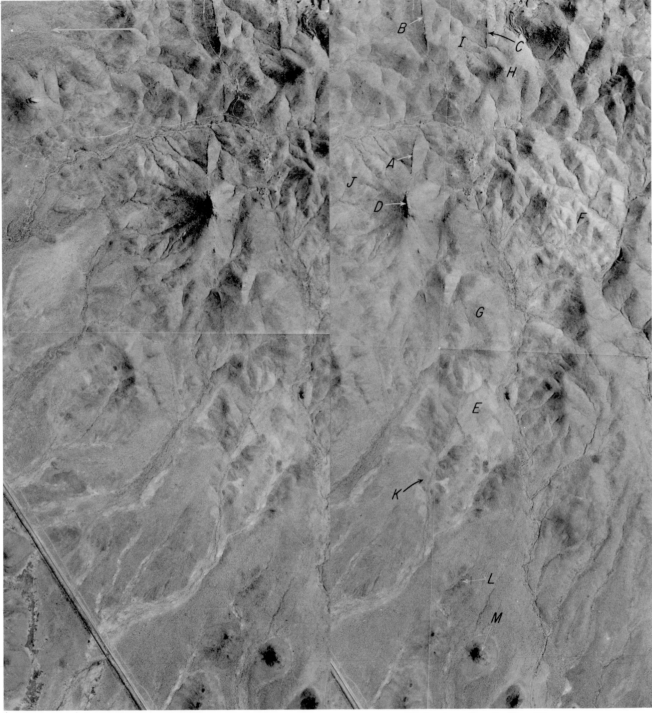

Figure 15-11. Stereogram of a complex area of basalts, granodiorite, intrusive rhyolite, dikes, and faults (some occupied by resistant vein materials) in a semiarid area. Four-lens photographs. (*Courtesy of U.S. Dept. of Agriculture, Soil Conservation Service.*)

COMPLEX AREA OF INTRUSIVE AND EXTRUSIVE ROCKS

The most impressive features in this area are the several spinelike ridges (features *A, B,* and *C*) and the high peak *D*. These resemble basic dikes. They are identified as resistant veins on published maps of the area.

Light-toned areas *E* and *F* are intrusive rhyolite bodies. Many of the medium-toned areas (i.e., areas *G* and *H*) are underlain by granodiorite. Weathered basalts lie in the northern and western low areas (i.e., areas *I* and *J*).

Much of the south lowland is a gravel-capped erosional surface. Dissection of this surface has uncovered several areas of bedrock (i.e., areas *K* and *L*). Hill *M* is a small volcanic plug.

EXERCISE

Obtain reference material and map this area in detail (latitude 32°20' N, longitude 108°46' W).

227

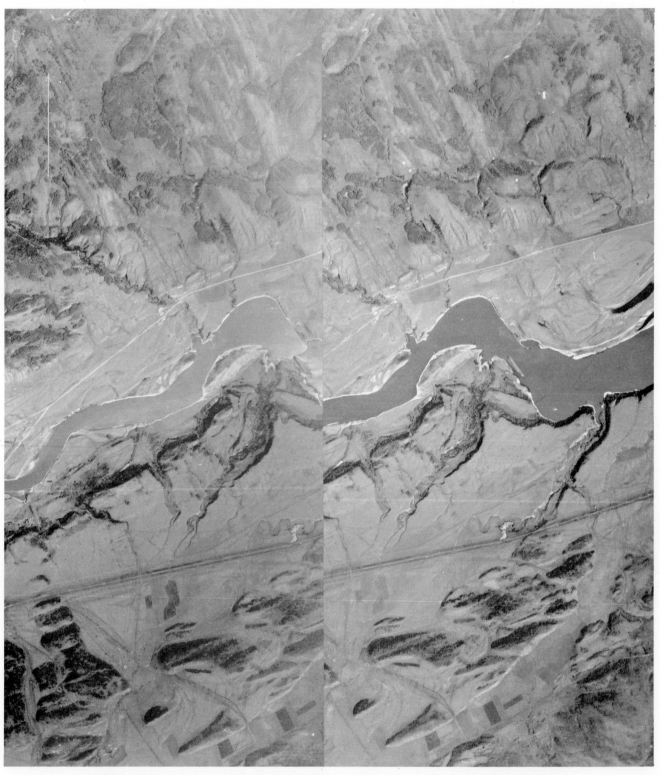

Figure 15-12. Stereogram of a glaciated lowland underlain by steeply dipping strata. (*Reproduced by courtesy of the Technical Division of the Department of Lands and Forests, Edmonton, Alberta.*)

STEEP DIPS IN GLACIATED LOWLAND AREA

This area lies just east of the front of the Rocky Mountains in southwestern Alberta, Canada.

The outstanding features shown in the stereo model are the northwest-trending ridges and valleys north of the river and the east-trending ridges and lowlands south of the river.

In the north, the topography reflects the strike of differentially eroded, steeply dipping sedimentary beds. The beds outcrop at several lowland places. Note the linear island.

The southern area is underlain by deposits derived from a glacier which overrode the area during Pleistocene time. This is drumlinoid topography, apparently partially destroyed by outwash runoff.

This is an important illustration. It should be studied carefully and fully understood.

Figure 15-13. Stereogram of a rhyolite intrusive in an area of bedded rhyolites and andesites. The climate here is semiarid. (*Courtesy of U.S. Dept. of Agriculture, Soil Conservation Service.*)

INTRUSIVE AND EXTRUSIVE IGNEOUS ROCKS

The central lowland is underlain by a jointed, light-toned, relatively nonresistant rhyolite intrusive. The slightly darker, highly jointed, more resistant rocks to the west, north, and northeast of the lowland are principally bedded rhyolites. The dark-toned, smoother slopes south of the lowland are developed in bedded andesites.

There is one large fault and several possible faults in the area.

Note the strange appearance of the larger streams. This is caused by reflections of the sun's rays into the camera. Why is it only apparent on the left photograph?

EXERCISES

1. Completely annotate the stereogram, showing structure, contacts, and drainage network.

2. Draw west-east and north-south vertically exaggerated topographic profiles and geologic cross sections across the stereomodel area, including the central intrusive lowland.

Figure 15-14. Geologic map of faulted Triassic strata and diabase sills. Ⱦa, red and olive shale, and some interbedded reddish-gray sandstone; Ⱦb, zone of baked shale adjacent to diabase sill; Ⱦc, diabase.

FAULTED SHALES AND DIABASE SILLS IN HUMID AREA

Despite a complete cover of thick residual soils, and widespread agricultural development and forest clearing, the topography of this area provides *some* indications of structure and rock-unit distribution.

In the north, note the low ridge *AB*. Its east edge is followed by an apparently subsequent segment of stream *C*. This ridge is underlain by diabase which dips eastward. The stream is probably adjusted along the diabase-baked shale contact zone.

The geologic map shows the diabase as a much wider unit than is suggested by the narrow ridge. The linear tree-covered steep slope at point *D* resembles a fault-line scarp.

The lower area *E*, to the west, could be underlain by sedimentary beds in fault contact with the diabase.

The relatively abrupt south end of ridge *AB* corresponds with the fault shown on the map; nonresistant shales underlie the lowland *F* just to the south.

The southern, largely tree-covered ridge *GH* loses its topographic identity near point *H*. Were this area part of a photogeologic mapping project for which reference maps were not available, it is probable that the photogeologist would indicate that the resistant ridge-forming unit (the diabase) appears to thin northward here, and perhaps pinches out completely. There is little to suggest that it extends northward, to be cut off by the fault.

It is difficult to detect topographic asymmetry along ridge *GH*. The lowland *I* to the west of the ridge is slightly lower

Figure 15-15. Stereogram of an area underlain by faulted Triassic shales and sandstones, baked shales, and diabase sills. This area is in the Piedmont Lowland in eastern United States. (*Courtesy of U.S. Department of Agriculture, Commodity Stabilization Service.*)

than the lowland *J* to the east. This difference may be explained by the gentle east dip indicated on the map. The eastward slope may be maintained and controlled by the resistant rocks. The lowering of the area to the west may have advanced more rapidly, since here the underlying strata are less resistant throughout.

EXERCISES

1. Draw and compare geologic cross sections along lines *KL* and *MN* on the map.

2. Discuss the possible fault along the west side of ridge *AB*.

231

APPENDIX

References to Part III Illustrations

Many of the line drawings used as illustrations in Part III are taken from published maps and sketches. Some were obtained from unpublished sources, by permission from the authors.

The aerial photographs and mosaics used were selected in several ways. Some were suggested by other geologists. Some were chosen from groups of photographs of large areas, kindly made available by commercial companies. Some were encountered during theses and other academic studies. A few were included in areas studied in the search for petroleum and minerals.

Some of the illustrations of Part III are not identified below. Reference to these illustrations is omitted for practical, personal, or ethical reasons.

Those which are identified may be obtained (if they are for sale) from the companies or government agencies listed below. Many of the maps and other technical publications may be consulted in technical or university libraries.

Each company and government agency is indicated by a key word or by initials.

The reference designations are as follows:

Alberta	Technical Division, Department of Lands and Forests, Edmonton, Alberta, Canada.
Ammann	Jack Ammann Photogrammetric Engineers, Inc.
CE	Corps of Engineers.
CSS	Commodity Stabilization Service, U.S. Department of Agriculture.
Fairchild	Fairchild Aerial Surveys, Inc.
FS	Forest Service, U.S. Department of Agriculture.
GSC	Geological Survey of Canada, Department of Mines and Technical Surveys, Ottawa, Ontario, Canada.
Muldrow	Muldrow Aerial Surveys Corporation.
MTS	Department of Mines and Technical Surveys, Map Distribution Office, Ottawa, Ontario, Canada.
TVA	Tennessee Valley Authority.
Tobin	Edgar Tobin Aerial Surveys.
RCAF	Royal Canadian Air Force (photos obtainable from Department of Mines and Technical Surveys, National Air Photo Library, Ottawa, Ontario, Canada).
SCS	Soil Conservation Service, U.S. Department of Agriculture.
USAF	U.S. Air Force (photos obtainable from U.S. Geological Survey).
USGS	U.S. Geological Survey.
VGS	Virginia Geological Survey, University of Virginia.

The following data should be sufficient to permit the student to locate and obtain original prints of most of the illustrations used in Part III.

Fig. 8-1 *SCS* — Photos CTF-3-30,31. 1:31,680. March 8, 1941. Otero County, N.Mex.

Fig. 8-2 *USGS* — Loveland Quadrangle (Topographic). 1:62,500, contour interval 20 feet. 1906. Larimer County, Colo.

Fig. 8-3 — Traced from part of the original manuscript maps prepared by C. Maynard Boos and Margaret Fuller Boos for the Carter Oil Company, Denver, Colorado. Maps reduced and published as part of their paper, "Tectonics of Eastern Flank and Foothills of Front Range, Colorado," *Bull. Am. Assoc. Petrol. Geologists*, vol. 41, no. 12, pp. 2603-2676. December, 1957.

Fig. 8-4 *CSS* — Photos AIL-10-19, 20. Latitude 40°28′ N, longitude 105°08′ W, Larimer County, Colo.

Fig. 8-8 *GSC* — Sectional Map No. 165 (Topographic), Rosebud, Alberta. Printed by the Surveyor General. 1:190,080, contour interval 50 feet. April, 1922. (Note: Original map does not show wells included in Figure 8-8.)

Fig. 8-9 *Alberta* — Photos 160-5108-1563-345, 346. Latitude 51°30′ N, longitude 112°40′ W, Drumheller area, Alberta, Canada.

Fig. 8-10 *GSC* — Map 581A (Geologic), Beaulieu River. 1:253,440. 1941. District of Mackenzie, Northwest Territories.

Fig. 8-11 *RCAF* — Photos A-8668-151, 152. Latitude 62°35′ N, longitude 113°36′ W, District of Mackenzie, Northwest Territories.

Fig. 8-12 *Tobin* — (Part of) Mosaic 8N, 15W. Northwest corner of Crockett County, Tex.

Fig. 8-13 *Tobin* — Photos 126-4-96, 97. Latitude 30°56′ N, longitude 101°52′ W, Northwest corner of Crockett County, Tex.

Fig. 8-14 *RCAF* — Photos A-11879-428, 429. Location of area not known.

Fig. 9-1   *Fairchild*   Photos C-13100X-3-136, 137. Latitude 36°09′ N, longitude 116°45′ W, Death Valley National Monument, Calif.

Fig. 9-2   *RCAF*   Photos A-12861-183, 184. Northwest Territories.

Fig. 9-3   *SCS*   Photos BT-1951, 1952, 1953. Coconino County, Ariz.

Fig. 9-4   *USGS*   Newberry Crater Quadrangle (Topographic). 1:125,000, contour interval 100 feet. 1948. Duschutes County, Ore.

Fig. 9-5   *FS*   Photos BAY-1H-200, 201, 202. 1:20,000. July 27, 1951. Latitude 43°44′ N, longitude 121°14′ W, Duschutes County, Ore.

Fig. 9-6   *FS*   Photos BAY-1H-202, 203, 204. 1:20,000. July 27, 1951. Latitude 43°42′ N, longitude 121°14′ W, Duschutes County, Ore.

Fig. 9-7   *USGS*   Sonora Quadrangle (Topographic). 1:24,000, contour interval 50 feet. 1949. Tuolumne County, Calif.

Fig. 9-8   *Fairchild*   Photos C-975-D-44, 45. Latitude 37°58′ N, longitude 120°26′ W, Tuolumne County, Calif.

Fig. 9-9   *USGS*   Orick Quadrangle (Topographic). 1:62,500, contour interval 50 feet. Humboldt County, Calif.

Fig. 9-11   *Fairchild*   Photos C-7490-705, 706. Latitude 41°17′ N, longitude 124°05′ W, Humboldt County, Calif.

Fig. 9-12   *CSS*   Photos CYO-4B-59, 60, 61. Sept. 19, 1946. Latitude 40°58′ N, longitude 112°53′ W, Tooele County, Utah.

Fig. 9-13   *FS*   Photos DOM-5-57, 58. Sept. 27, 1951. Latitude 37°59′ N, longitude 107°17′ W, Hinsdale County, Colo.

Fig. 9-14   *RCAF*   Photos A-12105-302, 303. North Canada. Location of area not known.

Fig. 9-15   *SCS*   Photos ALJ-10996, 10997. 1:31,680, focal length 6 inches. Oct. 13, 1937. Latitude 39°02′ N, longitude 108°05′ W, Mesa County, Colo.

Fig. 9-16   *USGS*   Varney Quadrangle (Topographic). 1:62,500, contour interval 40 feet. 1949. Madison County, Mont.

Fig. 9-17   *Fairchild*   Photos C-10950-F-39-13-33 and C-10950-F-40-13-32. Latitude 45°11′ N, longitude 111°55′ W, Madison County, Mont.

Fig. 9-18   *CSS*   Photos BOI-150-37, 38. 1:20,000, focal length 8.25 inches. Sept. 21, 1938. Latitude 43°50′ N, longitude 102°15′ W, Pennington County, S.Dak.

Fig. 9-19   *FS*   Photos CL-22-33, 34. Latitude 37°27′ N, longitude 104°54′ W, Spanish Peaks Area, Las Animas County, Colo.

Fig. 9-20   *RCAF*   Photos A-15052-146, 147. North Canada. Location of area not known.

Fig. 9-21   *Alberta*   Photos 160-5211-1823-150, 151. Location of area not known.

Fig. 10-1   *USGS*   Mt. Gunnison Quadrangle (Topographic). 1:62,500, contour interval 50 feet. 1952. Gunnison County, Colo.

Fig. 10-2   *USGS*   Geologic Map of Colorado. 1:500,000. 1935. Delta and Gunnison Counties, Colo.

Fig. 10-3   *FS*   Photos DRO-1-39,40. Latitude 38°48′ N, longitude 107°22′ W, Gunnison County, Colo.

Fig. 10-4   *GSC*   Map 868A (Geologic), Prosperous Lake. 1:63,360. District of Mackenzie, Northwest Territories.

Fig. 10-5   *RCAF*   Photos A-5619-36, 37. Latitude 62°44′ N, longitude 114°02′ W, District of Mackenzie, Northwest Territories.

Fig. 10-6   *TVA*   Mendota Quadrangle 197 NE (Topographic). 1:24,000, contour interval 20 feet. 1939. Scott and Washington Counties, Va.

Fig. 10-7   *TVA*   Photos 197-4-12, 13. Latitude 36°38′ N, longitude 82°19′ W, Scott and Washington Counties, Va.

Fig. 10-8   *TVA*   Same as Figure 10-6 above.

Fig. 10-9   *TVA*   Photos 197-3-11, 12. Latitude 36°40′ N, longitude 82°19′ W, Scott and Washington Counties, Va.

Fig. 10-10   *TVA*   Hansonville Quadrangle 205 SW and Wallace Quadrangle 206 NW (Topographic). 1:24,000, contour intervals 40 feet (Hansonville) and 20 feet (Wallace). 1939. Washington County, Va.

Fig. 10-11   *TVA*   Photos 206-1-6, 7. Latitude 36°44′ N, longitude 82°12′ W, Washington County, Va.

Fig. 10-12   *SCS*   Rio Grande Area Photos 7985, 7986. 1:31,680. 1935. Latitude 33°03′ N, longitude 107°33′ W, Sierra County, N.Mex.

Fig. 10-13   *Fairchild*   Photos C-3883-16, 17. Latitude 35°08′ N, longitude 119°40′ W, San Luis Obispo County, Calif.

Fig. 11-1   *USGS*   Photos GS-ID-24-74, 75. Aug. 2, 1949. Latitude 40°14′ N, longitude 105°12′ W, Boulder County, Colo.

Fig. 11-2   *USGS*   Photos GS-HJ-5-188, 189. Oct. 13, 1948. Latitude 40°14′ N, longitude 105°12′ W, Boulder County, Colo.

Fig. 11-3   *USGS*   Miscellaneous Geologic Investigations Map I-54, "Photogeologic Map of the Bluff-11 Quadrangle, San Juan County, Utah," by C. F. Miller. 1:24,000. 1955.

Fig. 11-4   *Fairchild*   Photos C-10560-10-73, 74. Latitude 37°13′ N, longitude 109°45′ W, San Juan County, Utah.

Fig. 11-5 *RCAF* Photos A-12260-437, 438. North Canada. Location of area not known.

Fig. 12-1 *CE* Derouen Quadrangle (Topographic). 1:62,500, contour intervals 5 and 20 feet (increasing at 20-foot contour). 1938. Iberia Parish, La.

Fig. 12-2 *CE* Same as Figure 12-1 above.

Fig. 12-3 *Tobin* Mosaic of the Weeks Island Area. Latitude 29°48′ N, longitude 91°48′ W, Iberia Parish, La.

Fig. 12-4 *USGS* Gibson Quadrangle (Topographic). 1:62,500, contour interval 5 feet. 1944. Terrebonne Parish, La.

Fig. 12-5 *Ammann* (Parts of) Mosaics covering southwest part of Unit Area 47. Latitude 29°35′ N, longitude 90°55′ W, Terrebonne Parish, La.

Fig. 12-6 *MTS* National Topographic Series, Olds and Bearberry Sheets, 82 O/16 West Half and 82 O/15 East Half. 1:50,000, contour interval 25 feet. 1956. Olds Area, Alberta, Canada.

Fig. 12-8 *Alberta* Photos 160-5114-1564-423, 424. Latitude 51°48′ N, longitude 114°29′ W, Olds Area, Alberta, Canada.

Fig. 12-9 *USGS* Photos 120-AK-31-4024, 4025. N.Mex. Location of area not known.

Fig. 12-10 *SCS* Photos DY-29-41, 42. Southwest N.Mex. Location of area not known.

Fig. 13-1 *FS* Photos CNM-2-74, 75. Latitude 36°20′ N, longitude 112°27′ W, Grand Canyon, Ariz.

Fig. 13-2 *SCS* Navajo Indian Reservation Survey Photos 6019, 6020. 1:31,680. 1934 and 1935 (date). Latitude 36°41′ N, longitude 108°50′ W, San Juan County, N.Mex.

Fig. 13-3 *Fairchild* Fifteen-minute Shiprock quadrangle mosaic. Latitudes 36°30′ to 36°45′ N, longitudes 108°45′ to 109°00′ W, San Juan County, N.Mex.

Fig. 13-4 *USGS* "Geology of Comb Ridge and Vicinity North of San Juan River, San Juan County, Utah," *Bull.* 1021-E, Plate 17, 1:63,360, by J. D. Sears, 1956.

Fig. 13-5 *Fairchild* Photos C-10560-SJR-FL-5-8, 9. 1:24,000. Aug. 16, 1946. Latitude 37°18′ N, longitude 109°38′ W, San Juan County, Utah.

Fig. 13-6 *SCS* Photos ALJ-12164, 12165. 1:31,680, focal length 6 inches. Jan. 9, 1938. Latitude 39°00′ N, longitude 110°36′ W, Emery County, Utah.

Fig. 13-7 *Fairchild* Photos C-19000-2983, 2984. Latitude 40°17′ N, longitude 108°37′ W, Moffat County, Colo.

Fig. 13-8 *USAF* Photos 131-AW-NK-13-1-12-1947, 1948. 1:60,000 (approx.). (These photographs are obtainable from the U.S. Geological Survey.) Latitude 43°33′ N, longitude 106°25′ W (approx.), Johnson County, Wyo.

Fig. 13-9 *USAF* Photos 131-AW-NK-13-1-11-1829, 1830. 1:60,000 (approx.). (These photographs are obtainable from the U.S. Geological Survey.) Latitude 43°30′ N, longitude 106°30′ W, Johnson and Natrona Counties, Wyo.

Fig. 13-10 *USGS* "Elk Basin Oil and Gas Field and Vicinity," Geologic and Structure Map, 1:31,680, 1944, by C. E. Dobbin, W. B. Kramer, and J. C. Miller.

Fig. 13-11 *Fairchild* Photos C-10400-2-8, 9. Latitude 44°57′ N, longitude 108°51′ W, Park County, Wyo.

Fig. 13-12 *USGS* Oil and Gas Investigations Preliminary Map 4, "Plains Adjacent to the Little Rocky Mountains, Montana," Figure 5, 1:48,000, 1944, by M. M. Knechtel, S. R. Brockunier, and S. W. Hobbs.

Fig. 13-13 *Ammann* Photos 36M-136, 137. Latitude 47°50′ N, longitude 108°35′ W, Phillips County, Mont.

Fig. 13-14 *USGS* Same as Figure 11-3 above.

Fig. 13-15 *Fairchild* Photos C-10560-4-128, 129. Latitude 37°08′ N, longitude 109°50′ W, San Juan County, Utah.

Fig. 13-16 *RCAF* Photos A-14368-51, 52. North Canada. Location of area not known.

Fig. 13-17 *Ammann* Photos 122W-44, 45. Latitude 44°40′ N, longitude 108°15′ W (approx.), Big Horn County, Wyo.

Fig. 13-18 *Fairchild* Photos C-19000-3363, 3364. Location of area not known.

Fig. 13-19 *CSS* Photos CKG-2-123, 124, 125. Latitude 34°21′ N, longitude 97°12′ W, Murray and Carter Counties, Okla.

Fig. 13-20 Same as Figure 8-3 above.

Fig. 13-21 *FS* Photos BOV-21-34, 35. Latitude 38°30′ N, longitude 105°15′ W (approx.), Fremont County, Colo.

Fig. 13-22 *GSC* Paper 47-16, Ross Lake, Northwest Territories. Geologic Map and Descriptive Notes. 1:31,680, 1947, by Y. O. Fortier.

Fig. 13-23 *RCAF* Photos A-8668-37, 38. Latitude 62°30′ N, longitude 113°12′ W, Ross Lake area, Northwest Territories.

Fig. 13-24 *SCS* Photos DMZ-3-67, 68. 1:20,000. 1951. N.Mex. Location of area not known.

Fig. 14-1 "Geomorphology and Structure of the West Kaibab Fault Zone and Kaibab Plateau, Arizona," by Arthur N. Strahler. Plate I, 1 inch to 5 miles, structure contour interval 100 feet. *Bull. Geol. Soc. Am.,* vol. 59, pp. 513-540, June, 1948.

Fig. 14-2 After Fig. 8, Strahler, 1948 (reference same as Figure 14-1 above).

Fig. 14-3 *FS* Photos CNM-7-37, 38. Latitude 36°55′ N, longitude 112°12′ W, Coconino County, Ariz.

Fig. 14-4   USGS   Wild Horse Mountain Quadrangle and Seminole Dam SW Quadrangle (Topographic). 1:24,000, contour interval 20 feet. 1953. Carbon County, Wyo.

Fig. 14-5   USGS   Photos GS-CM-5-137, 138. Latitude 42°04′ N, longitude 107°00′ W, Carbon County, Wyo.

Fig. 14-6   USGS   Walden Quadrangle (Topographic). 1:24,000, contour interval 20 feet. 1955. Jackson County, Colo.

Fig. 14-7   USGS   Photos GS-VM-2-103, 104. Latitude 40°42′ N, longitude 106°19′ W, Jackson County, Colo.

Fig. 14-8   RCAF   Photos A-12040-246, 247. Northwest Territories. Location of area not known.

Fig. 14-9   FS   Photos COC-BBL-1A-195, 196. Latitude 42°37′ N, longitude 111°00′ W, Lincoln County, Wyo.

Fig. 14-10   USGS   Oil and Gas Investigations Preliminary Map 90, "Regional Geologic Map of Parts of Culberson and Hudspeth Counties, Texas," 1:150,000 (approx.), 1949, by Philip B. King.

Fig. 14-11   Muldrow   Photos A-154, 155. Latitude 31°52′ N, longitude 105°25′ W, Hudspeth County, Tex.

Fig. 14-12   USGS   Geologic Map of Colorado. 1:500,000. 1935.

Fig. 14-13   SCS   Photos ALJ-13247, 13248. Latitude 40°35′ N, longitude 108°05′ W, Moffat County, Colo.

Fig. 14-14   "Geologic Map of the Rawlins Uplift, Carbon County, Wyoming," by James A. Barlow, Jr., December, 1952. Scale: 2 inches to 1 mile.

Fig. 14-15   Ammann   Photos 116W-8, 9. Latitude 41°50′ N, longitude 107°10′ W, Carbon County, Wyo.

Fig. 14-16   Fairchild   Photos C-19000-3010, 3011. Latitude 40°47′ N, longitude 108°40′ W, Moffat County, Colo.

Fig. 14-17   Fairchild   Photos C-19000-3011, 3012. Latitude 40°51′ N, longitude 108°41′ W, Moffat County, Colo.

Fig. 14-18   SCS   Rio Grande Area Photos 8023, 8024. 1:31,680. 1935. Latitude 33°08′ N, longitude 107°35′ W (approx.), Sierra County, N.Mex.

Fig. 15-1   "Preliminary Photogeologic Reconnaissance Map of the Banff-Exshaw Area, Alberta," scale, 1 inch to 1 mile, prepared in 1957 by V. C. Miller & Associates Photogeologists, Ltd.

Fig. 15-2   Alberta   Photos 160-5103X-1892-55, 56. Latitude 51°10′ N, longitude 115°18′ W, Banff-Exshaw area, Alberta, Canada.

Fig. 15-3   Same as Figure 15-1 above.

Fig. 15-4   Ground photograph taken by L. M. Clark, Pacific Petroleums, Ltd., Calgary, Alberta, Canada.

Fig. 15-5   Alberta   Photos 160-5104X-1892-24, 25. Latitude 51°12′ N, longitude 115°08′ W, Banff-Exshaw area, Alberta, Canada.

Fig. 15-6   SCS   Photos 29-125, 126. 1:31,680. 1939. N.Mex. Location of area not known.

Fig. 15-7   SCS   Photos ALJ-13825, 13826. Latitude 40°51′ N, longitude 108°35′ W, Moffat County, Colo.

Fig. 15-8   USGS   "Hanna and Carbon Basins, Geology, Coal and Oil Resources." U.S. Geol. Survey Bull. No. 804, Plate 27, 1:62,500, 1929, by C. F. Bowen, C. E. Dobbin, and H. W. Hoots.

Fig. 15-9   Ammann   Photos 23W-92, 93. Latitude 41°57′ N, longitude 106°25′ W, Carbon County, Wyo.

Fig. 15-10   SCS   Whitewater-Animas Area Photos DDR-7-89, 90. 1:31,680. 1946. Latitude 32°25′ N, longitude 108°30′ W, Grant County, N.Mex.

Fig. 15-11   SCS   Gila Area Photos 2682, 2683. 1:31,680. 1935. Latitude 32°20′ N, longitude 108°46′ W, Hidalgo County, N.Mex.

Fig. 15-12   Alberta   Photos 160-5103-1562-312, 313. Latitude 51°12′ N, longitude 114°48′ W, southwest Alberta, Canada.

Fig. 15-13   SCS   Photos DY-29-94, 95. N.Mex. Location of area not known.

Fig. 15-14   VGS   "Geology and Mineral Resources of the Warrenton Quadrangle, Virginia," Plate I, 1:62,500, Virginia Geol. Survey Bull. 54, 1939, by A. S. Furcron.

Fig. 15-15   CSS   Photos DJD-4G-44, 45. Latitude 38°32′ N, longitude 77°48′ W, Fauquier and Culpeper Counties, Va.

Bibliography

Abrams, Talbert (1944): "Essentials of Aerial Surveying and Photo Interpretation," McGraw-Hill Book Company, Inc., New York.

Ahrens, T. P. (1936): "The Utilization of Aerial Photographs in Mapping and Studying Land Features," Resettlement Administration, Land Utilization Division, Land-use Planning Section, Publication 6, Washington, D.C.

Alexander, J. B., and W. D. Proctor (1955): Investigations upon a Proposed Dam Site in Klang Gates, Federation of Malaya, *Colonial Geol. and Mineral Resources (Gt. Brit.),* vol. 5, no. 4, pp. 409–415.

Alliger, J. (1955): Application of Photogeology to Oil Exploration in Western Canada, *J. Alberta Soc. Petrol. Geol.,* vol. 3, no. 10, pp. 179–184, 194.

American Society of Photogrammetry (1947): College and University Courses in Geologic Uses of Aerial Photos, and General Discussion, *Photogram. Eng.,* vol. 13, no. 4, pp. 621–628.

——— (1952): "Manual of Photogrammetry," 2d ed., George Banta Publishing Company, Menasha, Wis.

——— (1960): "Manual of Photographic Interpretation," George Banta Publishing Company, Menasha, Wis.

Andrews, E. C. (1938): The Aerial, Geological, and Geophysical Survey of Northern Australia, *Econ. Geol.,* vol. 33, no. 1, pp. 81–86.

Armstrong, John E., and Howard W. Tipper (1948): Glaciation in North Central British Columbia, *Am. J. Sci.,* vol. 246, pp. 283–310.

Aschenbrenner, C. M. (1952): The Interpretation of Tridimensional Form from Stereo Pictures, *Photogram. Eng.,* vol. 18, no. 3, pp. 469–472.

——— (1952a): A Review of Facts and Terms Concerning the Stereoscopic Effect, *Photogram. Eng.,* vol. 18, pp. 818–823.

Auden, J. B. (1954): Erosional Patterns and Fracture Zones in Peninsular India, *Geol. Mag.,* vol. 91, pp. 89–101.

——— (1954a): Drainage and Fracture Patterns in North-West Scotland, *Geol. Mag.,* vol. 91, pp. 337–351.

Baetsle, P. L. (1956): L'Exagération apparente du relief dans l'observation des stéréogrammes, *Bull. soc. belge photogrammetrie,* no. 43 (extract).

Bagley, James W. (1941): "Aerophotography and Aerosurveying," McGraw-Hill Book Company, Inc., New York.

Barlow, James A. (1952): "Geologic Map of the Rawlins Uplift, Carbon County, Wyoming" (privately printed).

Barton, Donald C. (1933): Surface Fracture System of South Texas, *Bull. Am. Assoc. Petrol. Geologists,* vol. 17, no. 10, pp. 1194–1212.

Bean, Russell K. (1955): Development of the Orthophotoscope, *Photogram. Eng.,* vol. 21, no. 4, pp. 529–535.

——— and Morris M. Thompson (1957): Use of the Orthophotoscope, *Photogram. Eng.,* vol. 23, no. 1, pp. 170–179.

Belcher, Donald J. (1944): Identifying Land Forms and Soils by Aerial Photographs, *Proc. 30th Ann. Purdue Road School,* March, pp. 133–154.

——— (1945): The Engineering Significance of Soil Pattern, *Photogram. Eng.,* vol. 11, no. 2, pp. 115–148.

——— (1946): Engineering Applications of Aerial Reconnaissance, *Bull. Geol. Soc. Am.,* vol. 57, no. 8, pp. 727–734.

——— (1948): Determination of Soil Conditions from Aerial Photographs, *Photogram. Eng.,* vol. 14, no. 4, pp. 482–488.

——— (1953): The Status of Interpretation in Natural Resources Inventories: Photo Magnetometer Interpretation, *Photogram. Eng.,* vol. 19, no. 3.

——— (1953a): Terrain Intelligence and the Future of Mineral Prospecting, in "Selected Papers on Photogeology and Photo Interpretation," GG 209/1, Committee on Geophysics and Geography, Research and Development Board, Washington, D.C.

——— (1953b): The Engineering Significance of Landforms, *Highway Research Board, Proc.,* no. 2 in *Bull. Acad. Sci.,* no. 13.

——— (1959): Microforms and Features, *Photogram. Eng.,* vol. 25, no. 5, pp. 773–778.

———, J. Amouzegar, R. J. Hodge, H. C. Ladenheim, and D. R. Lueder (1951): "A Photo-analysis Key for the Determination of Ground Conditions"; vol. 1, "Coastal Plain Beaches"; vol. 2, "Pocket Beaches"; vol. 3, "Coral Beaches, Glaciated Beaches, River Mouth Beaches, Terrace Beaches," Beach Series, *Tech. Rept.* 3, U.S. Office of Naval Research, Cornell University, Ithaca, N.Y.

———, L. E. Greeg, and K. B. Woods (1943): The Formation, Distribution and Engineering Characteristics of Soil, *Purdue Univ. Research Ser.* 87, *Highway Research Board Bull.* 10, January, chap. 4, Aerial Photographs in Soil Mapping, pp. 61–80.

———, Ta Liang, R. B. Costello, G. L. Fallon, R. J. Hodge, H. C. Ladenheim, D. R. Lueder, and J. D. Mollard (1951): "A Photo-analysis Key for the Determination of Ground Conditions"; vol. 1, "General Analysis"; vol. 2, "Sedimentary Rocks"; vol. 3, "Igneous Rocks"; vol. 4, "Waterlaid Materials"; vol. 5, "Glacial Materials"; vol. 6, "Windlaid Materials," Landform Series, *Tech. Rept.* 3, U.S. Office of Naval Research, Cornell University, Ithaca, N.Y.

———, et al. (1957): Panel on Photo Interpretation, *Photogram. Eng.,* vol. 23, no. 1, pp. 100–121.

Beltman, B. J. (1952): Comments on "The Interpretation of Tridimensional Form from Stereo Pictures," (by Aschenbrenner, 1952), *Photogram. Eng.,* vol. 18, no. 5, pp. 823–825.

Bench, B. M. (1948): Discovery of Oil Structures by Aerial Photography, *Oil Gas J.,* vol. 49, no. 17, August, pp. 98–100 and 146–152.

——— (1948–1949): Oil Structure Discovered by Aerial Photography, *Mines Mag. (Denver),* vol. 38, no. 12, pp. 101–108; vol. 39, no. 1, pp. 13–15, and no. 2, pp. 13–16.

——— and D. W. Bell (1953): Interpretation of a Stereo Pair of Cross Mountain, Colorado, *Photogram. Eng.,* vol. 19, no. 3, pp. 461–463.

Benninghoff, William S. (1950): Use of Aerial Photographs in

Mapping Vegetation and Surficial Geology in Subarctic Regions, *Photogram. Eng.,* vol. 16, no. 3, pp. 428–429.

———— (1953): Use of Aerial Photographs for Terrain Interpretation Based on Field Mapping, *Photogram. Eng.,* vol. 19, no. 3, pp. 487–490.

Bentor, Y. K. (1952): Air-photographs and Geologic Mapping with Special Reference to the Geological Conditions in the Negev (Southern Israel), *Bull. Research Council Israel,* vol. 2, no. 2, pp. 157–169.

Bijlaard, P. P. (1948): On the Linear Patterns of the Earth's Crust, *Proc. Koninkl. Akad. Wetenschap. Amsterdam,* vol. 51, no. 4.

Black, L. D. (1955): Regional Keys Are Valid Geographical Generalizations, *Photogram. Eng.,* vol. 21, no. 5, pp. 706–708.

Black, Robert F. (1952): Polygonal Patterns and Ground Conditions from Aerial Photographs, *Photogram. Eng.,* vol. 18, no. 1, pp. 123–134.

———— and W. L. Barksdale (1949): Oriented Lakes in Northern Alaska, *J. Geol.,* vol. 57, pp. 105–118.

Blanchet, P. H. (1955): Photogeologic Exploration by Multiplex, *J. Alberta Soc. Petrol. Geol.,* Alberta, Canada.

———— (1957): Development of Fracture Analysis as Exploration Method, *Bull. Am. Assoc. Petrol. Geologists,* vol. 41, no. 8, pp. 1748–1759.

Boos, C. Maynard, and Margaret Fuller Boos (1957): Tectonics of Eastern Flank and Foothills of Front Range, Colorado, *Bull. Am. Assoc. Petrol. Geologists,* vol. 41, no. 12, pp. 2603–2676.

Bowen, C. F., C. E. Dobbin, and H. W. Hoots (1929): Hanna and Carbon Basins, Geology, Coal and Oil Resources, *U.S. Geol. Survey, Bull.* 804.

Brasseur, R., and J. Flandrin (1955): "Photogeology and Its Use," French Petroleum Institute, France.

Brock, C. C. (1952): "Physical Aspects of Air Photography," Longmans, Green & Co., Ltd., London.

Browning, W. F., Jr. (1951): Mapping Geologic Formations by the Application of Aerial Photography, *Highway Research Board Bull.* 46.

Brundall, Lawrence (1946): Photogeology Aids Oil Exploration, *The Oil Weekly,* Dec. 2, pp. 18–23; Dec. 9, pp. 52–53.

———— (1947): Photogeology Aids Oil Exploration, *Photogram. Eng.,* vol. 13, pp. 275–285.

———— (1956): Photogeology Permits Rapid Mapping of Wide Areas, *World Oil.*

———— and B. P. Harder (1953): Photogeologic Evaluation in the Montana Plains Area, *Proc. 4th Ann. Field Conf., Billings Geol. Soc.,* pp. 150–155.

———— and A. R. Wasem (1950): Photogeology's Place in Petroleum Exploration, *World Petrol.,* vol. 21, no. 3, pp. 51–54; no. 4, pp. 41–44.

Buringh, P. (1955): Some Problems Concerning Aerial Photo-interpretation in Soil Survey, *Neth. J. Agr. Sci.,* vol. 3, no. 2, pp. 100–106.

Bushnell, T. M. (1951): Use of Aerial Photography for Indiana Land Studies, *Photogram. Eng.,* vol. 17, no. 5, pp. 725–738.

Cabot, E. C. (1947): The Northern Alaskan Coastal Plain Interpreted from Aerial Photographs, *Geograph. Rev.,* vol. 37, pp. 639–648.

Cady, W. M. (1945): Aerial Photos as an Adjunct to Arctic and Subarctic Geologic Reconnaissance, *Trans. N.Y. Acad. Sci.,* vol. 7, ser. 2, pp. 135–138.

Cameron, H. L. (1949): Air Photograph Interpretation in the Chimney Corner–Cheticamp Area, Cape Breton Island, N.S., *Photogram. Eng.,* vol. 15, no. 2, pp. 238–249.

———— (1952): Airphoto Interpretation in Mining and Engineering Geology in Canada, (abstract), *Photogram. Eng.,* vol. 18, no. 3, p. 458.

———— (1953): Air-photo Interpretation in Natural Resources Inventories, *Photogram. Eng.,* vol. 19, no. 3, pp. 481–486.

Cattelain, F. (1952): Contribution à l'étude des courants et bancs de sable au littoral et dans un fleuve soumis à marée, par la photographie aérienne, Ministère des Travaux Publics, Service de Topographie et de Photogrammetrie, Belgique, *7th Congr. intern. photogrammetrie,* Washington, D.C.

Cheney, Theodore A. (1957): A New Interpretation of the Interpretation Situation, *Photogram. Eng.,* vol. 23, no. 1, pp. 101–105.

Choubert, Boris (1957): Essai sur la morphologie de la Guyane, "Memoires pour servir à l'explication de la carte géologique détaillée de la France," Département de la Guyane Française, Paris, Imprimerie Nationale.

Christensen, D. J. (1956): Eagles of Geology, *Photogram. Eng.,* vol. 22, no. 5, pp. 857–865.

Church, E., and A. O. Quinn (1948): "Elements of Photogrammetry," Syracuse University Press, Syracuse, N.Y.

Churchill, E. A., and R. L. Stitt (1955): Association Analysis Applied to the Interpretation of Aerial Photographs, *Photogram. Eng.,* vol. 21.

Cobb, Genevieve C. (1943): Bibliography on the Interpretation of Aerial Photographs and Recent Bibliographies on Aerial Photography and Related Subjects, *Bull. Geol. Soc. Am.,* vol. 54, pp. 1195–1210.

Coleman, Charles G., and Earl J. Rogers (1956): Report of Commission VII (Photographic Interpretation) to the International Society of Photogrammetry, *Photogram. Eng.,* vol. 22, no. 1, pp. 67–122 (especially "Natural Resources," pp. 87–97).

Colwell, R. N. (1946): The Estimation of Ground Conditions from Aerial Photographic Interpretation of Vegetation Types, *Photogram. Eng.,* vol. 12, p. 151.

———— (1953): Aerial Photographic Interpretation of Vegetation as an Aid to the Estimation of Terrain Conditions, in "Selected Papers on Photogeology and Photo Interpretation," GG 209/1, Committee on Geophysics and Geography, Research and Development Board, Washington, D.C.

———— (1954): A Systematic Analysis of Some Factors Affecting Photographic Interpretation, *Photogram. Eng.,* vol. 20, no. 3, pp. 433–454.

———— (1955): The PI Picture in 1955, *Photogram. Eng.,* vol. 21.

———— (1959): The Future for Photogrammetry and Photo Interpretation, *Photogram. Eng.,* vol. 25, no. 5, pp. 712–736.

Committee on Geophysics and Geography (1953): "Selected Papers on Photogeology and Photo Interpretation," Research and Development Board, GG 209/1, Washington, D.C.

Cozzens, W. L. (1937): Aerial Mapping in Relation to Geological Exploration, *Pacific Mineralogist,* vol. 4, no. 1, pp. 2284–2317.

Craig, Dwin R. (1955): Logetronics, *Photogram. Eng.,* vol. 21, no. 4, pp. 556–563.

Custer, S. A., and Sylvia R. Mayer (1955): "A Comparative Analysis of Curricula and Techniques Used in the Training of Photographic Interpreters," Boston University, Optical Research Laboratory, Technical Note 119.

DeBlieux, C. (1949): Photogeology in Gulf Coast Exploration, *Bull. Am. Assoc. Petrol. Geologists,* vol. 33, no. 7, pp. 1251–1259.

———— and G. F. Shepherd (1951): Photogeologic Study of Kent County, Texas, *Oil Gas J.,* vol. 50, no. 10, part I, pp. 86, 88, 98–100.

DeMartonne, E. (1948): "Géographie Aérienne," Editions Albin Michel, Paris.

Desjardins, Louis (1940): The Contouring Problem, *Photogram. Eng.,* vol. 6, no. 4, pp. 163–165.

———— (1943): Measurements of Dip Angles on Aerial Photographs, *Bull. Am. Assoc. Petrol. Geologists,* vol. 27, no. 11, pp. 1534–1538.

———— (1943a): Contouring and Elevation Measurement on Vertical Aerial Photographs, *Photogram. Eng.,* vol. 9, no. 4, pp. 214–224.

———— (1944): Notes on Parallax and Stereo-elevations, *Photogram. Eng.,* vol. 10, pp. 90–91.

———— (1945): Useful Graphical Constructions on Aerial Photographs, *Photogram. Eng.,* vol. 11, no. 3, pp. 194–229.

———— (1950): Techniques in Photogeology, *Bull. Am. Assoc. Petrol. Geologists,* vol. 34, no. 12, pp. 2284–2317.

———— (1950a): Structural Contour for the Photogeologist, *Photogram. Eng.,* vol. 16, no. 4, pp. 784–796.

———— (1950b): Photogeology on the Texas Gulf Coast, *Mines Mag. (Denver),* vol. 40, no. 10, pp. 97–101.

———— (1951): The Measurement of Formational Thickness by Photogeology, *Photogram. Eng.,* vol. 17, no. 5, pp. 821–830.

———— (1952): Aerial Photos of Multiple Surface Faults May Locate Deep-seated Salt Domes, *Oil Gas J.,* vol. 51, no. 13, pp. 82–84.

———— and S. G. Hower (1939): Geologic Mapping from the Air, *Oil Gas J.,* vol. 37, no. 52, pp. 44–59.

———— (1939a): Geologic, Topographic, and Structural Mapping from Aerial Photographs, "Finding and Producing Oil," *Proc. Am. Petrol. Inst.,* 1st ed., pp. 29–33.

Dietz, Robert S. (1947): Aerial Photographs in the Geological Study of Shore Features and Processes, *Photogram. Eng.,* vol. 13, no. 4, pp. 537–545.

Dirmeyer, R. D. (1945): Military Applications of Photo-geology, *Military Engr.,* vol. 37, pp. 392–397.

Dunbar, Moira, and Keith R. Greenaway (1956): "Arctic Canada from the Air," Canada Defense Research Board.

Eardley, A. J. (1941): "Interpretation of Geologic Maps and Aerial Photographs," Edwards Bros., Inc., Ann Arbor, Mich.

———— (1942): "Aerial Photographs—Their Use and Interpretation," Harper & Brothers, New York.

———— (1943): Aerial Photographs and the Distribution of Constructional Materials, *Highway Research Board, Proc. 23rd Ann. Meeting,* November, pp. 557–568.

Elias, M. M. (1953): The Use of Air Photos in Terrain Interpretation at Long Range, *Photogram. Eng.,* vol. 19, no. 3.

Eliel, Leon T. (1930): Aerial Photography and Its Importance to California Geologists, *Mining in California,* vol. 26, no. 1, pp. 64–71.

Elliott, D. H. (1952): Photogeologic Interpretation Using Photogrammetric Dip Calculations, *Calif. Dept. Natl. Resources Div. Mines Spec. Rept. No. 15.*

Fairbridge, R. W., and Curt Teichert (1948): The Low Isles of the Great Barrier Reef: A New Analysis, *Geograph. J. (London),* vol. 111, pp. 67–88.

Fang, C. (1955): Photogrammetry as Applied to Geography and Geology, *Chinese Soc. of Phot. Tech. Bull.*

Fischer, W. A. (1953): Photogeologic Studies of Arctic Alaska and Other Areas, in "Selected Papers on Photogeology and Photo Interpretation," GG 209/1, Committee on Geophysics and Geography, Research and Development Board, Washington, D.C.

———— (1955): Photogeologic Instruments Used by the U.S. Geological Survey, *Photogram. Eng.,* vol. 21, no. 1, pp. 32–39.

———— et al. (1956): Panel on Photogeology, *Photogram. Eng.,* vol. 22, no. 5, pp. 841–865.

———— (1958): Color Aerial Photography in Photogeologic Intepretation, *Photogram. Eng.,* vol. 24, no. 4, pp. 545–549.

Fisk, H. N. (1944): "Geological Investigation of the Alluvial Valley of the Lower Mississippi River," U.S. War Dept., Corps of Engineers, Mississippi River Comm., Vicksburg, Miss.

Fitch, A. A. (1942): Geological Observations of Air Photographs of the Peace River Area, British Columbia, *Photogram. Eng.,* vol. 8, pp. 156–159.

———— et al. (1944): Aerial Photography in Petroleum and Mineral Prospecting, *Empire Mining Met. Congr., Proc. 4th Congr.,* London.

Fortier, Y. O. (1947): Geological Mapping of the Ross Lake Area, Using Aerial Photographs, *Photogram. Eng.,* vol. 13, no. 4, pp. 545–548.

———— (1947a): "Ross Lake NWT, Geologic Map and Descriptive Notes," *Can. Dept. Mines and Tech. Surveys Geol. Survey Can. Paper 47–16.*

Friztag Drabbe, C. A. J. von (1951–1952): Some New Aspects in Stereoscopic Vision, *Photogrammetria,* vol. 8, no. 4, Special Congress Number.

———— (1953): Aerial Photographs and Photo Interpretation, in "A Photostudy of the World's Erosion by Water," J. H. de Bussy, Amsterdam.

Frost, R. E. (1946): Identification of Granular Deposits by Aerial Photography, *Highway Research Board Proc. 25th Ann. Meeting,* pp. 116–126, National Academy of Sciences of the United States.

———— (1952): Discussion of Photo Recognition, Analysis and Interpretation and Photo Keys, *Photogram. Eng.,* vol. 18, no. 3, p. 502.

———— (1953): Factors Limiting the Use of Aerial Photographs for Analysis of Soil and Terrain, *Photogram. Eng.,* vol. 19, no. 3, pp. 427–436.

———— et al. (1953): "A Manual on the Airphoto Interpretation of Soils and Rocks for Engineering Purposes," School of Civil Engineering and Engineering Mechanics, Purdue University, Lafayette, Indiana.

———— and O. W. Mintzer (1950): Influence of Topographic Position in Airphoto Identification of Permafrost, *Highway Research Board, Bull. 28,* November.

———— and J. D. Mollard (1947): New Glacial Features Identified by Air Photos in Soil Mapping Program, Joint Highway Research Project No. 29 (*Highway Research Board, Proc.,* vol. 26, pp. 562–578, 1946).

———— and K. B. Woods (1948): "Airphoto Patterns of Soils of the Western United States," Purdue University, Tech. Development Rept. 85, U.S. Dept. of Commerce, Civil Aeronautics Administration.

Furcron, A. S. (1939): Geology and Mineral Resources of the Warrenton Quadrangle, Virginia, *Virginia Geol. Survey, Bull. 54.*

Gandillot, J. (1952): The Airplane, Geologist's Eye, *Geography,* no. 9, French Geological Society, France.

———— (1954): Aerial Photographs in Geological Research, *Bull. soc. géol. France,* col. 1–3, 1–4, French Geological Society, France.

———— (1955): Geology and Aviation, *Ann. univ. Paris,* no. 1, University of Paris, France.

Gill, Donald (1932): Aerial Survey in Relation to Economic Geology, *Bull. Inst. Mining Met.,* preliminary paper, pp. 2–48.

Goodale, E. R. (1953): An Equation for Approximating the Vertical Exaggeration Ratio of a Stereoscopic View, *Photogram. Eng.,* vol. 19, pp. 607–616.

Goodman, R. E. (1960): Photo/Field Prospecting, *Photogram. Eng.,* vol. 26, no. 1, pp. 100–105.

Grantham, D. R. (1953): Aerial Photography, Vegetation, and Geology, *Mining Mag. (London),* vol. 88, no. 6, June, pp. 329–336.

Gravenor, C. P. (1956): Air Photographs of the Plains Region of Alberta, *Prelim. Rept. 56–5, Research Council Alberta (Can.),* Edmonton.

Gross, W. H. (1951): A Statistical Study of Topographic Linears and Bedrock Structures, *Proc. Geol. Assoc. Can.,* vol. 4, pp. 77–87.

Hack, John T. (1948): Photo-interpretation in Military Geology, *Photogram. Eng.,* vol. 14, no. 4, pp. 488–496.

Hackman, Robert J. (1956): The Graphic Construction of Controlled Stereoscopic Models, *Photogram. Eng.,* vol. 22, no. 2, pp. 387–391.

———— (1956a): The Stereo-slope Comparator—An Instrument for Measuring Angles of Slope in Stereoscopic Models, *Photogram. Eng.,* vol. 22, no. 5, pp. 893–898.

Harder, E. C. (1906): The Joint System in the Rocks of Southwestern Wisconsin and Its Relation to the Drainage Network, *Univ. Wisconsin Bull.* 138, Science Series, vol. 3, pp. 207–246.

Hartman, Ronald R., and Kalman N. Isaacs (1958): System in Photogeology, *Bull. Am. Assoc. Petrol. Geologists*, vol. 42, no. 5, pp. 1083–1093.

Heath, G. R. (1950): The Stereo-mosaic, a New Mapping Technique, *Photogram. Eng.*, vol. 16, no. 2, pp. 152–154.

——— (1955): An Associative Method of Regional Photo Interpretation, *Photogram. Eng.*, vol. 21, no. 4, pp. 589–598.

——— (1956): A Comparison of Two Basic Theories of Land Classification and Their Adaptability to Regional Photo Interpretation Key Techniques, *Photogram. Eng.*, vol. 22, no. 1, pp. 144–168.

——— (1957): Improvements in the Stereo-mosaic, *Photogram Eng.*, vol. 23, no. 3, pp. 536–542.

Helbling, R. I. (1949): "Studies in Photogeology in Connection with Geological Mapping in Switzerland, Specifically of the Todi Range," published under commission by the Federal Institute of Technology, Zurich, Art. Inst., Orell Fussl, A. G., Zurich (translated by N. E. Odell).

Hellding, R. (1935): Application de la photogrammetrie pour la construction des cartes géologiques, *Bull. soc. belge photogrammetrie*, Bruxelles; no. 1 (extrait).

Hemming, H. (1937): Air Survey as a Factor in Empire Development, *Mine & Quarry Eng.*, vol. 2, no. 7, pp. 254–263.

Hemphill, William R. (1958): Determination of Quantitative Geologic Data with Stereometer Type Instruments, *U.S. Geol. Survey Bull.* 1043-C.

——— (1958a): Small-scale Photographs in Photogeologic Interpretation, *Photogram. Eng.*, vol. 24, no. 4, pp. 562–567.

Henderson, G. (1960): Air-photo Lineaments in Mpanda Area, Western Province, Tanganyika, Africa, *Bull. Am. Assoc. Petrol. Geologists*, vol. 44, no. 1, pp. 53–71.

Henderson, L. H. (1939): Detailed Geological Mapping and Fault Studies of the San Jacinto Tunnel Line and Vicinity, *J. Geol.*, vol. 47, no. 3, pp. 314–324.

Herzog, G. W. (1940): The Uses of Aerial Photogrammetry in the Petroleum Industry, *Photogram. Eng.*, vol. 6.

Hittle, J. E. (1949): Air Photo Interpretation of Engineering Sites and Materials, *Photogram. Eng.*, vol. 15, no. 4, pp. 589–603.

Hobbs, W. H. (1905): Examples of Joint-controlled Drainage from Wisconsin and New York, *J. Geol.*, vol. 13, p. 363.

Holman, W. W., and H. C. Nikola (1953): Airphoto Interpretation of Coastal Plain Areas, *Highway Research Board, Bull. No. 83*, January.

Hopkins, D. M. (1953): "Interim Report, Airphoto Pattern Reconnaissance of Northwestern Canada," vols. I and II, Purdue University.

——— et al. (1955): "Permafrost and Ground Water in Alaska," *U.S. Geol. Survey Profess. Paper* 264F.

Howard, Arthur D. (1960): Photogeology at Stanford University, *Photogram. Eng.*, vol. 26, no. 1, pp. 72–73.

Howe, Robert H. L., et al. (1956): Application of Air Photo Interpretation in the Location of Ground Water, *J. Am. Water Works Assoc.*, vol. 48.

Howe, Robert H. L. (1958): Procedures of Applying Air Photo Interpretation in the Location of Ground Water, *Photogram. Eng.*, vol. 24, no. 1, pp. 35–49.

——— (1960): The Application of Aerial Photographic Interpretation to the Investigation of Hydrologic Problems, *Photogram. Eng.*, vol. 26, no. 1, pp. 85–95.

Hunt, Charles B. (1951): Military Geology, *Geol. Soc. Am. Eng. Geol.* (Berkey volume), pp. 302–306.

Jenkins, D. S., D. J. Belcher, L. E. Gregg, and K. B. Woods (1946): "The Origin, Distribution, and Airphoto Interpretation of United States Soils," Tech. Develop. Rept. No. 52, U.S. Dept. of Commerce, Civil Aeronautics Administration, Washington, D.C.

Johnson, George R., and R. R. Platt (1930): "Peru from the Air," *Am. Geograph. Soc., Spec. Publ. No. 12*.

Johnstone, W. E. (1953): A Geological Interpretation of an Air Photograph of British Somaliland, *Photogram. Eng.*, vol. 19, no. 3, pp. 466–468.

——— (1953a): Photogeology and Mineral Exploration, *Mining Mag.* (London), vol. 88, no. 5, pp. 265–270.

Jolliffe, A. W. (1942): Structures in the Canadian Shield, *Trans. Am. Geophys. Union*, part II, pp. 699–707.

——— (1945): Aeroprospecting in the Yellowknife Area, *Trans. Can. Inst. Mining Met.*, vol. 48, pp. 588–609.

Judson, Sheldon, and George W. Andrews (1955): Pattern and Form of Some Valleys in the Driftless Area, Wisconsin, *J. Geol.*, vol. 63, no. 4, pp. 328–336.

Kedar, Yehuda (1958): The Use of Aerial Photographs in Research in Physiogeographic Conditions and Anthropogeographic Data in Various Historic Periods, *Photogram. Eng.*, vol. 24, no. 4, pp. 584–587.

——— (1958a): A Geographic Approach to the Study of Photo Interpretation, *Photogram. Eng.*, vol. 24, no. 5, pp. 821–824.

Kelly, W. A., and D. J. McGuire (1955): Exceptional Meander Scars and Their Significance in Determining the Direction of Stream Flow, *Photogram. Eng.*, vol. 21, no. 1, pp. 110–112.

Kent, B. H. (1957): Experiments in the Use of Color Aerial Photographs for Geologic Study, *Photogram. Eng.*, vol. 23, no. 5, pp. 865–868.

Kesseli, J. E. (1952): Use of Air Photographs by Geographers, *Photogram. Eng.*, vol. 18, no. 4, pp. 737–742.

Kistler, Philip S. (1947): Viewing Photographs in Three Dimensions, *Photogram. Eng.*, vol. 13, pp. 127–134.

Kuenen, P. H. (1950): Stereoscopic Projection for Demonstration in Geology, Geomorphology, and Other Natural Sciences, *J. Geol.*, vol. 58, pp. 49–54.

Kupsch, W. O., and J. Wild (1958): Lineaments in Avonlea Area, Saskatchewan, *Bull. Am. Assoc. Petrol. Geologists*, vol. 42, no. 1, pp. 127–134.

Lahee, F. H. (1952): "Field Geology," 5th ed., chap. 17, pp. 531–572, McGraw-Hill Book Company, Inc., New York.

Lake, M. C. (1950): Cerro Bolivar—U.S. Steel's New Iron Ore Bonanza, *Eng. Min. J.*, August, pp. 73–83.

Landen, David (1956): New Developments in Photogrammetric Training for Geologists, *Photogram. Eng.*, vol. 22, no. 2, pp. 271–279.

Landis, G. (1955): Concept and Validity of Association Photographic Interpretation Keys in Regional Analysis, *Photogram. Eng.*, vol. 21, no. 5, pp. 705–706.

Lane, A. L. (1945): Use of Aerial Photographs, *Military Engr.*, vol. 37, pp. 263–266.

Lang, A. H. (1947): Air Photographs in Geological Mapping of Cordilleran Region, Western Canada, *Photogram. Eng.*, vol. 13, no. 4, pp. 548–550.

Lang, A. H., H. S. Bostock, and Y. O. Fortier (1947): "Interim Catalogue of the Geological Survey Collections of Outstanding Air Photographs," *Can. Dept. Mines and Tech. Surveys, Geol. Survey Can.*, Paper 47-26, Ottawa.

Lattman, Laurence H. (1956): Improved Pocket Lens Stereoscope, *Bull. Am. Assoc. Petrol. Geologists*, vol. 40, no. 8, pp. 2000–2002.

——— (1958): Technique of Mapping Geologic Fracture Traces and Lineaments on Aerial Photographs, *Photogram. Eng.*, vol. 24, no. 4, pp. 568–576.

Lattman, L. H., and R. P. Nickelsen (1958): Photogeologic Fracture-trace Mapping in Appalachian Plateau, *Bull. Am. Assoc. Petrol. Geologists*, vol. 42, no. 9, pp. 2238–2245.

Lattman, Laurence H., and Wilds W. Olive (1955): Solution-widened Joints in Trans-pecos Texas, *Bull. Am. Assoc. Petrol. Geologists*, vol. 39, no. 10, pp. 2084–2087.

Laylander, P. A. (1952): How Colored Aerial Photographs

Make Newest Ore-search Method, *Mining World,* June, pp. 41–43.

—— (1956): A Performance Estimate Comparing Conventional Geologic Mapping with That Accomplished with the Aid of Color Photographs, *Photogram. Eng.,* vol. 22, no. 5, pp. 853–857.

Lee, W. T. (1922): The Face of the Earth as Seen from the Air, *Am. Geograph. Soc., Spec. Publ. No. 4,* New York.

Leroy, L. W. (1952): Photostratigraphy, *World Oil,* vol. 134, no. 7, pp. 96–98.

Levings, W. S. (1944): Aerogeology in Mineral Exploration, *Quart. Colo. School Mines,* vol. 39, no. 4, pp. 7–77.

—— and K. S. Herness (1953): Air Photo Criteria of Ore Localization in the Corbin-Wickes Mining District, Jefferson County, Montana, *Photogram. Eng.,* vol. 19, no. 3, pp. 449–460.

Light, Richard U. (1941): Focus on Africa, *Am. Geograph. Soc., Spec. Publ. No. 25.*

Lobeck, A. K. (1939): "Geomorphology," McGraw-Hill Book Company, Inc., New York.

—— and W. J. Tellington (1944): "Military Maps and Air Photographs," McGraw-Hill Book Company, Inc., New York.

Loel, Wayne (1938): "Use of Aerial Photographs in Geologic Mapping," *Am. Inst. Mining Met. Engrs., Tech. Publ. 890.*

—— (1941): Use of Aerial Photographs in Geologic Mapping, *Trans. Am. Inst. Mining Met. Engrs.,* vol. 144, pp. 356–409.

Low, Julian W. (1957): "Geologic Field Methods," Harper & Brothers, New York.

Lueder, D. R. (1953): Airphoto Interpretation as an Aid in Mineral Reconnaissance and Development, *Photogram. Eng.,* vol. 19, no. 5, pp. 819–830.

—— (1954): "Determination of Beach Conditions by Means of Aerial Photographic Interpretation," vols. 1 to 5, U.S. Office of Naval Research, Tech. Rept. 6, Cornell University, Ithaca, N.Y.

—— (1958): The Future of Color Aerial Photography, *Eng. News-Record,* Apr. 10.

—— (1959): "Aerial Photographic Interpretation; Principles and Applications," McGraw-Hill Book Company, Inc., New York.

Lundahl, Arthur C., et al. (1950): Symposium: Information Relative to Uses of Aerial Photographs by Geologists, *Photogram. Eng.,* vol. 16, no. 5, pp. 721–806.

Lyon, Duane (1959): "Basic Metrical Photogrammetry," Duane Lyon, St. Louis, Mo.

MacFadden, C. H. (1952): The Uses of Aerial Photographs in Geographic Research, *Photogram. Eng.,* vol. 18, no. 4, pp. 732–737.

Matthes, G. H. (1928): Aerial Photography as an Aid in Geological Studies, *Bull. Am. Inst. Min. Met. Engrs.*

McBeth, Frank H. (1956): A Method of Shoreline Delineation, *Photogram. Eng.,* vol. 22, no. 2, pp. 400–405.

McCurdy, P. G. (1947): "Manual of Coastal Delineation from Aerial Photographs," U.S. Navy Dept., Hydrographic Office Publication No. 592.

McInnes, D. W. (1952): Geological Mapping from Air Photographs, *Mining Geol. J. Victoria,* March, pp. 4–9; September, pp. 4–8.

McNeil, G. T. (1949): "ABC's of Photogrammetry," part I, Edwards Bros., Inc., Ann Arbor, Mich.

Melton, Frank A. (1936): An Empirical Classification of Floodplain Streams, *The Geograph. Review,* vol. 26, no. 4, pp. 593–609.

—— (1940): A Tentative Classification of Sand Dunes, Its Application to Dune History in the Southern High Plains, *J. Geol.,* vol. 48, no. 2, pp. 113–174.

—— (1945): Preliminary Observations on Geological Use of Aerial Photographs, *Bull. Am. Assoc. Petrol. Geologists,* vol. 29, pp. 1756–1765.

—— (1950): Photogeological Study of the Flatlands, *Mines Mag. (Denver),* vol. 40, no. 10, pp. 37–49.

—— (1950a): The Geomorphology and Photo-geological Study of the "Flat-lands," *Photogram. Eng.,* vol. 16, no. 5, pp. 722–744.

—— (1953): Geologic Exploration and Mapping with Aerial Photographs, in "Selected Papers on Photogeology and Photo Interpretation," GG 209/1, Committee on Geophysics and Geography, Research and Development Board, Washington, D.C.

—— (1955): Photogeology in "Flatland" Regions of Low Dip, *Shale Shaker,* vol. 6, no. 3, pp. 5–39.

—— (1956): Problems of the Photogeologist in "Flatland" Regions of Low Dip, *Photogram. Eng.,* vol. 22, no. 1, pp. 52–63.

Melville, P. L. (1948): An Airphoto Study of the Triassic Area in Albemarle County, Virginia, *Highway Research Board, Bull. No. 13,* p. 30.

Merritt, Everett L. (1958): "Analytical Photogrammetry," Pitman Publishing Corporation, New York.

Miller, Charles I. (1958): The Stereoscopic Space-image, *Photogram. Eng.,* vol. 24, no. 5, pp. 810–815.

Miller, Victor C. (1950): Rapid Dip Estimation in Photogeological Reconnaissance, *Bull. Am. Assoc. Petrol. Geologists,* vol. 34, no. 8, pp. 1739–1743.

—— (1953): Some Factors Causing Vertical Exaggeration and Slope Distortion on Aerial Photographs, *Photogram. Eng.,* vol. 19, pp. 592–607.

—— (1953a): "A Quantitative Geomorphic Study of Drainage Basin Characteristics in the Clinch Mountain Area, Virginia and Tennessee," Tech. Rept. 3, Contract N6 ONR 271-30, Dept. of Geology, Columbia University.

—— (1955): A Brief Consideration of the Geomorphology of the Glacier Park–St. Mary Area, Montana, *Guidebook 6th Ann. Field Conf., Billings Geol. Soc.,* pp. 211–219.

—— (1957): Photogeomorphic Interpretation of the Plains, *J. Alberta Soc. Petrol. Geologists,* vol. 6, no. 3, pp. 44–47.

Minard, James P. (1960): Color Aerial Photographs Facilitate Geologic Mapping on the Atlantic Coastal Plain of New Jersey, *Photogram. Eng.,* vol. 26, no. 1, pp. 112–116.

Moessner, Karl E. (1955): A Simple Test for Stereoscopic Perception, *Photogram. Eng.,* vol. 21, no. 3, pp. 331–339.

Moffitt, Francis F. (1959): "Photogrammetry," International Textbook Company, Scranton, Pa.

Mollard, J. D. (1949): Photo Interpretation of Transported Soil Materials, *Eng. J. (Montreal),* June.

—— (1952): How We Identify Geologic Features in Vertical Aerial Photographs, *The Compass of Sigma Gamma Epsilon,* Indiana University, p. 248.

—— (1956): Airphoto Analysis and Interpretation in Engineering-geology Investigations, *Eng. Digest,* July and August.

—— (1957): A Study of Aerial Mosaics in Southern Saskatchewan and Manitoba, *Oil in Canada,* vol. 9, Aug. 5, pp. 26–50 (pp. 18140–18164).

—— (1957a): Aerial Photographs Aid Petroleum Search, *Can. Oil and Gas Ind.,* vol. 10, no. 7, pp. 89–96.

—— (1959): Photogeophysics: Its Application in Petroleum Exploration over the Glaciated Plains of Western Canada, *Proc. 2nd Williston Basin Conf.,* Conrad Publishing Company, Bismarck, N.Dak.

Moore, Raymond C. (1947): Aerial Photographs as Aids in Stratigraphic Studies, *Photogram. Eng.,* vol. 13, no. 4, pp. 550–557.

Nichols, D. A. (1932): Solifluction and Other Features in Northern Canada Shown by Photographs from the Air, *Trans. Roy. Soc. Can., IV,* 3rd series, vol. 26, pp. 267–275.

Nouhuys, J. J. van (1937): Geological Interpretation of Aerial Photographs, *Trans. Am. Inst. Mining Met. Eng.,* vol. 126, pp. 607–624; Mining Technology, vol. 1, no. 4, *Am. Inst. Mining Met. Engrs. Tech. Publ. 825,* July.

Nugent, L. E., Jr. (1947): Aerial Photographs in Structural

Mapping of Sedimentary Formations, *Bull. Am. Assoc. Petrol. Geologists,* vol. 31, pp. 478–494.

Parvis, M. (1947): "Airphoto Interpretation of Drainage Features of Switzerland County, Indiana," State Highway Commission of Indiana and Joint Highway Research Project, Purdue University, Lafayette, Indiana.

——— (1950): Drainage Pattern Significance in Airphoto Identification of Soils and Bedrocks, *Photogram. Eng.,* vol. 16, no. 3, pp. 387–409.

Pasto, J. K. (1954): Soil Mapping by Stereoscopic Interpretation of Air Photos, *Soil Sci. Soc. Am. Proc.,* April, pp. 135–138.

Patrick, W. W. (1954): English?, *Bull. Am. Assoc. Petrol. Geologists,* vol. 38, no. 12, pp. 2558–2561.

Pillmore, C. L. (1957): Application of High Order Stereoscopic Plotting Instruments to Photogeologic Studies, *U.S. Geol. Survey Bull.* 1043-B, pp. 23–34.

Pincus, Howard J. (1959): Some Applications of Terrestrial Photogrammetry to the Study of Shorelines, *Photogram. Eng.,* vol. 25, no. 1, pp. 75–82.

Pomerening, J. A., and M. G. Cline (1953): The Accuracy of Soil Maps Prepared by Various Methods That Use Aerial Photograph Interpretation, *Photogram. Eng.,* vol. 19, no. 5, pp. 809–817.

Powers, William E. (1951): A Key for the Photo-identification of Glacial Landforms, *Photogram. Eng.,* vol. 17, no. 5, pp. 776–779.

——— and Clyde F. Kohn (1959): Aerial Photo-interpretation of Landforms and Rural Cultural Features in Glaciated and Cultural Regions, *Northwestern Univ. Studies in Geography,* no. 3, Northwestern University Press.

Prusok, Rudi A., and John R. Ege (1960): A Simple Stereophotographic Field Method of Rock Outcrop Description for the Geologist, *Photogram. Eng.,* vol. 26, no. 1, pp. 98–100.

Putnam, William C. (1947): Aerial Photographs in Geology, *Photogram. Eng.,* vol. 13, no. 4, pp. 557–565.

Raasveldt, Henri C. (1956): The Stereomodel, How It Is Formed and Deformed, *Photogram. Eng.,* vol. 22, no. 4, pp. 708–726.

——— (1959): Determination of the Angle of Dip of Seemingly Vertical Strata on Vertical Aerial Photographs, *Photogram. Eng.,* vol. 25, no. 1, pp. 49–53.

Rabben, E. L. (1955): The Eyes Have It, *Photogram. Eng.,* vol. 21, no. 4, p. 574.

Raup, H. M., and C. S. Denny (1950): Photointerpretation of the Terrain along the Southern Part of the Alaskan Highway, *U.S. Geol. Survey Bull.* 963D.

Ray, Richard G. (1956): Photogeologic Procedures in Geologic Interpretation and Mapping, *U.S. Geol. Survey Bull.* 1043-A.

——— (1956a): Status of Photogeology in the U.S. Geological Survey, *Photogram. Eng.,* vol. 22, no. 5, pp. 846–853.

——— (1958): Scale and Instrument Relationship in Photogeologic Study, *Photogram. Eng.,* vol. 24, no. 4, pp. 577–584.

——— (1958a): Color Aerial Photography, *Western Miner and Oil Review,* vol. 31, no. 3, pp. 35–37.

Ray, Richard G., and William A. Fischer (1957): Geology from the Air, *Science,* vol. 127, no. 3277, pp. 725–735.

——— (1960): Quantitative Photography—A Geologic Research Tool, *Photogram. Eng.,* vol. 26, no. 1, pp. 143–150.

Rea, Henry Carter (1941): Photogeology, *Bull. Am. Assoc. Petrol. Geologists,* vol. 25, pp. 1796–1799.

Reed, J. C. (1940): The Use of Airplane Photographs in the Geological Study of the Chichagof Mining District, Alaska, *Photogram. Eng.,* vol. 6, no. 1, pp. 35–44.

Rice, A. H. (1945): Air Photography in Geographical Exploration and Geological Surveying, *Am. J. Sci.,* vol. 243-A, pp. 486–494.

Rich, J. L. (1914): Certain Types of Streams and Their Meaning, *J. Geol.,* vol. 22, pp. 469–497.

——— (1928): Jointing in Limestones as Seen from the Air, *Bull. Am. Assoc. Petrol. Geologists,* vol. 12, no. 8, pp. 861–862.

——— (1939): A Bird's-eye Cross Section of the Central Appalachian Mountains and Plateaus, Washington to Cincinnati, *Geograph. Rev.,* vol. 29, no. 4, October, pp. 561–586.

——— (1941): The Aerial Traverse—An Application of Aerial Photography in Geographic Studies, *Ohio J. Sci.,* vol. 41, no. 3, pp. 212–224.

——— (1942): The Face of South America, an Aerial Traverse, *Am. Geograph. Soc. Spec. Publ.* 26, New York.

——— (1947): Geological Applications of Oblique Photography, *Photogram. Eng.,* vol. 13, no. 4, pp. 565–570.

——— (1947a): Reconnaissance Mapping from Oblique Aerial Photographs without Ground Control, *Photogram. Eng.,* vol. 13, no. 4, pp. 600–609.

——— (1947b): A Method of Preparing Stereoscopic Aerial Photographs for Reproduction in Quantity, *Photogram. Eng.,* vol. 13, no. 4, pp. 619–621.

——— (1951): Geomorphology as a Tool for the Interpretation of Geology and Earth History, *Trans. N.Y. Acad. Sci.,* ser. 2, vol. 13, no. 6, pp. 188–192.

Rogers, E. J. (1953): A Plan for Research in Aerial Photo Interpretation, *Photogram. Eng.,* vol. 19, no. 5, pp. 801–805.

——— (1956): Problems in Comparing Photo Interpretation Research Results from Different Studies, *Photogram. Eng.,* vol. 22, no. 1.

Rooney, G. W., and W. S. Levings (1947): Advances in the Use of Air Survey by Mining Geologists, *Photogram. Eng.,* vol. 13, no. 4, pp. 570–584.

Roscoe, John H., et al. (1955): Panel: Photo Interpretation, *Photogram. Eng.,* vol. 21, no. 4, pp. 564–610.

Russell, Richard J. (1949): Geographical Geomorphology, *Ann. Assoc. Am. Geographers,* vol. 39, pp. 1–11.

——— (1958): Geological Geomorphology, *Bull. Geol. Soc. Am.,* vol. 69, no. 1, pp. 1–22.

Rydlun, E. G. (1928): Aerial Photography as Applied to Mining and Geology, *Eng. Mining J.,* vol. 126, pp. 204–209.

Sager, R. C. (1951): Aerial Analysis of Permanently Frozen Ground, *Photogram. Eng.,* vol. 17, no. 4, pp. 551–571.

Salzman, M. H. (1950): Note on Stereoscopy, *Photogram. Eng.,* vol. 16, no. 3, pp. 475–477.

Sanders, R. G. (1942): Orient Your Stereoscope Correctly, *Photogram. Eng.,* vol. 7, no. 4, pp. 240–245.

Schneeberger, W. F. (1952): Aerial Survey and Oil Exploration, *Photogram. Eng.,* vol. 18, no. 4, pp. 753–759.

Scott, H. S. (1957): The Role of Aerial Survey Methods in Canada's Northward Development, *Eng. Inst. Can. J.,* November.

Sears, J. D. (1956): Geology of Comb Ridge and Vicinity North of San Juan River, San Juan County, Utah, *U.S. Geological Survey Bull.* 1021-E.

Sharp, H. O. (1951): "Practical Photogrammetry," The Macmillan Company, New York.

Shaw, S. H. (1953): The Value of Air Photographs in the Analysis of Drainage Patterns, *Photogrammetric Record,* vol. 1, no. 2, pp. 4–17.

Shearer, E. M. (1957): Stereo-structural Contouring, *Bull. Am. Assoc. Petrol. Geologists,* vol. 41, no. 8, pp. 1694–1703.

Shepard, Francis P. (1950): Photography Related to the Investigation of Shore Processes, *Photogram. Eng.,* vol. 16, no. 4, pp. 756–769.

Sibinga, Smit G. L. (1948): On the Geomorphic and Geologic Analysis and Interpretation of Aerial Photographs, *Tijdschr. Koninkl. Ned. Aadrijkskundig Genoot.,* pp. 692–700.

Singleton, Robert (1956): Vertical Exaggeration and Perceptual Models, *Photogram. Eng.,* vol. 22, no. 1, pp. 175–178.

Smith, H. T. U. (1941): Aerial Photographs in Geomorphic Studies, *J. Geomorphology,* vol. 4, no. 3, pp. 171–205.

——— (1943): "Aerial Photographs and Their Applications," Appleton-Century-Crofts, Inc., New York.

——— (ed.) (1947): Symposium on Uses of Aerial Photographs by Geologists, *Photogram. Eng.,* vol. 13, no. 4, pp. 531–628.

——— (1947a): Aerial Photos in Geologic Training, *Photogram. Eng.,* vol. 13, no. 4, pp. 615–619.

——— (1948): Giant Glacial Grooves in Northwest Canada, *Am. J. Sci.,* vol. 246, pp. 503–514.

——— et al. (1949): Trends and Needs in Photogeology and Photo-interpretation; Discussion Forum, *Photogram. Eng.,* vol. 15, no. 4, pp. 567–578.

——— (1950): Progress and Problems in Photogeology, *Photogram. Eng.,* vol. 16, no. 1, pp. 111–118.

——— (1950a): Notes on Recent Literature Relating to Photogeology, *Photogram. Eng.,* vol. 16, no. 4, pp. 781–783.

——— et al. (1951): Symposium: Air Photos in Geography and Soil Science, *Photogram. Eng.,* vol. 17, no. 5, pp. 715–779.

——— (1952): Photo-interpretation in Applied Earth Science, *Photogram. Eng.,* vol. 18, no. 3, pp. 418–428.

——— (1952a): Air Photos in Geology (Summary), *Tulsa Geol. Soc. Dig.,* vol. 20, pp. 47–48.

——— (1953): Photo Interpretation of Terrain, in "Selected Papers on Photogeology and Photo Interpretation," GG 209/1, Committee on Geophysics and Geography, Research and Development Board, Washington, D.C.

——— (1953a): Photo Interpretation in Relation to Geologic Research, *Photogram. Eng.,* vol. 19, no. 1, pp. 108–111.

——— (1953b): Present Status of Photo Interpretation in Earth Science, *Photogram. Eng.,* vol. 19, no. 1, pp. 137–143.

Smith, N. C., and K. M. Renfro (1955): Photogeology: Matured Exploration Tool, *Petrol. Eng.,* September, pp. B 94–96.

Smith, Norman C., and Sherman A. Wengerd (1947): Photogeology Aids Naval Petroleum Exploration, *Bull. Am. Assoc. Petrol. Geologists,* vol. 31, no. 5, pp. 824–828.

Southard, Rupert B., Jr. (1958): Orthophotography—Its Techniques and Applications, *Photogram. Eng.,* vol. 24, no. 3, pp. 443–451.

Spooner, C. S., S. W. Dossi, and M. G. Misulia (1957): Let's Go over the Hill—Potential Benefits of Profile Scanning the Stereo-model, *Photogram. Eng.,* vol. 23, no. 5, pp. 909–920.

Steers, J. A. (1945): Coral Reefs and Air Photography, *Geograph. J.* (London), vol. 106, pp. 232–235.

Stone, Kirk H. (1951): Geographical Air-photo Interpretation, *Photogram. Eng.,* vol. 17, no. 5, pp. 754–759.

——— (1954): A Selected Bibliography for Geographic Instruction and Research by Air-photo Interpretation, *Photogram. Eng.,* vol. 20, no. 3, pp. 561–565.

——— (1961): World Air Photo Coverage, 1960, *Photogram. Eng.,* vol. 27, no. 2, pp. 214–227.

——— (1956): Air-photo Interpretation Procedures, *Photogram. Eng.,* vol. 22, no. 1, pp. 123–132.

Strahler, Arthur N. (1948): Geomorphology and Structure of the West Kaibab Fault Zone and Kaibab Plateau, Arizona, *Bull. Geol. Soc. Am.,* vol. 59, pp. 513–540.

Stringer, K. V. (1951): The Combined Stereo-pair in Photogeology, *Colonial Geol. and Mineral Resources* (Gt. Brit.), vol. 2, no. 1, pp. 31–32.

Strobell, John D. (1947): The Multiplex Compilation of Geologic Maps, *Photogram. Eng.,* vol. 13, no. 4, pp. 609–614.

Summerson, C. H. (1954): A Philosophy for Photo Interpreters, *Photogram. Eng.,* vol. 20, no. 3, pp. 396–397.

Tanner, William F. (1953): Estimating Low Dips on Air Photographs, *Bull. Am. Assoc. Petrol. Geologists,* vol. 37, no. 12, pp. 2743–2746.

Tator, Benjamin A. (1949): University Instruction in Photogeology, *Photogram. Eng.,* vol. 15, no. 4, pp. 603–614.

——— (1950): Photogrammetry and Photo Interpretation in Geology Curricula, *Bull. Am. Assoc. Petrol. Geologists,* vol. 34, no. 12, pp. 2351–2356.

——— (1951): Some Applications of Aerial Photographs to Geographic Studies in the Gulf Coast Region, *Photogram. Eng.,* vol. 17, no. 5, pp. 716–725.

——— (1954): Drainage Anomalies in Coastal Plains Regions, *Photogram. Eng.,* vol. 20, no. 3, pp. 412–417.

——— (1958): The Aerial Photograph and Applied Geomorphology, *Photogram. Eng.,* vol. 24, no. 4, pp. 549–561.

Teichert, Curt, and R. W. Fairbridge (1950): Photo-interpretation of Coral Reefs, *Photogram. Eng.,* vol. 16, no. 4, pp. 744–755.

Thompson, Morris M. (1958): Photogrammetric Mapping of Sand Beds in a Hydraulic Test Flume, *Photogram. Eng.,* vol. 24, no. 3, pp. 468–475.

Thorén, Ragnar (1959): Frost Problems and Photo Interpretation of Patterned Ground, *Photogram. Eng.,* vol. 25, no. 5, pp. 779–786.

Threet, Richard L. (1956): Graphical Template for Determination of Dip from Aerial Vertical Photographs, *Bull. Am. Assoc. Petrol. Geologists,* vol. 40, no. 5, pp. 1009–1016.

Thurrell, R. F., Jr. (1953): Vertical Exaggeration in Stereoscopic Models, *Photogram. Eng.,* vol. 19, pp. 579–588.

——— (1953a): Procedures and Problems of Photogeologic Evaluation, *Photogram. Eng.,* vol. 19, no. 3, pp. 443–449.

——— (1953b): Procedures and Problems in Photogeologic Evaluation, in "Selected Papers on Photogeology and Photo Interpretation," GG 209/1, Committee on Geophysics and Geography, Research and Development Board, Washington, D.C.

Thwaites, F. T. (1947): Use of Aerial Photographs in Glacial Geology, *Photogram. Eng.,* vol. 13, no. 4, pp. 584–586.

Treece, Walter A. (1955): Estimation of Vertical Exaggeration in Stereoscopic Viewing of Aerial Photographs, *Photogram. Eng.,* vol. 21, no. 4, pp. 518–527.

Truesdell, Page E. (1950): Naval Interest in Photogeology, *Photogram. Eng.,* vol. 16, no. 3, pp. 431–433.

——— (1959): Working Group No. 3; Interpretation of Surface Configuration, Drainage, Soils, Geology—Interim Progress Report for Commission VII, *Photogram. Eng.,* vol. 25, no. 1, pp. 121–128.

Twenhofel, William S., and C. L. Sainsbury (1958): Fault Patterns in Southeastern Alaska, *Bull. Geol. Soc. Am.,* vol. 69, no. 11, pp. 1431–1442.

U.S. Air Force (1946): "Index to Aerial and Ground Photographic Illustrations of Geologic and Topographic Features throughout the World," Headquarters U.S. Army Air Force, mimeographed (supplement 1, 1949).

——— (1953): "Regional Photo Interpretation Series—Antarctica," AFM 200–30, TM 30–250, Department of the Air Force.

Vincent, Norman (1957): Economic Aspects of Aerial Exploration, *Photogram. Eng.,* vol. 23, no. 1, pp. 105–108.

Waldo, Cullen E., and Robert P. Ireland (1955): Construction of Landform Keys, *Photogram. Eng.,* vol. 21, no. 4, pp. 603–606.

Wallace, R. E. (1950): Determination of Dip and Strike by Indirect Observations in the Field and from Aerial Photographs; A Solution by Stereographic Projection, *J. Geol.,* vol. 58, pp. 269–280.

Wanless, Harold R. (1950): Selection of Aerial Photographs for Teaching Geology, *Photogram. Eng.,* vol. 16, no. 4, pp. 796–802.

——— (1950a): Aerial Photograph Collection, *Photogram. Eng.,* vol. 16, no. 4, pp. 803–806.

——— et al. (1951): Outstanding Aerial Photographs in North America, *Natl. Acad. Sci., Natl. Research Council, Rept. 5,* American Geological Institute.

——— (1953): Development of Methods and Materials for Teaching Photogeologic Interpretation, in "Selected Papers on Photogeology and Photo Interpretation," GG 209/1, Committee on Geophysics and Geography, Research and Development Board, Washington, D.C.

Wasem, A. R. (1949): Petroleum Photogeology, *Photogram. Eng.,* vol. 15, no. 4, pp. 579–589; also *World Oil,* vol. 130, no. 5, pp. 64–72, 1950.

Washburn, A. L. (1947): "Reconnaissance Geology of Parts of Victoria Island and Adjacent Regions, Arctic Canada," *Geol. Soc. Am. Mem.* 22.

Weiner, H. (1955): The Mechanical Aspect of Photo Interpretation Keys, *Photogram. Eng.,* vol. 21, no. 5, pp. 708–712.

Wengerd, Sherman A. (1947): Geologic Interpretation of Trimetrogon Photographs—Northern Alaska, *Photogram. Eng.,* vol. 13, no. 4, pp. 586–600.

——— (1947a): Newer Techniques in Aerial Surveying, *World Oil,* vol. 127, no. 3, pp. 37–42; no. 4, pp. 46–54; no. 5, pp. 49–54; no. 6, pp. 136–142; no. 8, pp. 131–136.

——— (1950): Photogeologic Characteristics of Paleozoic Rocks on the Monument Upwarp, Utah, *Photogram. Eng.,* vol. 16, no. 5, pp. 770–781.

Wermund, E. G. (1955): Fault Patterns in Northwest Louisiana, *Bull. Am. Assoc. Petrol. Geologists,* vol. 39, no. 11, pp. 2329–2336.

Wheeler, R. R., and N. C. Smith (1952): Finding Faded Structures, Part I, *World Oil,* vol. 135, no. 1, pp. 73–76, 82.

Willcox, H. C. (1925): Value of Aerial Photographic Surveying and Mapping to Petroleum Companies and Their Geologists, pp. 78–81 in "Production of Petroleum in 1924," American Institute of Mining and Metallurgical Engineers, New York.

Willett, R. W. (1940): Air Photography and Geology, *N.Z. J. Sci. Tech.,* vol. 22, no. 1B, pp. 21–33.

Wilson, J. Tuzo (1948): Some Aspects of Geophysics in Canada with Special Reference to Structural Research in the Canadian Shield, Part 2, *Trans. Am. Geophys. Union,* vol. 29, pp. 691–726.

Wood, Edward S. (1949): Photogrammetry for the Non-photogrammetrist, *Photogram. Eng.,* vol. 15, no. 2, pp. 249–275.

Wright, Prof. W. D. (1954): Stereoscopic Vision Applied to Photogrammetry, *The Photogrammetric Record,* vol. 1, no. 3, pp. 29–49.

Zeller, M. (1952): "Textbook of Photogrammetry," (E. A. Misken and R. Powell trans.), H. K. Lewis & Company, Ltd., London.

Zernitz, E. R. (1932): Drainage Patterns and Their Significance, *J. Geol.,* vol. 40, no. 6.

Zonneveld, J. I. S., and A. Cohen (1952): Geological Reconnaissance in Surinam, Symposium in *Photogram. Eng.,* vol. 18, no. 1, pp. 151–157.

Index